Grade Aid with Practice Tests

for

Baron, Branscombe, and Byrne

Social Psychology

Twelfth Edition

prepared by

Virginia Gills Centanni
Oakwood College and Virginia College

Boston   New York   San Francisco
Mexico City   Montreal   Toronto   London   Madrid   Munich   Paris
Hong Kong   Singapore   Tokyo   Cape Town   Sydney

ISBN-13: 978-0-205-58180-1
ISBN-10:   0-205-58180-3

Printed in the United States of America

10 9 8 7 6 5 4 3 2 1   12 11 10 09 08

Contents

Your instructor has chosen a classic, internationally-respected social psychology text. Most social psychologists regard the Baron and Byrne *Social Psychology* text as one of the best—if not *the best*—in the field. This text will inform you about the exciting and important field of social psychology. I am also confident that you'll find it quite helpful in years to come with respect to your future academic and career endeavors.

This GradeAid Student Workbook with Practice Tests has been designed to help you get the most out of your text. By offering a four part learning system:

- "Before You Read..." This section should literally be reviewed prior to your text reading. This section provides a concise summary of the chapter, highlights the key learning objectives and provides a list of key terms with page references.
- "As You Read..." Will be most effective if you work on the exercises *while* you read your text chapters. These exercises were designed so that you could complete them as you go along with your readings to reinforce and solidify the material presented. New to this Edition, *a full answer key is provided for this section!*
- "After You Read..." Has a brand new section titled: *MyPsychLab Connection* where I have given you three great MyPsychLab assets that are especially pertinent to the material in the chapter as a fun, multimedia break from the text reading. There are also four Practice Tests with multiple choice and completion questions. The answers to all of these quizzes can be found at the end of the corresponding GradeAid chapter.
- "When You Have Finished..." This section rounds out the studying experience with a little vocabulary booster (Crossword Puzzle) and a new and unique section: *You Be the Researcher* that takes you beyond the text to deepen your knowledge of the material presented in your reading, to encourage critical thinking, and to provide you with a glimpse into psychology as a *true* science!

It is my sincere hope that you use this GradeAid to its full advantage and enjoy a better understanding of the material presented in *Social Psychology, 12th Edition*.

Virginia Gills Centanni
Oakwood College and Virginia College

CHAPTER 1

SOCIAL PSYCHOLOGY:
THE SCIENCE OF THE SOCIAL SIDE OF LIFE

Before You Read...Chapter Summary

At the beginning of Chapter One you will be introduced to a film entitled, *Legally Blonde*. This film was chosen by the author to illustrate some of the concepts to which you will be exposed throughout this textbook. In particular, the author use this film to acquaint you with social psychology as a discipline that studies and attempts to grasp the role that our thoughts, feelings and actions play in our lives.

Social psychology is formally defined as "the scientific field that seeks to understand the nature and causes of individual behavior and thought in social situations." Within the first chapter you will gain valuable insight into the role of social psychology as a science and discover the four core values that social psychology embodies allowing it to be classified as a true science. In addition, you will read of the wide variety of factors that can impact our thoughts and actions, including the social, cognitive, environmental, cultural, and biological factors. Quite interestingly, you will find out that our thoughts and actions are not only impacted by things we see, hear, or experience; they are also influenced by processes of which we are not conscious.

Social psychologists often are found conducting research in an effort to provide additional insight into our thoughts and actions. You will learn of the ways in which social psychologists go about conducting this research through a discussion of the methods of systematic observation, correlation and experimentation. You will next become aware of the role of theory in social psychology. As a final point, the authors discuss the ethical standards by which the social psychologist conducts research. The chapter concludes with the authors giving the reader a concise guide concerning how to get the most from your social psychology learning experience.

Before You Read... Learning Objectives

After reading this chapter, you should be able to:

- Define *social psychology* and discuss the topics social psychologists ponder.
- Explain the four core values that make social psychology a true science.
- Discuss the variables that affect our thoughts and actions as social human beings.
- State and discuss three of the primary research methods used by social psychologists.
- Provide illustrative examples of the research trends in social psychology.
- Define the word *theory* and the route taken to build a theory.
- Give an overview and discuss the significance of the ethical principles to which social psychologists are held.

As You Read...Term Identification

Important Terms to Know
Below is a list of some of the key terms and concepts from this chapter. Make flashcards in order to enhance your recall ability of these terms. Refer to the definitions that are either in boldface or in the margins of this chapter for help. You may also want to include additional terms from this chapter as you deem necessary.

social psychology (p. 6)	social diversity (p. 18)	experimentation / **experimental method** (p. 25)
science (p. 6)	multicultural perspective (p. 18)	dependent variable (p. 25)
accuracy (p. 6)	instincts (p. 19)	independent variable (p. 25)
objectivity (p. 6)	social norms (p. 19)	random assignment (p. 26)
skepticism (p. 6)	cognitive dissonance (p. 20)	external validity (p. 27)
open-mindedness (p. 6)	attribution (p. 20)	mediating variables (p. 28)
evolutionary psychology (p. 10)	environmental psychology, (p. 20)	theory (p. 29)
social behavior (p. 14)	systematic observation (p. 21)	deception (p. 31)
social thought (p. 14)	naturalistic observation (p. 21)	informed consent (p. 32)
warmth (p. 15)	survey method (p, 22)	debriefing (p. 32)
competence (p. 15)	correlational method (p. 23)	
implicit processes (p. 16)	hypothesis (p. 23)	

As You Read...Practice Activities

Let's Go To The Movies...
(Introduction, page 3)

1.   The authors open Chapter One with an analysis of the movie, *Legally Blonde*, from a social psychology perspective. In an effort to facilitate your knowledge of social psychology and the social psychology perspective, think of a movie you have seen that lends itself to a similar analysis. Name the movie and write a short analysis of the movie, explaining why you believe this movie fits in well with the social psychology perspective. For example, your analysis may include, but in no way should be limited to, the effect of the environment on character behavior, or the influence of character appearance on the response of others.

_____

_____

_____

_____

SOCIAL PSYCHOLOGY: WHAT IT IS AND WHAT IT DOES

Providing a Formal Definition...
(Introduction, page 6)

2.   There are two factors that make providing a formal definition difficult for social psychology. These include the broadness of the scope of the field of social psychology and the rapid speed of change in the field. Your author, though, does provide a formal definition. What formal definition does your author give for social psychology? Restate the definition in your own words.

_____

_____

_____

The Science of Social Psychology...
(Social Psychology is Scientific in Nature, page 6)

3.   There are four values that are central to the determination of any discipline as a science. They are: accuracy, objectivity, skepticism, and open-mindedness. After reading the definitions provided by the author, provide a definition for each in your own words.

1. **Accuracy**: _____

2. **Objectivity**: _____

3. **Skepticism**: _____

The Science of Social Psychology...Continued

   4. Open-Mindedness: _____

Isn't It All Just Common Sense?
(Social Psychology is Scientific in Nature, page 8)

4.   Define "common sense". Ponder the common sense saying: "One cannot put a quart in a pint cup." What does this saying mean? Do you agree with the statement? In what way does the statement represent the concept of common sense? Why do social psychologists use the scientific method as an alternative to using common sense?

   _____

   _____

   _____

   _____

Finish the Sentence...
(Social Psychology Focuses on the Behavior of Individuals, page 9)

5.   Fill in the blank:

   "...the field's major interest lies in understanding the factors that shape the

   actions and thoughts of _____ in social settings."

   Why is this entity the major focus of social psychology? _____

   _____

   _____

Matching the Research with the Researcher...
(Social Psychology Seeks to Understand the Causes of Social Behavior and Thought, pages 9 – 13)

   6.   Match the researchers with the research findings:

   _____   McCall (1997)

   _____   Swann and Gill (1997)

   _____   Tesser and Martin (1996)

   _____   Anderson, Bushman, and
           Groom (1997)
   _____   Buss (2004)

   _____   Baron (1997)

   _____   Buss and Shackleford (1997)

   _____   Pettijohn and Jungeberg (2004)

Matching the Research with the Researcher…Continued

A. There are certain qualities that are representative of "good genes". One having these qualities is more prone to being viewed as healthy and vigorous.

B. How we react to other people based is often based on their appearance.

C. Social cognition is one of the areas most central to social psychology.

D. Being exposed to an agreeable odor tends to make individuals exhibit more helping behavior toward others.

E. Though we do have inherent tendencies to behave in a certain manner, these tendencies can be superseded by cognitive factors and experience.

F. Individuals tend to exhibit more irritability and aggression when the outside climate is hot and humid.

G. Biological issues play a significant role in social behavior.

H. Early in life children have the tendency to bear a resemblance to their fathers. The reason for this is that it aids in the reduction of any doubt that the child belongs to a specific man.

Categorically Speaking…
(Social Psychology Seeks to Understand the Causes of Social Behavior and Thought, page 10)

7. Your author describes five categories under which most variables that effect our behavior and thought fall. Name each category and give an example of each.

1. _____

2. _____

3. _____

4. _____

5. _____

A New Branch of Psychology…
(Social Psychology Seeks to Understand the Causes of Social Behavior and Thought, page 11)

8. Buss (2004) and Buss and Shackleford (1997) found evidence that biological factors contribute to our social behavior. Findings such as this have led to the development of a new branch of psychology. Name this branch and discuss its beliefs related to evolved psychological mechanisms.

_____

_____

_____

SOCIAL PSYCHOLOGY: ITS CUTTING EDGE

The Dance...
(Cognition and Behavior: Two Sides of the Same Social Coin, page 14)

9.   The music has begun. The couple involved in the waltz is in perfect unison. Their names are social behavior and social thought. Describe each and explain the interplay between the two.

_____

_____

_____

Tools of the Trade...
(Social Neuroscience: Where Social Psychology and Brain Research Meet, page 14)

10.   In conducting research into the neural foundations of the processes of social thought and behavior, social psychologists use a number of tools in an effort to determine how events in the brain are related to the two processes. Name two of these tools. Why do social psychologists NOT use these tools for ALL aspects of social thought and behavior?

_____

_____

_____

You Were a Participant...
(Social Neuroscience: Where Social Psychology and Brain Research Meet, page 15)

11.   In 2006, you had the opportunity to participate in the study, *Dehumanizing the lowest of the low*, which was conducted by L.T. Harris and S.T. Fiske. As part of the study, after signing an informed consent, you were shown the following two faces.

FACE A   FACE B

You Were a Participant...Continued

Assuming you found Face A more attractive than the Face B, according to Harris and Fiske, what pattern did your brain scan most likely show?

_____

_____

_____

According to the Research...
(The Role of Implicit (Nonconscious) Processes, page 17)

12.   Match the researcher / researchers with their findings.

_____   Pelham et al. (2003)   _____   Ruder & Bless (2003)

_____   Richeson & Shelton, 2003)   _____   O'Sullivan (2003)

_____   Bar-Ham, Ziv, Lamy, and
        Hodes (2006)

A.   Implicit processes can influence our career choice.
B.   Babies show a partiality for the faces of people of their own racial group.
C.   We tend to believe that other peoples' behavior reflects their underlying traits rather than suggesting their reaction to their present set of circumstances.
D.   We are much better at recognizing faces of people within our own racial group.
E.   If we are in a bad mood, we show the tendency to remember negative things about others.

Social Psychology and the Legal System...
(The Role of Implicit (Nonconscious) Processes, page 17)

13.   What does the author of the textbook mean by implicit processes?

_____

_____

Allison, an African American, was robbed at gunpoint a year ago. When she reported the incident to the police she was asked to give a description of the assailant, who was noted to be Caucasian. Using research findings described in this section, explain why this might be difficult for Allison.

_____

_____

Social Diversity...
(Taking Full Account of Social Diversity, page 18)

14.   Describe the *multicultural perspective*. Why have social psychologists adopted this perspective? What are the three important differences that the multicultural perspective takes into account?

_____

_____

_____

_____

A BRIEF LOOK AT HISTORY: THE ORIGINS AND EARLY DEVELOPMENT OF SOCIAL PSYCHOLOGY

A Timeline...
(The Early Years: Social Psychology Emerges, page 19)

15.   Between 1908 and 1924, two important texts were written in which the words "social psychology" appeared in the titles. Name the authors of these two books and describe the role each played in the emergence of the field of social psychology.

_____

_____

_____

_____

_____

_____

And The Beat Goes On...
(Social Psychology's Youth: The 1940's, 1950's, and 1960's. pages 19 – 20)

16.   Describe the directions in which the emerging field of social psychology traveled during the 1940's, 1950's, and the 1960's.

_____

_____

_____

_____

A Turn Toward Modernity...
(The 1970s, 1980s, and 1990s: A Maturing Field, page 20)

17.   Describe the two large scale trends that began during this time period.

_____

_____

_____

_____

_____

HOW SOCIAL PSYCHOLOGISTS ANSWER THE FASCINATING QUESTIONS THEY RAISE: RESEARCH AS THE ROUTE TO INCREASED KNOWLEDGE

What Did You Observe?
(Systematic Observation: Describing the World Around Us, page 21)

18.   *Naturalistic observation* is a type of systematic observation often employed by social
       psychologists. Describe the concepts of *systematic observation* and *naturalistic observation*.
       What is the most important idea that the researcher must remember if he or she is conducting a
       naturalistic observation?

_____

_____

How would you evaluate your school's cafeteria? How would you evaluate your professor's
personality? What would your assessment of the latest movie be? Another type of systematic
observation is the survey method of conducting research. All of these questions could be
answered using the survey method. What is one of the advantages of the survey method?

_____

_____

Correlation Comparison...
(Correlation: The Search for Relationships, page 23)

19.   As a project for his social psychology class, Dr. Mullins assigned each student to conduct a study
       investigating the relationship between shyness and school grade point average (GPA). One
       student, Martinez, conducted the study and, upon analyzing his data, found a correlation of .69
       exists. Another student, Anthony, also conducted the study. Anthony, though, found a
       correlation of .97. Compare the two results. Which of the results shows a stronger relationship?

Correlation Comparison...Continued

How do you know? Because the correlation is positive, what do you know about the relationship between the two variables?

_____

_____

_____

_____

Are You Going in My Direction?
(Correlation: The Search for Relationships, page 23)

20. Identify the direction and interpret the correlation in the following scenario:

Dr. Alonzo conducted a study investigating the hypothesis that drinking diet drinks contributes to the occurrence of heart attacks. He found that for every diet drink consumed by the participant, the risk of the occurrence of a heart attack increases by a small percentage.

_____

_____

_____

Let's Practice...
(Experimentation: Its Basic Nature, pages 25 - 26)

21. In the following, identify the independent and dependent variables. In addition, state the levels of the independent variable.

Marquis is investigating the role that the number of people in a group can play in cooperative behavior. He has two research questions: (1) Does the number of people in a group affect cooperation within the group? (2) Does a group with an odd number of participants exhibit more cooperative behavior than a group with an even number of participants?

Marquis has hypothesized that the number of people in a group will affect cooperative behavior within the group. He also expects to find that a group with an even number of participants will exhibit more cooperative behavior than a group with an odd number of participants.

Marquis has divided his participants into two groups. Group I consists of 5 participants – an odd number. Group II consists of 6 participants – an even number.

a.   The independent variable (IV) in this experiment is _____

_____

Let's Practice…Continued

b. How many levels of the IV are there? What are those levels? _____

_____

c. The dependent variable (DV) in this experiment is _____

_____

d. If you were to perform this experiment, would your hypotheses agree with those of

Marquis? If not, what would you hypothesize? _____

_____

e. Often one of the criteria for conducting research is that the researcher's sample must be representative of the population from which it was chosen. In light of this, first tell what a representative sample is. Then discuss how Marquis might go about finding a representative sample for the study described above.

_____

_____

_____

The Issue of Confounding…
(The Experimental Method: Knowledge through Systematic Intervention, page 27)

22. Patrice conducted a study investigating whether, after viewing a cartoon, children (ages 5 – 7 years of age) would demonstrate the tendency to recall more positive or negative information from the cartoon. She began the study be dividing the children into two groups based on their age. All children between 5 and 6 were placed in group I. All children between 6 and 7 were placed in group II. Prior to having the children view the cartoon, Patrice gave the children a snack. She felt the snack, consisting of a cola beverage and some crackers, would provide an incentive for the children and would contribute to their patience during the study. Unfortunately, Patrice ran out of the cola beverage while serving group I and had to serve the children in group II water instead of the cola beverage.

She, then, proceeded with the study. Patrice analyzed her data and found a statistically significant difference between the two groups. Group I remembered a significantly greater amount of positive information than did group II.

When drawing her conclusions, Patrice, at first, attributed the difference between groups to the age disparity of the two groups. She, then, remembered something she had learned in her biology class – that sugar can cause physiological arousal in children. She began to wonder: Could the sugar ingestion be group I have contributed to her results? In other words, Patrice recognized the presence of a potential confounding variable.

The Issue of Confounding...Continued

Define the term *confounding* and use this knowledge to suggest what some possible confounds in this experiment might have been.

_____

_____

_____

_____

Assessing the Generalizability of an Experiment...
(Two Key Requirements for Its Success, page 27)

23. Beth has conducted an experiment investigating the construct of self esteem in teenage girls.   In light of the fact that the study is being conducted in the psychology lab at her college, Beth is concerned that the external validity might be too low.

Define the concept of *external validity.*

_____

_____

_____

Why is the external validity of experiments often in question?

_____

_____

_____

Mediating the Situation...
(Further Thoughts on Causality: The Role of Mediating Variables, page 27)

24. Oftentimes, the terms *confounding variable* and *mediating variable* get confused.

Define each and use an example to demonstrate the difference between the two types of variables.

_____

_____

_____

Let Me Explain…
(The Role of Theory in Social Psychology, page 28)

25.   Rewrite the following paragraph, correcting all mistakes.

A hypothesis is defined as a framework for explaining events or processes. In social psychology, as well as in other fields of psychology, researchers seek to prove theories. In light of this, acceptance of a theory based on the collected data is not what a social psychologist seeks and studies are performed to gather evidence that is contrary to the theory.

_____

_____

_____

_____

_____

Evaluating Your Knowledge of The Research Methods used in Social Psychology…
(Systematic Observation: Describing the World around Us; Correlation: The Search for Relationships; The Experimental Method: Knowledge through Systematic Intervention, pages 21 - 25)

26.   Fill each blank square with the appropriate word or words.

METHOD	USAGE	EXAMPLE
Correlation		Is there a relationship between headaches and number of books read?
	Gather information about behavior	
Experiment		

THE QUEST FOR KNOWLEDGE AND THE RIGHTS OF INDIVIDUALS: SEEKING AN APPROPRIATE BALANCE

Deception Connection...
(page 31)

27. In order to investigate the particular issue in question, the researcher must sometimes deceive the participants. Define *deception*. Why is using deception sometimes essential?

_____

_____

_____

Your Ethics are Showing...
(page 31)

28. Psychologists, including social psychologists, are bound by the American Psychological Association to adhere to certain ethical guidelines. The issue of deception can bring some significant ethical issues to the forefront.

Two of these issues are discussed in your textbook. Name and describe each of them.

1. _____

_____

2. _____

_____

Resolving the Issue...
(page 31)

29. Because there are studies that cannot be performed without the use of deception, psychologists have two safeguards that can be used to resolve the issues associated with the use of deception. Name and discuss these two safeguards.

1._____

_____

2. _____

_____

Let Me Be Your Guide...
(page 31)

30. LaTonia is conducting a research assignment for her social psychology class. She has found that she must incorporate deception into her study. She has spoken with you to get your advice. You remember that there is a list of guidelines for using deception found within your textbook. LaTonia asks that you write the list down for her and provide her with a brief description of each of the items. Help LaTonia by providing her with this information. In other words, list and describe the guidelines for using deception.

_____

_____

_____

Your Proposal is Acceptable...
(page 32)

31. Finish the sentence below:

If a student at a university in the United States wishes to receive federal funding

for his or her research, he or she must have a (n) _____

evaluate the ethics of the proposed research.

After You Read… MyPsychLab Connection

Did you know that your textbook has a MyPsychLab CourseCompass, which correlates relevant assets to each of the chapters in your textbook?

In order to take advantage of the site, you must purchase an access code online (or purchase a new textbook with a complimentary access code), register and create a username and password.

For more information about MyPsychLab, go to the following web address: http://www.ablongman.com/mypsychlab/whatis.html.

(1)   Due to the American Psychological Association's guidelines for research, an informed consent form is today required in certain types of psychological research. Years ago, though, this was not the case. One study that poignantly demonstrates the reasoning behind the concept of the informed consent is the Tuskegee Experiment.   For information regarding this study, visit the link in *WATCH* entitled, *Before Informed Consent.*

2.   Have you ever wondered what the relationship is between caffeine (coffee) and test performance? If so, you will be interested in the link in *EXPLORE* entitled, *Interactive Correlation*. This link will not only help diminish your curiosity, it will also enhance your understanding of the correlation method of research.

3.   Everyone makes predictions. We listen to the weather on TV and attempt to make reasonably educated decisions about what we will wear the next day. Unfortunately, predictions about the weather are not without error. Our predictions are no different. In *STIMULATE, Predicting Results of Scientific Research*, you will find information on the use of predictions in research and gain a valuable understanding that predictions are just that – predictions – and they are not infallible.

After You Read… Practice Test #1

_____1.   Science is defined
A.   by social psychology differently than other disciplines.
B.   by the adoption of specific core values.
C.   by **ALL** scientists as a special group of highly advanced fields.
D.   by any field that uses intuition to arrive at valid conclusions.

_____2.   A large number of variables mold an individual's social behavior and thought. These variables can be categorized into five distinct groupings. These categories include **ALL** of the following **EXCEPT**
A.   the actions and characteristics of others.
B.   the economic status of individuals in society.
C.   the environmental influence on behavior.
D.   **ALL** of the above represent categories into which variables that mold an individual's social behavior and thought can be placed.

_____3.   Systematic observation involves the careful observation of behavior as it occurs. One type of systematic observation is the survey method of conducting research. In order, though, to conduct a first-rate survey research project there are certain requirements the study **MUST** meet. These include
A.   the participants **MUST** be a representative sample of the population from which they were obtained.
B.   the survey **MUST** be short with 4 – 5 questions, at most.
C.   the survey **MUST** be well worded.
D.   Both A and C are requirements of a survey study.

_____4.   The correlational approach and the experimental approach to research are dissimilar to each other in one important area. That difference is
A.   correlational research is used to determine if a cause / effect relationship exists within the study.
B.   both of the approaches can be used to determine if a cause / effect relationship exists between variables of interest.
C.   experimental research is the only type of study that can be used to determine a cause / effect relationship.
D.   both the correlational approach and the experimental approach are used to determine a relationship between variables without assessing causation.

_____5.   Leon is investigating the way social factors are involved in the incidence of depression in the elderly. To do this, he will conduct an experiment in which he will manipulate an important determinant of the occurrence of depression, social support. He will divide his participants into 3 groups. Group one will be visited by two community workers during a two week period. Group two will be visited by 4 community workers during the same two week period. Community workers will **NOT** visit together; rather, they will visit on different days. After the two weeks, Leon will give the participants a measure of depression and compare the two groups. In this study, the independent variable is
A.   the days of the week in which the community workers visit.
B.   the measurement of depression.
C.   the number of community workers visiting each group.
D.   the age of the participants.

_____6.   Which of the following represents the strongest correlation in which both variables increase together?
A.   - .97
B.   +.97
C.   - .38
D.   +.38

_____7.   Which of the following best defines the term, dependent variable?
A.   The factor(s) that is/are systematically altered by the researcher.
B.   The factor(s) that is/are standardized by the researcher.
C.   The aspects of behavior that are systematically altered by the researcher.
D.   The aspects of behavior that are measured by the researcher or produced by the participant.

_____8.   As stated in your textbook, the reason random assignment is used in the selection of participants in an experiment is
A.   without random assignment, the data collected is virtually worthless.
B.   without random assignment, the researcher may find concluding the differences found between the participants/groups were due to the impact of the independent variable impossible.
C.   without random assignment, the participants may be able to determine the researcher's purpose in conducting the experiment and this may skew the data.
D.   Both A and B are true of random assignment of participants within an experiment.

_____9.   The procedure for the formation of a theory consists of 5 steps. **ALL** of the following are regarded as steps taken toward the formation of a theory, **EXCEPT**
A.   the theory is tested by evaluating hypothesis (es).
B.   if the results of the hypothesis (es) testing are consistent with the theory, there is increased confidence in the accuracy of the theory.
C.   ultimately, the theory is proven and no further analyses are needed.
D.   theories reflect existing evidence of their accuracy.

_____10.   There are two safeguards that are used whenever deception is used. They are a consent form and a careful debriefing. The consent form is designed to

A.   give the participants information regarding the deception that will be used within the study as a means of persuading their participation within the study.

B.   provide participants with a full description of the purposed of the study after they have participated.

C.   let the participants know that information will be held from them until the study has ended.

D.   provide the participants with as much information as possible about the procedure that will be employed within the study.

11.   Deception is used only after the researcher has been given the "go-ahead" by the

_____.

12.   The stronger the correlation, the closer the correlation coefficient is to positive or

negative _____.

13.   Adriane is conducting a study in which has hypothesized that if one spends 30 minutes or more per day reading, the amount of stress they are experiencing will be reduced. She plans to have participants divided into three groups: those who will read for 30 minutes per day, those who will read for 1 hour per day and those who will read for 1 ½ hour per day. In this study, the time per day spent reading is the _____ variable.

14.   The above study can best be categorized as a(n) _____.

15.   If one were to study a phenomenon in social psychology through the

_____, one would take into

account race, ethnicity, gender, sex, and cultural values of his or her participants.

After You Read... Practice Test #2

_____1. Marvin has conducted a study investigating the relationship between the hours of sun per day and pro-social behavior. He collected data, analyzed it and came to a conclusion. If Marvin found a correlation coefficient of -.03, how would you interpret the findings?
- A. The correlation is very low.
- B. As sun hours decrease, so does pro-social behavior.
- C. As sun hours increase, pro-social behavior decreases.
- D. Both A and B are true of the correlation coefficient of -.03.

_____2. The textbook states that our cognitive processes play a central role in our thoughts and behaviors. According to the cognitive perspective, our reactions to various situations are often based on
- A. our brain wave patterns.
- B. our memories of past events.
- C. how pretty we think someone is.
- D. our racial heritage.

_____3. According to your textbook, deception in research raises the following ethical issue(s):
- A. Harm to the participant.
- B. Resentment on the part of the participant for not being told the truth from the beginning.
- C. Loss of anonymity.
- D. All of the above are correct.

_____4. The _____ provides the participant with important information on the study prior to participation; while the _____ provides the participant with important information after participation in the study.
- A. debriefing; consent form.
- B. consent form; debriefing.
- C. informational briefing form; post-briefing form.
- D. consent form; post-briefing form.

_____5. Joshua is an undergraduate student who is majoring in psychology. Presently, he is taking a social psychology course. As part of his class, Joshua has conducted a study investigating smoking behavior and stress. Joshua found a positive correlation between stress and smoking behavior. He, therefore, concluded that stress causes smoking. Is there a problem with this interpretation?
- A. No, Joshua can definitely say that stress causes smoking behavior.
- B. Yes, Joshua's results simply show a relationship between stress and smoking; therefore, he cannot say stress causes smoking.
- C. Yes, though Joshua found a positive correlation, this probably is an inaccurate finding and there is really no relationship between stress and smoking.
- D. Both B and C represent problems with Joshua's interpretation of the results.

_____6.   Social psychology
A.   seeks to understand **ALL** of its major topics of interest in terms of brain activity.
B.   seeks to understand **ALL** of its major topics of interest in terms of nervous system activity.
C.   uses brain activity and nervous system activity to provide understanding in **SOME** of its major topics.
D.   does not use brain activity or nervous system activity to understand **ANY** of its topics. In fact, the field does not use any biological measures at all.

_____7.   Juan is conducting an investigation to determine if there are differences between the display of compassion toward animals in male and female participants. The research method best suited to this investigation would be
A.   a correlational study in which Juan determines if there is a relationship between compassionate behavior towards animals and sex.
B.   an experiment in which Juan varies the type of animals to which he exposes the participants.
C.   a survey in which Juan asks questions regarding compassion toward animals.
D.   a naturalistic observation in which Juan observes both males and females interacting with animals.

_____8.   Social psychologists use the scientific method for one very important reason. The reason is that
A.   it provides definitive evidence that a theory is true.
B.   social psychologists do **NOT** use the scientific method. This method is only used by such fields as chemistry and biology.
C.   it yields much more conclusive evidence than would an interpretation from a common sense standpoint.
D.   they are strongly committed to proving theories and the scientific method is the best way to do this.

_____9.   Social psychology seeks to explain or describe human behavior by investigating **ALL** of the following **EXCEPT**
A.   the actions of others.
B.   characteristics of others.
C.   environmental variables.
D.   ALL of the above are investigated by social psychologists in an effort to explain or describe human behavior.

_____10.   Evolutionary psychology suggests that humans have evolved psychological mechanisms that help us deal with problems of survival. The components which make up our biological heritage include **ALL** of the following **EXCEPT**
A.   consistency throughout life.
B.   inheritance.
C.   senses.
D.   childhood experiences.

11. Wesley is interested in the relationship between exposure to the mental health and exposure to the sun. Since he is interested solely in finding a possible relationship, you would suggest that he conduct a(n) _____ study.

12. In order for systematic observation to deliver useable and reliable results, the participants must be a _____ sample of the population from which they were chosen.

13. A(n) _____ is given to all participants of an experiment prior to the study to acquaint them with what is involved in participation in the study.

14. To determine the biological components of our behavior, social psychologists often rely on measurements of _____.

15. You are told that the correlation between drinking alcohol and aggressive behavior shows that the more alcohol one drinks, the more aggressive one will become. The correlation coefficient in this case will be _____.

After You Read… Practice Test #3

_____1.   Which of the following questions lends itself best to the correlational method of research?
   A.   How should intelligence be measured?
   B.   What is Timothy's intelligence quotient?
   C.   Is intelligence inherited?
   D.   What is the relationship between intelligence and creativity?

_____2.   Alex is conducting a study for his psychology class. He is sitting in the food court at the mall and counting the number of women and men who purchase salads for their lunchtime meal. The type of research study Alex is conducting can best be described as a(n)
   A.   correlational study.
   B.   experiment.
   C.   survey study.
   D.   naturalistic observation.

_____3.   The evolutionary perspective is well suited to the study of
   A.   why we choose the mate we choose.
   B.   why children resemble their parents.
   C.   why we display aggression.
   D.   **ALL** of the above lend themselves well to study through the evolutionary perspective.

_____4.   If social behavior and thought are influenced by social factors, variables that would fit into this category include **ALL** of the following **EXCEPT**
   A.   socioeconomic status.
   B.   your environment.
   C.   your genetic heritage.
   D.   your relationships with others.

_____5.   Dr. Allen is your social psychology professor. Presently, he is studying the physiological events related to grief. He has proposed a hypothesis which would require him to assess the occurrence of these events. During class, Dr. Allen is describing his research to the class and is asked by a student how he is going to evaluate the occurrence of physiological events. Dr. Allen states that he is going to use the same basic tools that other scientists use in their research and gives the class the assignment of determining what these basic tools are. Which of the following would be considered the basic tool(s) of this type of research?
   A.   PET scan
   B.   MRI scan
   C.   X-rays
   D.   Both A and B are correct.

_____6.   If the students are to get the previous question's assignment correct, they should give **ALL** of the following answers **EXCEPT**
A.   assessment of brain scans.
B.   interpretation of surveys.
C.   determination of correlation.
D.   Both B and C should not have been given as answers to the question.

_____7.   The core value that is defined as "a commitment to obtaining and evaluating information in a manner that is as free from bias as humanly possible" is
A.   accuracy.
B.   objectivity.
C.   skepticism.
D.   open-mindedness.

_____8.   In the past, social psychologists were divided into two categories. These categories are
A.   those who study social behavior and those who study social thought.
B.   those who study social behavior and those who study how people attempt to make sense of their social world.
C.   those who study social thought and those who study how people act in social situations.
D.   **ALL** of the above are correct.

_____9.   Which of the following would be **MOST** appropriate for a correlational research study?
A.   How is preference in art related to preference in music?
B.   What are some of the causes of musical preference?
C.   Why do people join church groups?
D.   Both A and B are **MOST** appropriate for correlational research studies.

_____10.   Herman has signed a consent form to participate in a research study investigating happiness in males over 65 years of age. As part of the consent form, Herman is advised that he will be viewing pictures designed to invoke the emotions of happiness and sadness. He is also informed that some of the pictures will be of females and some will be of males. The design of this study is
A.   correlational.
B.   experimental.
C.   survey.
D.   naturalistic observation.

11.   A _____ demonstrates a relationship between variables.

12.   An unverified prediction is more commonly known as a(n) _____.

13.   When every person in a population has an equal chance of being exposed to each level of the independent variable, the researcher is employing _____ to the experimental conditions.

14.   When conducting a survey, the accuracy of results relies strongly on survey _____.

15.   _____ involves withholding or concealing information from participants.

After You Read... Practice Test #4

_____1. Cynthia, John, Leon, and Martha each conducted a correlational study investigating the relationship between social interaction and drug abuse. The correlation coefficients for each study were as follows: -.91, -.69, -.82, -.78. Upon comparing all four coefficients, what can you say about the correlation?
   A.   The correlation is strong and falls in the negative direction.
   B.   Due to the negative numbers, the correlation is relatively low.
   C.   If **ALL** of the coefficients were positive, the correlation would be strong.
   D.   The correlation is strong and show as social interaction increases, do does drug abuse.

_____2. Social psychologists would investigate **ALL** of the following **EXCEPT**
   A.   the role of heredity in the development of a psychological disorder.
   B.   how our personality affects our health.
   C.   the role of heredity in our social interactions with others.
   D.   the link between depression and memory for negative information.

_____3. Deception is used in a research study
   A.   **only** when necessary.
   B.   whenever the experimenter thinks it is appropriate.
   C.   **only** after the study gains the acceptance of the institutional review board.
   D.   Both A and C are correct.

_____4. Wyatt is very excited. Using 25 participants, he recently conducted a study in an effort to answer the question, "does eating alone cause one to eat more than one would eat when with another person?" Upon careful analysis of his data, Wyatt found that the participants in his study did eat more when alone than with someone else. He meets with his best friend for lunch that day and tells her that he has proven his hypothesis. Wyatt's friend, though, is a psychology major and she immediately corrects his mistake. What is Wyatt's mistake?
   A.   He did not have enough participants to say he has proven his hypothesis.
   B.   In psychological research, one never proves a hypothesis.
   C.   Rather than proving his hypothesis, he has, in actuality, proven a theory.
   D.   He should have kept the information that he has proven his hypothesis to himself because he should respect the confidentiality of his participants.

_____5. A study is conducted in which participants are exposed to either one hour of cartoons, two hours of cartoons, a one hour documentary, a two hour documentary, or no media at all.
   A.   In this study, the dependent variable is media exposure.
   B.   In this study, the independent variable is media exposure.
   C.   In this study, the dependent variable is the number of participants.
   D.   In this study, the independent variable is the cartoon exposure.

_____6. Your author states that providing a formal definition for social psychology is difficult. The reasoning behind this statement is
  A. social psychology is a relatively new branch of psychology and is too narrow in its scope.
  B. social psychology is a relatively new branch of psychology and is changing and progressing too slowly, at present to provide a definition.
  C. social psychology is a very broad field and is continually changing.
  D. **NONE** of the above is correct.

_____7. Researchers use deception
  A. whenever possible because it provides for the "best", most comprehensive research studies.
  B. only after the institutional review board, which assesses the ethical principles of a study, gives its approval.
  C. only when doing an observational study.
  D. Both B and C are correct.

_____8. Social psychology seeks to explain human behavior. Which of the following would a social psychologist investigate?
  A. How our attitudes and our behaviors at times can be inconsistent.
  B. Prejudice and discrimination.
  C. Behavior inconsistent with gender role expectations.
  D. **ALL** of the above would be studied by a social psychologist.

_____9. The branch of evolutionary psychology was founded on the belief that all humans have, overtime, developed psychological mechanisms that are designed to help us survive in the world surrounding us. This has been called our biological heritage. Our biological heritage includes which of the following?
  A. Selection.
  B. Stability.
  C. Strength.
  D. Senses.

_____10. Which of the following represents the weakest correlation?
  A. -.23
  B. +.23
  C. -.98
  D. Both A and B are correct in that they represent an equally weak correlation.

11. Social psychology investigates the influences of social factors on our _____,
_____ and _____.

12. The primary focus of social psychology is the _____.

13. The field of evolutionary psychology suggests that our species has developed
_____ to help us survive.

14. Implicit processes are _____ processes that influence our thoughts and behaviors.

15.   A multicultural perspective recognizes the role of factors including _____,
_____, and _____ ethnicity on our thoughts and
behaviors.

When you have finished... Crossword Puzzle

Across

5. A commitment to obtaining and evaluating such information in a manner that is as free from bias as humanly possible
7. This technique involves efforts by researchers to withhold or conceal information about the purposes of a study from participants

Down

1. A commitment to gathering and evaluating information about the world
2. Refers to a tendency for one event to change as the other changes
3. Branch of psychology that suggests that our species has been subject to the process of biological evolution throughout its history
4. Refers to a set of values, and several methods that can be used to study a wide range of topics
6. How people attempt to make sense out of the social world and to understand themselves and others

Created by Puzzlemaker at DiscoverySchool.com

| *When you have finished… You be the Researcher* |

Earlier in Chapter One, in the section entitled *Taking Full Account of Social Diversity*, we are informed that 64% of the populace in the United States identifies itself as White (of European ancestry). The remaining 36% of the U.S. population categorizes themselves as being from some other descent.

Using your knowledge of the survey method, conduct your own study. Below you will find a simple questionnaire designed to be used to ascertain ethnicity. You are to make copies of this questionnaire and give the survey to at least 25 people. Your participants may be students, professors, or friends. After at least 25 people have completed your questionnaire, you are to determine the percentages of those who categorize themselves as White (of European ancestry) and the percentages of those who categorize themselves as being from some other ethnicity. Percentages can be determined by applying formulas found below:

Identification as White = <u>Number of participants describing themselves as White</u>
Total number of participants

Identification as Other = <u>Number of participants describing themselves as other than White</u>
Total number of participants

Finally, provide answers to the following:

(1)   How does your sample compare to the sample described in your textbook?

_____

_____

_____

(2)   Do you think you would have gotten different percentages if you were to give this survey in another part of the country? If so, why?

_____

_____

_____

(3)   What is one advantage of using the survey method?

_____

_____

(4)   What is one of the requirements that must be met when using the survey method?

_____

_____

ETHNICITY QUESTIONNAIRE

Please DO NOT put your name or any other identifying information on this form

My ethnicity can best be described as (please check one):

____ **African American (Origins in Black racial groups)**

____ **Asian (Origins in the Far East, South East Asia, or India)**

____ **Hispanic / Latino (Origins in Cuba, Mexico, Puerto Rico, South or Central America)**

____ **Native American / Alaskan Native (Origins in the original people of North and South America)**

____ **Native Hawaiian / Pacific Islander (Origins in Hawaii, Guam, Samoa, or other Pacific Islands)**

____ **White (Origins in Europe, the Middle East, or North Africa)**

Ethnic categories based on The 1997 Standards for Collection of Federal Data on Race and Ethnicity: http://www.whitehouse.gov/omb/inforeg/race.pdf

Answers - As You Read...Practice Activities

1. Discuss any movie – paying special attention to character behavior.

2. Formal definition: "The scientific field that seeks to understand the nature and causes of individual behavior and thought in social situations." Restate this definition in your own words.

3. Make sure you restate the definitions in your own words. This will increase your ability to learn the material.

4. Common sense presents a confusing and inconsistent picture of human behavior. It yields much less conclusive evidence than does the scientific method.

5. Individuals. Societies vary greatly in terms of the levels of certain behaviors; but, the individual performs these acts.

6. B, C, A, F, H, D, G, E

7. The actions and characteristics of other people; cognitive processes, environmental variables, cultural context, and biological factors.

8. Evolutionary psychology – strongly believes that biological factors play an important role in social behavior. Evolutionary psychology suggests that we are products of the process of biological evolution and because of this we now possess a number of evolved psychological mechanisms that aid us in dealing with problems related to our survival.

9. Social behavior is defined as how people act in social situations. Social thought is defined as how people attempt to make sense out of the social world and understand themselves and others. Today, social psychologists see a strong connection between the two concepts. They believe we cannot understand how people act without considering their thoughts. The two are inseparable.

10. PET and MRI are two tools used to determine how events in the brain are related to social behavior and social thought. The reason social psychologists do not use these tools to study all aspects of social thought and behavior is that there are many aspects of social thought and behavior, such as attitudes, attributes, and reciprocity that cannot easily be connected to activity in specific areas of the brain.

11. The areas of the brain known to be involved in social thought would be activated for Face A, but would not be activated for Face B.

12. A, D, B, E, C

13. Implicit processes are unconscious processes or those of which we are unaware. Allison is an African American and the assailant was Caucasian. According to Richeson and Shelton (2003), we are much better at recognizing faces of people within our own racial group.

14. The multicultural perspective takes into account the importance of gender, age, ethnicity, sexual orientation, disability, socioeconomic status, religious orientation, and many other social and cultural dimensions. Social psychologists have adopted this perspective because of the changing ethnic makeup of society. The multicultural perspective takes into account the individual's cultural, ethnic, and racial heritage.

15. William McDougall's book written in 1908, espoused the view that social behavior stems from instincts or innate tendencies.

Floyd Allport (1924) wrote that social behavior stems not only from instincts, it also stems from numerous other factors. These include the presence of other people and their specific actions. Allport's book also emphasized the importance of experimentation and contained information on studies that had already been conducted in the field of social psychology.

16. In the 1950's and the 1960's, there was a strong emphasis on group influence on behavior. Also during this time the theory of cognitive dissonance was espoused by Festinger. The tumultuous period of the 1960's is viewed as the epoch in which social psychology actually came into its own. The number of social psychologists rose dramatically as did the topics of consideration.

17. In the 1970's emphasis was placed on gender differences and sex discrimination. The 1980's saw a growing influence on cognitive perspective and application.

18. Systematic observation is careful observation of behavior as it occurs. Naturalistic observation is the observation of behavior in natural settings. A researcher conducting a naturalistic observational study must not, in any way, change the natural behavior of the persons being observed.

One advantage of the survey method is that information can be easily gathered.

19. Anthony's correlation shows a stronger relationship than does that of Martinez. The reason one can interpret this is that Anthony's correlation coefficient is .97 and Martinez's is .69. The coefficient that is closer to 1.0 is strongest. Because both correlations are positive, we know that in both studies that shyness and GPA are positively related with both variables increasing together.

20. The direction is positive and the correlation shows a relationship between the two variables. Also, as one variable increases, so does the other.

21.
a. Number of people in each group
b. There are two levels – participants and 6 participants
c. Cooperative behavior
d. Answers will vary.
e. A representative sample is one in which every member of the population has an equal chance of participating in the study.

22. A confounding variable makes determining causality difficult. When present, a confounding variable makes it difficult to interpret the data.

23. External validity is defined as the extent to which findings of an experiment can be generalized to the "real" world. Experiments are conducted in highly controlled settings which are often highly unlike the setting outside of the laboratory.

24. A mediating variable is a factor that is influenced by the IV and has an effect on the DV.

25. The paragraph should read as follows:

A ~~hypothesis~~ **theory** is defined as a framework for explaining events or processes. In social psychology, as well as in other fields of psychology, researchers seek to ~~prove~~ **assess** theories. In light of this, acceptance of a theory based on the collected data is ~~not~~ what a social psychologist seeks and studies are performed to gather evidence that is ~~contrary~~ **relevant** to the theory.

26. In the "EXAMPLE" box, your answers are probably not going to be the same as the answers given. An example is provided to you simply for comparison purposes.

METHOD	USAGE	EXAMPLE
Correlation	Relationship between variables	Is there a relationship between headaches and number of books read?
Survey	Gather information about behavior	Attitudes toward political candidates
Experiment	Cause and effect	Do people with depression have better memories during summer months?

27. Deception is a technique in which researchers make an effort to withhold information about the purpose(s) of the study. Researchers sometimes use deception because if the participants know the true intent of the study, valid information about the behavior(s) being studied may not be able to be obtained.

28. Two issues involved in the use of deception are that the deception may result in harm to the participants and if a participant feels that he or she was tricked due to the deception, they may develop a negative opinion of social psychology, specifically, and psychology, in general.

29. Two safeguards that should be used whenever deception is used are the informed consent and a careful debriefing. The informed consent gives participants as much information as possible about the study and the procedure that will be used in gaining data. A debriefing provides participants with a detailed description of the study after they have participated in the study.

30. Use deception only if necessary. Be cautious when using deception and, if deception is used, make sure that all precautions are taken to protect the rights, safety and well-being of all participants.

31. The statement should read: If a student at a university in the United States wishes to receive federal funding for his or her research, he or she must have *an Institutional Review Board* evaluate the ethics of the proposed research.

Answers – Cross-Word Puzzle

Across
5. accuracy
7. deception

Down
1. objectivity
2. correlation
3. evolutionary
4. thought
6. science

Answers - After You Read... Practice Test #1

1. B
2. B
3. D
4. C
5. C
6. B
7. A
8. D
9. C
10. D
11. institutional review board
12. one
13. independent
14. experiment
15. multicultural perspective

Answers - After You Read... Practice Test #2

1. D
2. A
3. D
4. B
5. B
6. C
7. D
8. C
9. D
10. A
11. correlational
12. representative
13. informed consent
14. brain activity
15. Positive

Answers - After You Read... Practice Test #3

1. D
2. D
3. D
4. C
5. D
6. B
7. D
8. A
9. B
10. B
11. correlation
12. hypothesis
13. random assignment
14. wording
15. deception

Answers - After You Read... Practice Test #4

1. A
2. A
3. D
4. B
5. B
6. C
7. B
8. D
9. A
10. D
11. thought, feelings, actions
12. individual
13. evolved psychological mechanisms
14. unconscious
15. age, gender, ethnicity

CHAPTER 2

SOCIAL COGNITION:
HOW WE THINK ABOUT THE SOCIAL WORLD

Before You Read...Chapter Summary

Social cognition is best defined as how we think about the social world, try to understand it, and understand ourselves and our place in it. In Chapter Two, your author identifies a few noteworthy issues related to social cognition. You will first become acquainted with the schema. A schema is an organizational framework that guides social thought. As humans, we have schemas for all sorts of experiences. We have schemas for going to the movies, studying, and preparing our favorite dish. In addition, we have schemas for other people, social roles and social groups as well as many other facets of our lives. Once we have developed a schema it becomes a powerful influence in our interpretation of our world, what information we remember, and how we use and interpret the information.

Next, your author identifies the role of heuristics or rules of thumb in speeding up the decision making process when making complex decisions. Some heuristics identified include the representative heuristic, the availability heuristic, and the anchoring and adjustment heuristic. You will, then, become acquainted with two modes of processing in social thought – automatic processing and controlled processing.

As with any other entities, social cognition is not without error. You will be exposed to some of the error involved in social cognition, including the negativity bias, the optimist bias, the escalation of commitment, and the idea of thought suppression, counterfactual and magical thinking. Finally, you will gain an understanding of how feelings can work to shape our thought and visa versa.

Before You Read... Learning Objectives

After reading this chapter, you should be able to:

- Define *schema* and discuss the impact schemas can have on social cognition
- Discuss how schemas direct our thoughts
- Define and discuss *priming* and *schema persistence*
- Explain what *heuristics* are and discuss various types of heuristics
- Clarify the two modes of social thought – automatic and controlled processing
- Discuss sources of error in social cognition including the *negativity bias* and the *optimist bias*, *thought suppression, magical thinking,* and *counterfactual thinking*
- Give details of how feelings can shape out thought and how thoughts shapes our feelings

As You Read...Term Identification

Important Terms to Know
Below is a list of some of the key terms and concepts from this chapter. Make flashcards in order to enhance your recall ability of these terms. Refer to the definitions that are either in boldface or in the margins of this chapter for help. You may also want to include additional terms from this chapter as you deem necessary.

social cognition, (p.38)	representative heuristic, (p. 46)	counterfactual thinking, (p. 55)
schemas, (p. 39)	availability heuristic. (p. 46)	upward counterfactuals, (p. 59)
heuristics, (p. 39)	anchoring and adjustment heuristic, (p. 47)	thought suppression, (p. 60)
affect, (p. 39)	automatic processing, (p. 49)	magical thinking, (p. 61)
priming, (p. 41)	negativity bias, (p. 54)	affect, (p. 63)
unpriming, (p. 41)	optimistic bias, (p. 55)	mood congruence effects, (p. 64)
perseverance effect, (p. 43)	overconfidence barrier, (p. 55)	mood dependent memory, (p. 64)
information overload, (p. 44)	planning fallacy, (p. 55)	terror management, (p. 62)

> ## *As You Read...Practice Activities*

Schemas: Mental Frameworks For Organizing – And Using – Social Information

Your Schema is showing...
(The Impact of Schemas and Social Cognition: Attention, Encoding, Retrieval, page 39)

1. Your author opens Chapter Two by telling a story about selling a used car. This story is well-suited to this chapter in that it provides a strong illustration of some of the concepts involved in social cognition. The author's story was guided by one of the concepts used in social cognition, a schema. In particular, the incident related in the story was guided by his schema for selling a used car. Define the term, **schema** and, using information included in the introduction, describe your schema for going to the movies.

    _____

    _____

    _____

    _____

    _____

    _____

Let's Process This...
(The Impact of Schemas on Social Cognition: Attention, Encoding, Retrieval, pages 40-41)

2. As proud Americans, all United States citizens should have a schema for what it means to be "patriotic." We know that we should stand up whenever *The Star Spangled Banner* is played and when reciting *The Pledge of Allegiance*. We also know that we should place our right hand over our heart and that males should take off their hats, if applicable, when reciting *The Pledge of Allegiance*. Our schema for what it means to be "patriotic", like all schemas, is influenced by **three** basic processes: Attention, encoding and retrieval. Describe each process.

    1._____

    _____

    2. _____

    _____

    3. _____

    _____

The Age Old Question...
(The Impact of Schemas on Social Cognition: Attention, Encoding, Retrieval, pages 40-41)

3.   Ponder the question: Are we more likely to remember information that is congruent with our schemas or do we display the tendency to remember information that is incongruent with our schemas? Within chapter two, your author provides research evidence on this topic. According to this research which do we exhibit the tendency to remember – that which is consistent with our schemas or that which is inconsistent? Describe the findings as delineated in your textbook

_____

_____

_____

Anyway You Slice It...
(The Impact of Schemas on Social Cognition: Attention, Encoding, Retrieval, pages 40-41)

4.   Tanya is a waitress at the local pizzeria. Her boss, Mr. Lashley, is a happy-go-lucky kind of guy and is always playing practical jokes on his staff. Mr. Lashley's personality and his willingness to have fun have contributed to the easy going environment in the restaurant. Today, though, Mr. Lashley arrived at work and noticed that the person who closed last night failed to turn on the main alarm system. Upon Tanya's arrival at work, she finds Mr. Lashley in the process of firing the person who closed.

       The rest of the day followed along those same lines. The tension in the pizzeria was very evident. Each of the employees found themselves walking on eggshells and in fear of "rubbing" Mr. Lashley the wrong way. According to the work of Stanger and McMillon (1992), why will Tanya tend to remember this incident?

_____

_____

_____

Priming...
(Priming: Which Schemas Guide Our Thoughts, pages 41-42)

5.   Priming can be a determinant in which schema becomes activated in a given situation. Describe what is meant by *priming* and give a scenario in which you might experience `the phenomenon of priming in your everyday life.

_____

_____

_____

Can it Last Forever?
(Priming: Which Schemas Guide Our Thoughts, page 41-42)

6. Some researchers have envisioned priming as having a lasting effect on one's thought patterns. Others have demonstrated that the effects of priming can be undone. The process through which schemas can be deactivated is known as un-priming. Using figure 2.3 and the information given within the textbook, discuss the concept of un-priming.

_____

_____

_____

Decrypt the Cryptogram...
(Priming: Which Schemas Guide Our Thoughts, page 41-42)

7. Complete the following cryptogram by matching the correct letter with a number. Some of the information is already provided.

A	B	C	D	E	F	G	H	I	J	K	L	M	N	O	P	Q	R	S	T	U	V	W	X	Y	Z
24		5		21			25	4				17						15	1						

```
S  C  H  E  M  A  S     A     E     C              I  T  I     E           A  M  E
15 5  25 21 17 24 15   24 12 21    5 16 3 19 4  1  4 26 21    20 12 24 17 21 6 16 12

      S     T  H  A  T     H  E           S     I     T  E           E  T
     13 15  1  25 24 1    25 21 10 7     2 15   4 19  1  21 12 7 12 21 1

A              S  E  S     C  I  A     I                 M  A  T  I            .
24 19 23      2  15 21    15 16 5  4  24 10   4 19 20 16 12 17 24 1  4  16 19
```

Created by Puzzlemaker at DiscoverySchool.com

Schemas are Not Always Constructive...
(Schema Persistence: Why Even Discredited Schemas Can Sometimes Influence Our Thoughts and Behavior, pages 42-43)

8. Prejudice, as the name implies, means pre – judging. It is pre – judging someone or something prior to gaining enough factual evidence to make an educated decision. Unfortunately, in society today, prejudice and the discriminatory acts associated with such are alive and well. It is noted by your author that schemas play a role in prejudice. What role do schemas play in the formation of prejudicial attitudes? Explain the connection between schemas and stereotypes.

_____

_____

_____

And You Thought That Was Bad?
(Schema Persistence: Why Even Discredited Schemas Can Sometimes Influence Our Thoughts and Behavior, pages 42-43)

9.   Whether constructive or not, schemas can and do affect our behavior. While learning about the connection between schemas and prejudice, you may have wondered how schemas that are less than constructive might influence behavior. The behavior often associated with prejudicial attitudes – discrimination - may have come to mind. The term *discrimination* can be interchanged with the concept of *self-fulfilling*.

Define the term, *self-fulfilling*. Then, draw a connection between the concepts of schemas, prejudice and the concept of self-fulfilling (discrimination, in this case).

_____

_____

_____

_____

_____

What Do Policemen and Ballet Dancers Have in Common? Not Much…That is, Usually…
(Schema Persistence: Why Even Discredited Schemas Can Sometimes Influence Our Thoughts and Behavior, pages 42-43)

10.   Captain McGill has been a police officer for the past twenty-five years. At a recent meeting designed to increase morale around the police station, all officers were to write down on a piece of paper something of which the other officers might not be aware of. The item the officers were to write was to be about themselves.

Officer Shaw wrote that he had recently traveled to Montana to do some hunting. Officer Jones wrote that she tutored an immigrant family in English in hopes that they may soon make the decision to become American citizens. Captain McGill threw caution to the wind and admitted that he has been taking ballet dancing every Wednesday night at the local YMCA. There were laughs and insulting comments when Captain McGill's statement was read. Over the next few days, Captain McGill noted that officers who usually treated him as "one of the guys" began keep their distance as if he had some sort of disease. In addition, though he was always invited to the Friday night visit to the local bar, Captain McGill was excluded. Explain why the phenomenon that may have occurred in this scenario.

_____

_____

_____

HEURISTICS: HOW WE REDUCE OUR EFFORT IN SOCIAL COGNITION

He is My Son…
(Representative: Judging by Resemblance, page 46)

11.   In the early 1970's, there was a joke going around that went something like this:

A young boy was playing football. While being tackled, he twisted his shoulder and had to be taken out of the game. Upon x-ray it was noted that the child had a separated shoulder and would need surgery to repair the injury. He was prepped for surgery; but, upon entering the room to examine the boy, the doctor exclaimed, "I cannot operate on this boy! He is my son!" Who is the doctor?

In that time period most people immediately answered, "The doctor is the boy's father." This answer, though, was incorrect. The correct answer is that the doctor is the boy's mother. Keeping in mind the time period – the early 1970's - according to the *representative heuristic*, why might this have happened?

_____

_____

_____

Can It Be Wrong?
(Representative: Judging by Resemblance, page 46)

12.   Address the issue of judgments based on the representative heuristics being accurate at times and inaccurate at others. Also, define the term *base rate* and explain the role the base rate plays.

_____

_____

_____

_____

Watch out – The New Candidate for Mayor Cheats…
(Availability: "If I Can Think of It, It Must Be Important", pages 46-47)

13.   There is an election coming up in his hometown and, being the responsible person he is, Tony has been doing some intense research into the candidates and their qualifications. When researching the background of one of the candidates, Conrad Ellison, Tony notes that approximately 20 years Mr. Ellison was kicked out of an ivy-league university for cheating on an exam.

If this is the only information Tony is able to find on Mr. Ellison, according to the *availability heuristic*, do you think Tony will vote for Mr. Ellison?

_____

Watch out – The New Candidate for Mayor Cheats...Continued

Defend your answer.

_____

_____

_____

Is it Available?
(Availability: "If I Can Think of It, It Must Be Important", page 46-47)

14.   Using your critical thinking skills, consider the following:

Allison Moore is an actress. In particular, she is an actress who is often seen in movies designed to teach children moral values. She is a highly religious individual and often speaks to audiences on the importance of morals in the lives of children and in the family. Recently, Allison was arrested for the murder of her 16 year old son.

According to the *availability heuristic*, would you think Allison was, indeed, guilty? Why or why not?

_____

_____

_____

Throw Me an Anchor...
(Anchoring and Adjustment: Where You Begin Makes a Difference, pages 47-48)

15.   In your own words, define what is meant by the *anchoring and adjustment* heuristic.

_____

_____

_____

To Err is Human...
(Anchoring and Adjustment: Where You Begin Makes a Difference, pages 47-48)

16.   "To err is human, to forgive – divine." The *anchoring and adjustment* heuristic can not always provide us with the most sufficient and efficient answer. Explain one of the problems with this heuristic and discuss an instance in which this problem may be greater than in other instances.

_____

_____

AUTOMATIC AND CONTROLLED PROCESSING OF SOCIAL THOUGHT

What is The Difference?
(Page 49)

17.   Define the following in your own words:

1. *Controlled Processing:* _____

_____

2. *Automatic Processing:* _____

_____

Can It Be Done?
(Page 49)

18.   Dr. Napier is a social psychologist who investigates various aspects of social thought by examining activity within the human brain. Today, Dr. Napier is conducting research on evaluative reactions. Explain the concept of *evaluative reactions*.

_____

_____

_____

If Dr. Napier is using EEG readings to evaluate her participants, according to Cunningham et al., 2003, where should activation of the brain show up if the judgment is automatic? If the judgment is more controlled?

_____

_____

According to Ferrita, Garcia-Marques, Sherman, and Sherman (2006), is it possible for Dr. Napier's participants to use both automatic and controlled processing at the same time? If so, when?

_____

_____

_____

In the Future...
(Automatic Processing and Automatic Social Behavior, pages 49-51)

19.   Conducting a partial replication of the study by Cesario, Plaks and Higgins (2006) as delineated in your textbook, Dr. Horton sought to assess the role automatic processing plays in the determination of behavior. The difference between the study conducted by Dr. Horton and that of Cesario et al. was that Dr. Horton used Iraq and America as the primes.

As is a characteristic of a good initial study, Dr. Horton's findings were consistent with those of Cesario et al. What do you think Dr. Horton's findings were?

_____

_____

_____

As If His Life Depends on It...
(The Benefits of Automatic Processing: Beyond Mere Efficiency, pages 51-53)

20.   Ricky is trying to remember the telephone number of a girl he met at a party two nights ago. He is beginning to get very frustrated with the process, though. According to the work of Djiksterhuis and Nordgren (2007), what advice would you give Ricky? Explain your answer.

_____

_____

_____

Your Capacity for the Concept of Capacity...
(The Benefits of Automatic Processing: Beyond Mere Efficiency, page 51-53)

21.   Discuss the role of capacity of information (automatic versus controlled processing) on thought.

_____

_____

_____

POTENTIAL SOURCES OF ERROR IN SOCIAL COGNITION: WHY TOTAL RATIONALITY IS RARER THAN YOU THINK

An Unpalatable Experience...
(Negativity Bias: The Tendency to Pay Extra Attention to Negative Information, pages 54-55)

22. Lana is out with Carlos tonight. They are celebrating her birthday at a new Italian restaurant. For dinner, Lana orders spaghetti and meatballs and a house salad. The spaghetti is wonderful and the meatballs have just the right amount of seasoning. Unfortunately, the house salad is not so wonderful. The lettuce is slightly wilted and the sole slice of tomato has a small bit of mold on it. According to work of Kunda, 1999, what is Lana most likely to remember about this restaurant? Why?

_____

_____

_____

_____

In Your Own Words...
(Optimistic Bias: Our Tendency to See the World Through Rose Colored Glasses, pages 55-57)

23. In your own words explain *the optimistic bias* and *the overconfidence effect*.

Optimistic bias: _____

_____

Overconfidence Effect: _____

_____

How might the optimistic bias play into the overconfidence barrier (Vallone et al., 1990)?

_____

_____

Could This Be Procrastination?
(Optimistic Bias: Our Tendency to See the World Through Rose Colored Glasses, pages 55-57)

24.   Julie, a sophomore at the local university, has been given an assignment for her literature class. She will have one week to complete the assignment and turn it into her professor. Rather than begin the assignment when it is given, Julie has chosen to go on a five day vacation with a friend. When Julie returns she is very tired and puts the assignment off, once again. Now, the day before the assignment is due, Julie sits down and begins her work. Unfortunately, though, Julie has fallen prey to the planning fallacy and is unable to complete her assignment in its entirety on that day. In class, the next morning, Julie pays for her ineptitude with a "0" on the assignment. Explain the *planning fallacy* and how Julie's decision was indicative of this phenomenon.

_____

_____

_____

The Best is Yet To Come...
(The Rocky Past versus The Golden Future, page 57)

25.   Your author notes that individuals tend to predict for themselves a happy future filled with positive occurrences. Why might this be true?

_____

_____

_____

_____

Number Three...
(The War in Iraq: Did The Optimistic Play a Role? pages 58-59)

26.   The third type of cognitive bias is *escalation of commitment*. Explain this concept and tell how it is relevant to a discussion of the war in Iraq.

_____

_____

_____

_____

When I Think About It...
(Counterfactual Thinking: Imaging "What Might Have Been", pages 57-60)

27.   Samantha is 45 years old. She is currently in the process of getting a divorce after 26 long years of marriage. During this period, Samantha is asked to baby sit for her younger sister's newborn. As Samantha rocks the baby, her thoughts turn to the fact that she and her soon to be ex-husband never had a child and now she feels that her "biological" clock has run out. Samantha begins to think what life would have been like with a child.

Samantha's thinking pattern exemplifies the concept of what type of thinking?

_____

How do you know?

_____

_____

_____

It Disappoints Me...
(Counterfactual Thinking: Imaging "What Might Have Been", pages 57-60)

28.   In the above scenario, why is it likely that Samantha is experiencing such great disappointment?

_____

_____

I Will Think About That Another Day...
(Thought Suppression: Why Efforts to Avoid Thinking Certain Thoughts Sometimes Backfire, pages 60-61)

29.   Define the term *thought suppression*. Then, name and describe the two components that the phenomenon involves.

_____

_____

_____

_____

_____

I Will Think About That Another Day...Continued

Name two reasons why people engage in thought suppression.

1. _____

_____

2. _____

_____

WOW...There are a Lot of Mistakes We Can, and Often Do, Make...
(Social Cognition: Some Optimistic Conclusions, page 62)

30.   Considering all of the errors we are prone to make in our social thinking, according to your textbook, in actuality, how good are we, really, when thinking of others? Should we worry?

_____

_____

_____

_____

AFFECT AND COGNITION: HOW FEELINGS SHAPE THOUGHT AND THOUGHT SHAPES FEELINGS

An Accomplished Cyclist...
(The Influence of Affect on Cognition, pages 62-65)

31.   According to your textbook, there is a plethora of research studies that have addressed the topic of thought shaping our state of affect and visa versa. To those who experience the illness of depression, it is a vicious cycle.

Having consistent depressive (negative) thought leads to feelings of depression. In turn, when one is depressed they tend to engage in an increase in depressive thought. In other words, there is a complex interplay between thought and feelings.

There are **five** ways in which feelings affect our thoughts. List each of them and describe each in your own words.

1. _____

_____

_____

An Accomplished Cyclist...Continued

2. _____

_____

_____

3. _____

_____

_____

4. _____

_____

_____

5. _____

_____

_____

Your Congruence is Dependent or is Your Dependence Congruent??!?
(The Influence of Affect on Cognition, pages 62-65)

32.   There are **two** kinds of effects that can occur due to the relationship between affective state and memory. Name and describe these **two** effects.

1. _____

_____

2. _____

_____

The New Job...
(The Influence of Affect on Cognition, pages 62-65)

33.   Dennis is experiencing increased physiological arousal whenever he has to be around his new boss, Kevin. Having some knowledge of the principles of social psychology, Dennis believes that this arousal is due to the fact that Kevin is unsure about Dennis' work and he wants to be there if (or maybe when) Dennis makes a mistake.

The New Job...Continued

Dennis' arousal is consistent with *Schachter's Two-Factor Theory of Emotion* **(1964)**. Discuss Schachter's **two** factors. Also, make up your own example of the theory at work.

1. _____

_____

2. _____

_____

Labeling and Discrimination...
(The Influence of Affect on Cognition, pages 62-65)

34. Cognition can effect emotions by activating our schemas. Explain this concept and, using your critical thinking skills, provide one issue in our society that illustrates this concept.

_____

_____

_____

You Scream, I Scream, We All Scream for Ice Cream...
(Cognition and The Regulation of Affective States, pages 66-67)

35. As human beings, we often find ourselves in situations in which we must control our moods. In an effort to accomplish this task, we must employ our cognitive mechanisms. One way we try to control, or regulate, our moods is through giving into temptation.

Let us consider the following situation:

Danielle has just broken up with her boyfriend of 3 years. She has been crying and, at present, feels depressed. To compensate for the depressed feelings, Danielle visits her local convenience store and purchases a half gallon of her favorite ice cream – cookies and cream. When she arrives back at her home, Danielle promptly sits down and consumes the entire half gallon of ice cream.

Why might Danielle be displaying such behavior? Discuss the research of Tice, Bratslavky and Baumeister (2000).

_____

_____

_____

Separate and Equal?
(Affect and Cognition: Social Neuroscience Evidence for Two Separate Systems, pages 67-68)

36.   There appear to be biological arguments that, rather than being a two-system interplay between cognition and affect, the two systems are separate. Cohen (2005) investigated this idea and your textbook gives an excellent account of the research.

Discuss Cohen's study on the existence of the two systems of affect and cognition as separate.

_____

_____

_____

MAKING SENSE OF COMMON SENSE: A SOCIAL PSYCHOLOGICAL PERSPECTIVE

Is It Wrong to Be Happy?
(Is Being in a Good Mood Always Beneficial? The Potential Downside of Being Up, page 68)

37.   If you were to ask anyone the question, "Do you prefer to be happy or sad?" You would most likely get the answer – "happy." Of course, the answer is "happy" – who actually chooses to be sad? Interestingly, one probably would not benefit from being happy **ALL** of the time.

List and clarify some of the potential downsides of happiness.

_____

_____

_____

_____

_____

_____

After You Read... MyPsychLab Connection

(1)   Basketball anyone?? *Watch Attention.* In this short video clip you will find out exactly how adept you are at paying attention. You will also find out to what details we have the tendency to pay attention. What will you notice?

(2)   Optimism versus pessimism...did you ever realize that your view on life, yourself, others, etc., can affect your health? Well, it can. View the video, *Wellness Study*, and see just how.

(3)   You have been told repeatedly that you are not very good at math since you were a small child. Throughout your schooling – elementary school, middle school, high school, and well into college your grades in math have been - well, let us say - less than optimal. Why might this be happening? *Watch Self-Fulfilling Prophecy* and find out.

After You Read... Practice Test #1

_____1.   Controlled processing tends to occur when
        A.   a situation is very important to us.
        B.   something unexpected happens.
        C.   we need to make a quick decision.
        D.   Both A and B are true of controlled processing.

_____2.   Schemas
        A.   are mental frameworks that allow us to organize large amounts of information.
        B.   are inefficient.
        C.   are almost never accurate.
        D.   are used only on rare occasions.

_____3.   Heuristics
        A.   are a means of reducing cognitive effort.
        B.   are slow and methodical.
        C.   are always accurate.
        D.   require a lot of effort.

_____4.   You have encountered a rather odd looking animal at the zoo. The animal has four legs, a long tail, sharp teeth, gray and white stripes, and a cat-like face. You believe this animal is a tiger because his features are most similar to the typical tiger features. You later find out that this animal was a white tiger. To place / name this animal, you employ the _____ heuristic.
        A.   availability
        B.   representative
        C.   anchoring and adjustment
        D.   congruent

_____5.   Information that does not fit into our schema is best described as
        A.   congruent
        B.   consistent
        C.   incongruent
        D.   reliable

_____6.   Peter has just had an argument with is girlfriend, Alisa, over the purchase of an engagement ring. It seems that Alisa has wanted a ring for a while and felt it was time for Peter to make the purchase. To apologize for the argument, Alisa suggests that Peter allow her to buy him dinner. Peter, showing great irritation, states he would prefer that she did not buy him dinner, citing it as a ploy for Alisa to get in "good" with him – so that he will consider buying the ring. Peter's reaction could be explained by the phenomenon of
        A.   priming.
        B.   cognitive load.
        C.   strength of schema.
        D.   unpriming.

_____ 7.   Brandy works at a local bar and grill. When she arrives at work every morning, she is required to complete her required assignments. She is expected to open the bar and kitchen and make sure all tables are clean and ready for customers. She first opens the kitchen because she will have to have items from the kitchen to open the bar. Finally, she will check all the tables. Brandy's methodical actions can be defined as her _____ for her job.

         A.   framework
         B.   schema
         C.   mental structure
         D.   All of the above are correct.

_____ 8.   The three basic processes influenced by schemas include all **EXCEPT** the following
         A.   encoding.
         B.   retrieval.
         C.   forgetting.
         D.   attention.

_____ 9.   According to a well-known study conducted by Rosenthal and Jacobson (1968), the students who were labeled as high in IQ and "blooming" academically eight months previous to a second testing
         A.   showed little gains in scores on the test.
         B.   showed great gains.
         C.   showed no gain.
         D.   showed a loss.

_____ 10.   Once primed, schemas
         A.   persist forever.
         B.   persist for approximately one year.
         C.   persist until expressed in thought or behavior.
         D.   persist for approximately one month and then are subject to rapid repriming.

11.   The _____ heuristic suggests that the easier it is to use information, the more important the information will seem.

12.   One's current mood can influence our tendency to employ _____ processing.

13.   Marie is thinking about what it would be like to have completed her college degree rather than getting married to Tim and having a child. Marie is engaging in _____ thinking.

14.   The _____ refers to our tendency to assume that things will turn out well in the end.

15.   Processing that is systematic and logical is known as _____ processing; processing that is fast and relatively unforced is known as _____ processing.

After You Read... Practice Test #2

_____ 1. Schemas are all of the following, **EXCEPT**
    A.   relatively consistent among particular cultures.
    B.   are invariant from one person to the next, regardless of cultural influences.
    C.   help us understand our social world.
    D.   reflect unique life experiences.

_____ 2. Schemas act as filters. All of the following are true of schemas as filters, **EXCEPT**
    A.   information consistent with them is more likely to be noticed.
    B.   information consistent with them is allowed to enter our consciousness.
    C.   inconsistent information that does not fit into our schema is **ALWAYS** ignored.
    D.   inconsistent information is noticed if it is extreme and we cannot help but notice it.

_____ 3. According to your author, we are prone to errors in thinking about others.
    A.   All in all, though, we tend to be pretty good at social thought.
    B.   These errors lead us to incorrect conclusions 99.9% of the time.
    C.   These errors, in no way, influence our social thought.
    D.   All in all, though, we tend to come to the correct conclusions approximately 100% of the time.

_____ 4. Sue feels that all physicians are egotistical, self-centered and rude. She comes in contact with a physician who shows great compassion and respect for his patients. Is this capable of altering Sue's schemas of physicians?
    A.   According to Kunda and Oleson (1995), yes.
    B.   According to Kunda and Oleson (1995), no.
    C.   While it does not alter the schema, it does create a new subtype of "physician."
    D.   Both B and C are correct.

_____ 5. James has been known to be rather sure of himself. He is also sure of what he wants in a girlfriend. He wants her to be flawlessly beautiful, tall, with blond hair, and to be highly intelligent. He, though, has learned that his "ideal" girlfriend is probably just a figment of his desires. He has, therefore, had to change his line of thinking and has, in his own words, "lowered his standards." Though this is probably not the way to go about finding a girlfriend, this is the path James has chosen. In addition, the scenario, though hopefully highly unrepresentative of the norm, provides an excellent example of the
    _____ heuristic.
    A.   representative
    B.   anchoring and adjustment
    C.   availability
    D.   fallacy

_____6.   Automatic processing is all of the following, **EXCEPT**
       A.   fast.
       B.   systematic.
       C.   relatively effortless.
       D.   intuitive.

_____7.   If one makes the judgment as to it something is good or bad, activation of the brain is
           seen primarily in the _____. If one makes a more controlled, logical
           judgment, activation is seen in the _____.
       A.   amygdala; temporal lobe
       B.   prefrontal cortex; amygdala
       C.   prefrontal cortex; temporal lobe
       D.   amygdala; prefrontal cortex

_____8.   Felicia has just graduated from high school. While in high school, she had many positive
           and many negative experiences. The experience she remembers with the most clarity is
           the time she was suspended for two weeks due to her participating in a prank on the
           principal. The _____ tells us that it is more likely that
           Felicia will, indeed, have a better memory for the negative material.
       A.   negativity fallacy
       B.   pessimistic bias
       C.   optimistic bias
       D.   negativity bias

_____9.   Using your knowledge of correlations, if you were to estimate the relationship between
           attention to and recall of negative information and social thought, what would your
           correlation tend to look like?
       A.   High and negative.
       B.   High and positive.
       C.   Low and negative.
       D.   Low and positive.

_____10.   How does one's level of motivation follow the idea of the planning fallacy?
       A.   The less motivated we are, the more optimistic our predictions.
       B.   The less motivated we are, the less optimistic our predictions.
       C.   The more motivate we are, the more optimistic our predictions.
       D.   Both B and C are correct.

11.   _____ can best be defined as the fact that once we make a

       decision, we tend to stick to the decision.

12.   Janice has decided to go to college and major in pre-med. When speaking with her admissions

       counselor, she is told that she may have a hard time at first since she did not take biology or

       chemistry in high school. Looking back, Janice has begun to regret her decision in high school

       not to take either of the two subjects. This represents

       _____thinking.

13. Sonya's mother is very ill and, recently, her thoughts have been utterly consumed with this fact. She has an exam tomorrow and just cannot get her mind off of her mother. Kirby advises Sonya to engage in _____ which should help her keep her mind on her exam.

14. The idea that mood influences what information is noticed in a given situation is called _____.

15. Research has found that the better one's mood, the more likely they are to use the _____ heuristic.

After You Read... Practice Test #3

_____1.   Your textbook notes that being in a good mood tends to encourage us to use heuristics. Which of the following can potentially be responsible for our use of heuristics when in a pleasant mood?
   A.   Being in a good mood greatly increases our cognitive load.
   B.   Being in a good mood increases our capacity for processing information
   C.   Being in a good mood reduces motivation to process information carefully.
   D.   Both A and B are correct.

_____2.   Select the downfall(s) of schemas.
   A.   They can, at times, be self-fulfilling.
   B.   They influence how we respond to the world in ways that make the world consistent with our schemas.
   C.   They are virtually useless for providing a basis for our perception of the world.
   D.   Both A and B are correct.

_____3.   Rachelle is enrolled in a child development course at The University of XYZ. She is participating in a study in which she will first be shows a video on the horrors of childhood abuse. This video was very powerful and made Rachelle wonder if her niece was being abuse, as she exhibited some of the symptoms described in the video as being indicative of abuse. When Rachelle leaves the classroom, she has to stop by the store. While in the store, she realizes something strange – she is paying a great deal of attention to children in the store and has even spotted a child she is sure is being abused. Why might this be occurring?
   A.   Schema Separation.
   B.   Self-Fulfilling.
   C.   Unpriming.
   D.   Priming.

_____4.   Robert is a shy, rather unassuming kind of guy. If you were to fill out an information form for Robert, applying the representative heuristic, which of the following would you most likely be asked to put on the form?
   A.   Football Player.
   B.   Captain of the Basketball Team.
   C.   Physics student.
   D.   Hockey Player.

_____5.   You are asked if you think the population of Sicily is less than or greater than 20 million. You are then asked what your estimate of the total population of Sicily is. According to this heuristic you will most likely say that the total population is somewhere near 20 million because the number – 20 million – in the previous question.
   A.   Representative heuristic.
   B.   Anchoring and adjustment heuristic.
   C.   Availability heuristic.
   D.   Numbering heuristic.

_____6.   _____ can be defined as our tendency to have a great deal of
            confidence in our beliefs.
            A.   Overconfidence bias
            B.   Confidence heuristic
            C.   Overconfidence barrier
            D.   Self-assuring heuristic

_____7.   Dr. Smith conducted a study investigating the impact of classical music on motivation.
            Dr. Smith's hypothesis was that increased exposure to classical music would result in
            greater motivation, depending on the task. Participants were exposed to classical music
            for differing lengths of time and were then asked to perform a task at their own pace –
            just as long as that task was completed within a thirty minute period. Half of the
            participants were given simple mathematical problems to solve; while the other half was
            given complex algebra problems to solve. When analyzing the data, Dr. Smith found that
            those given simple mathematical problems to solve showed the tendency to
            underestimate the amount of time it would take them to complete the task. This form of
            optimism is known as the _____.
            A.   planning fallacy.
            B.   estimated error.
            C.   self-confidence bias.
            D.   chronological error.

_____8.   People tend to engage in thought suppression
            A.   as a means of influencing their own behavior.
            B   because suppression makes them feel better.
            C.   because they are told to do so.
            D.   All of the above are correct.

_____9.   The relationship between affect and cognition can best be defined as
            _____.
            A.   one does not affect the other.
            B.   one affects the other.
            C.   the two have no relationship.
            D.   A and C are correct.

_____10.   Though studies have shown that a happy mood tends to _____ creativity
            while a sad or negative mood tends to _____ creativity, Pablo Picasso
            would have, indeed, been the exception to the rule during his "blue" period.
            A.   increase; decrease
            B.   decrease; increase
            C.   Mood has no affect on creativity.
            D.   Any state of mood, no matter if it is negative or positive, will increase creativity.

11.   _____ refers to the information that we tend to notice;

       _____ refers to the process responsible for storing information in our

memory; and _____ refers to the process we use to recover information

already stored in memory.

12.   Larry is an avid TV watcher. Recently he has seen commercials on TV stating that four of every five college students use a certain type of pen. Today, Larry is going shopping for some school supplies and is planning on buying the advertised pen. This is a simple example of the _____ heuristic.

13.   _____ is our tendency to remember negative over positive information.

14.   Tim believes that if he thinks about someone calling him, they will do it. It is quite possible that this may happen by coincidence, but the fact that Tim actually believes that he can control others by thought represents a form of _____.

15.   Research findings have found that two distinct systems may exist for processing social information. One system is concerned with _____, while the other is concerned with _____.

After You Read... Practice Test #4

_____1.   Social thought can occur two ways. One of the ways requires effort and time. The other way is fairly effortless and requires little time. The first definition refers to _____ thought; while the second refers to _____.thought.
   A.   controlled; automatic
   B.   automatic; controlled
   C.   increased; decreased
   D.   decreased; increased

_____2.   In their study, Bargh, Chen and Burrows (1996) investigated the phenomenon of
   A.   schema formation.
   B.   priming.
   C.   the representative heuristic.
   D.   the availability heuristic.

_____3.   Conscious thought can accommodate _____; while unconscious thought can accommodate _____.
   A.   an unlimited amount of information; a very limited amount of information.
   B.   both conscious thought and unconscious thought can accommodate the same amount of information.
   C.   a limited amount of information; an unlimited amount of information.
   D.   None of the above is correct.

_____4.   The negativity bias refers to all of the following **EXCEPT**
   A.   that it has an evolutionary explanation.
   B.   that it suggests that we tend to pay more attention to negative information.
   C.   that it is powerful in influencing our social thought.
   D.   All of the above are correct.

_____5.   Peter, a native and long-time resident of New York, is going to visit his aunt in New Orleans. He has met several people around campus who are from the "deep" south and has found that they are all kind of laid back and, in his words, "slow-moving." According to the _____ heuristic, Peter thinks that all southerners are laid back and "slow-moving."
   A.   anchoring and adjustment
   B.   representative
   C.   availability
   D.   bias

_____6.   Research has shown that we have the tendency to think of our future as
   A.   bleak and full of failure
   B.   full of possibilities even if our past has been filled with both ups and downs
   C.   full of possibilities only if our past has been positive
   D.   full of possibilities only if our past has been primarily negative

_____7. In the 1980's, there was what could best be termed as an AIDS "scare." Everyone was aware of the disease and everyone was concerned. While coming to the forefront, AIDS was not as rampant as diseases such as cancer and heart disease. Due to the scare, though, one would certainly not have been aware of this difference and would have assumed that AIDS was more rampant than the other two diseases.
This is an example of the _____ heuristic.
A. representative
B. anchoring and adjustment
C. bias
D. availability

_____8. Alex is getting ready to change his major from political science to biology. He is going over his transcripts and finds that he has only taken 6 hours of science and is going to have to really push hard to make up for what he lacks. He wants to kick himself for not making the decision to change his major sooner. Alex is engaging in _____ thinking.
A. counterfactual
B. counterproductive
C. perspective
D. foresight

_____9. Michael has recently lost his grandfather and is experiencing depression. Tonight he is going to a play with his girlfriend, Maria, who bought the tickets in hopes of bringing Michael out of his depressed mood. Maria plans to take Michael out to dinner and then to the play. Unfortunately, according to the _____ effect, Michael is not very likely to remember much of the positives about the night.
A. mood incongruent
B. mood dependent
C. mood congruent
D. mood independent

_____10. One's current mood, whether negative or positive,
A. can influence our interpretation of others' behavior.
B. can influence our interpretation of the motives behind others' behavior.
C. can cause us to influence another person's behavior as being opposite of our present mood.
D. Both A and B are correct.

11. When we are depressed we oftentimes demonstrate the tendency to engage in behaviors that are _____ for us, but which, in actuality, tend to make us feel _____.

12. The heuristic that leads us to use a particular starting point and then alter this point is the _____ heuristic.

13   The research of Ohman, Lundquist and Esteves (2001) showed that we are more accurate

       at perceiving _____ facial expressions.

14.   Quinn has recently moved from California to New Jersey. He is very unhappy, but is

       going to "hang in there" and plans to remain in New Jersey for at least two years. This is a

       demonstration of the _____.

15.   The term _____ refers to our current moods and feelings.

When you have finished... Crossword Puzzle

Across

4.   Effect in which the unwanted thoughts occur at an even higher rate than was true before efforts to suppress them began

6.   Mental frameworks developed through experience that, once formed, help us to organize social information

7.   Refers to the processes through which we recover information from memory in order to use it in some manner

Down

1.   A bias that represents a powerful predisposition to expect things to turn out well, overall

2.   Simple rules-of-thumb we often use to make decisions or draw inferences quickly, and with minimal effort

3.   Transitory increases in the ease which specific schemas can be activated produced by experiences relevant to the schemas

5.   Our current feelings or moods

Created by Puzzlemaker at DiscoverySchool.com

When you have finished... You be the Researcher

You have arrived on planet **Sociocog**. There are two types of people on this planet, **the Socargians and the Cogmorians.** The Socargians tend to be a peace-loving people. They are hard-workers, involved in their community through volunteer work and make wonderful parents. On the other hand, the Cogmorians tend to be more aggressive than their Socargian counterparts. They also have the propensity towards being lazy, uninvolved in their community and are not what one would term model parents.

Your task is to conduct a research study investigating the phenomenon of priming using a brief narrative that explains characteristics of either the Socargians or the Cogmorians and a second narrative that includes a story in which there are displays of both pro and anti-social behavior. All of the tools required for this study can be found below.

The procedure is as follows:

(1)   You are to recruit 10 participants.

(2)   You will provide each participant with one of the two narratives describing either the Socargians or the Cormorians. Your participants are to read, silently, the narratives. You will then give each participant the second narrative.

It is your assignment to add to the procedure to make this an experimental study, make the determination as to your hypothesis. You are also to identify your independent variable(s) and its/their levels and your dependent variable(s). (1) Answer the question, why is this study best suited to the experimental method? (2) Also, provide an explanation as to the priming mechanism at work in this study. (3) Do you think that the priming in this study would be successful or not? Explain your reasoning.

<u>Procedure</u>:

_____

_____

_____

_____

_____

<u>Hypothesis(es):</u>

_____

_____

Independent Variable(s):

_____

_____

Levels of the Independent Variable(s):

_____

_____

_____

Dependent Variable(s):

_____

_____

1. _____

_____

_____

2. _____

_____

_____

3. _____

_____

_____

Answers – After You Read...Practice Activities

1. A schema is a mental structure that helps us organize social information and guides the processing of that information. Schemas are developed through our experiences. Your schema might begin with your arrival at the theatre, paying for your ticket, buying popcorn and a drink, and finding a seat within the auditorium.

2. Attention refers to what information we choose to pay attention to. Encoding refers to the process through which information gets stored in our memory. Retrieval refers to the process through which we recall information that has been stored in our memory.

3. Research shows people tend to report information that is consistent (congruent) with our schemas; but, at the same time, information that is inconsistent (incongruent) with our schemas may also be present in memory.

4. Tanya will remember the information because it is inconsistent with her schema for Mr. Lashley.

5. Priming occurs when recent experiences make some schemas more active than they would otherwise be, and, as a result, they exert stronger effects on our current thinking.

6. Un-priming is undoing priming which seems to only persist until the thoughts or actions primed are expressed.

7. Schemas are cognitive frameworks that help us interpret and use social information.

8. Schemas can alter our perception of the social world. This can lead to prejudice, which, unfortunately, is resistant to change as are the schemas from which they are formed.

9. Self-fulfilling = influences our responses to the social world in ways that make it consistent with the schema.

   Schema leads to the formation of prejudicial attitudes which, in turn, lead to discriminatory practices/actions.

10. Captain McGill's admission that he has been taking ballet classes was inconsistent with the schema of a policeman. Policemen are thought of as strong and tough. Ballet dancers are thought of as fragile and frail. The inconsistency of the two as seen in the person of Captain McGill influenced the reaction of others in the precinct to him and he was treated differently than he had been prior to his declaration.

11. According to the representative heuristic, the closer the resemblance between an individual and a typical member of a group, the more likely he or she is to be perceived as being part of the group. In the 1970's, doctors were more often men than women, so the doctor was presumed to be a man and the boy's father.

12. Accuracy occurs because there are often certain traits that are embodied by people in certain occupations. Inaccuracy can occur because people tend to ignore base rates. Base rates represent the frequency with which events or patterns occur in the total population.

13. He will not vote for Mr. Ellison because the information available is inconsistent with the schema of what would be considered a "good" elected official.

14. Probably not. Positive information available here is inconsistent with what would our typical schema of a murderer.

15.   Receive a base and then adjust it.

16.   Adjustments are often not sufficient to overcome the initial anchor. One instance of when this would be used is when one is less capable of engaging in effortful thought.

17.   Controlled processing = systematic, logical, careful, effortful

        Automatic processing = fast, effortless, intuitive

18.   Evaluative reactions are social judgments relating to where we tend to like or dislike something.

        If automatic – activation should show up in the amygdale. If the judgment is controlled, the activation should be in the frontal cortex, especially in the medial prefrontal cortex and the ventrolateral prefrontal cortex.

        Yes, in situations involving uncertainty.

19.   Participants should show greater hostility if they were primed with the "GAY" faces than they would if they were primed with the "STRAIGHT" faces.

20.   Ricky should direct his attention elsewhere. This is sometimes superior to careful and deliberate thought.

21.   Conscious thought has precise limits in terms of the quantity of information it can handle. Unconscious thought has a larger capacity than does conscious thought.

22.   Lana is most likely to remember the negative information. This is because we tend to pay more attention to negative information than we do to positive information.

23.   Optimistic bias = tendency to believe that everything will turn out well.

Overconfidence effect = tendency to have greater confidence in our beliefs than is justified.

Individuals tend to believe everything will turn out well and have great confidence in this belief.

24.   Planning fallacy is our tendency to underestimate how long it will take us to do something. Julie underestimated the amount of time it would take her to complete her assignment. She thought she had enough time and went on a vacation and, in light of this, she was not able to complete the assignment on time and received a "0".

25.   When we think about our past, we tend to recall negative events. When we think about the future, we tend to think about positive things. The dominance of positive thoughts makes us highly optimistic about our future.

26.   Escalation of commitment is a bias that states if we make a decision, we tend to stick with that decision even if there are negative outcomes.

        This is what happened to President Bush in Iraq. He committed troops and, though there have been a high number of casualties, he has not brought the troops home.

27.   Samantha's thinking if indicative of counterfactual thinking. She is thinking about what could have been.

28.   Samantha is experiencing such great disappointment because counterfactual thinking can influence our affective state.

29.   Thought suppression involves restraining thoughts from coming into our consciousness.

People engage in thought suppression are that thought suppression is a means of influencing our feelings. Also, people engage in thought suppression when they are told to do so, maybe a therapist or a counselor.

30. We tend to be better than thought when thinking of others despite all of the errors that we can make. Therefore, we should not be worried at all.

31.
(1) Mood congruence effect
(2) Creativity
(3) Our tendency to engage in heuristic processing
(4) Influence our interpretation of the behavior of others
(5) Influence our emotions

32. Mood congruent effects and mood dependent memory.. Affective states serve as retrieval cues influencing what we can remember.

33. According to Schachter's theory, we experience the emotion and then interpret our emotion from the situation.

34. Cognition activates schemas containing strong affective components which, in turn, affect our current feelings.

35. Danielle is acting as she is because emotional distress can reduce our capacity to control our impulses. Tice, Bratslavky and Baumeister (200) argued that we choose to engage in the behavior; therefore, it is not automatic.

36. According to Cohen (2005), one system is concerned with reason; while the other is concerned with emotion.

37. Downsides to happiness include:

(1) When we are happy, we are more likely to do what others ask of us.
(2) It may also decrease our capacity to process information which increases our use of heuristics.
(3) It reduces motivation to process information carefully.

Answers – Cross Word Puzzle

Across

4. rebound
6. schemas
7. retrieval

Down

1. optimistic
2. heuristics
3. priming
5. affect

Answers – Practice Test #1

1.	D
2.	A
3.	A
4.	B
5.	C
6.	D
7.	D
8.	C
9.	B
10.	C
11.	availability
12.	automatic
13.	counterfactual
14.	optimistic bias
15.	controlled; automatic

Answers – Practice Test #2

1.	B
2.	C
3.	A
4.	D
5.	B
6.	B
7.	D
8.	D
9.	B
10.	D
11.	escalation of commitment
12.	counterfactual
13.	thought suppression
14.	mood congruence
15.	availability effect

Answers – Practice Test #3

1.	B
2.	D
3.	D
4.	C
5.	B
6.	A
7.	A
8.	D
9.	B
10.	A
11.	attention, encoding, retrieval
12.	availability
13.	negativity bias
14.	magical thinking
15.	logic, intuition

Answers – Practice Test #4

1.	A
2.	B
3.	C
4.	D
5.	B
6.	B
7.	D
8.	A
9.	B
10.	D
11.	bad, better
12.	anchoring and adjustment
13.	negative
14.	escalation of commitment
15.	affect

CHAPTER 3

SOCIAL PERCEPTION:
PERCEIVING AND UNDERSTANDING OTHERS

Before You Read...Chapter Summary

In Chapter Three, your author presents the topic of social perception by focusing on three of its most central aspects: nonverbal communication; attributions; and impression formation. In section one, you will become familiar with the notion of nonverbal communication. Nonverbal communication is just what you probably think it is – communicating without the use of speech. Your author will introduce you to five "channels" of nonverbal communication: facial expressions, eye contact, body movements, posture, and touching. You will learn that there are five basic emotions that are linked with recognizable facial expressions. One such pairing would be the emotion of happiness and the smile. You will also learn that some of these pairings are exhibited cross-culturally. What this means is that if you were to visit another part of the world, let's say China, and smile, everyone in China would perceive the fact that you are experiencing happiness as opposed to some other emotion. As is seen with facial expressions as "channels" of nonverbal communication, your author goes into the four other "channels" and some of the research backing for each of these concepts. Finally, this section ends with a discussion of the use of nonverbal cues in deception and a short dialogue concerning gender differences in reading nonverbal cues.

Section 2 of this chapter deals with attributions. Here you will be introduced to several theories of attributions; including Jones and Davis's Theory of Correspondent Inference (1965) and Kelley's Theory of Causal Attributions (1972). You will also learn of some of the biases that can exist when using attributions. One such bias is the Fundamental Attribution Error. If one is operating under the Fundamental Attribution Error, they tend to believe that if someone never scores when playing basketball, it is the player's fault – he or she is just not good at basketball. On the other hand, in accordance with this bias, if you are a basketball player and not scoring, it is because the referee keeps calling penalties on you. In other words, in the first situation, the player is personally responsible. Not scoring is due to something internal – the player his or herself. In the situation involving you, though, not scoring is not your fault. Instead it is due to something external – the referee.

The final section of Chapter Three provides discussion of impression formation. Your author presents the phenomenon of the first impression and its importance. You will also learn how one can go about presenting his or herself in the best light. That is, you will learn what one needs to do to put that unforgettable best foot forward.

Before You Read... Learning Objectives

After reading this chapter, you should be able to:

- Discuss how nonverbal cues aid in our perception of others.
- Elaborate on the types of nonverbal cues, including those that are considered universal.
- Define the term *attribution*.
- Explain the main concepts behind two classic attributional theories – *The Theory of Correspondent Inference* and *The Theory of Causal Attributions*.
- Describe the *Fundamental Attribution Error*.
- Explain the *Actor-Observe Effect* and the *Self-Serving Bias*.
- Elaborate on the self-defeating pattern of attributions.
- Discuss *impression formation* and also how impressions can be managed.

As You Read...Term Identification

Important Terms to Know
Below is a list of some of the key terms and concepts from this chapter. Make flashcards in order to enhance your recall ability of these terms. Refer to the definitions that are either in boldface or in the margins of this chapter for help. You may also want to include additional terms from this chapter as you deem necessary.

nonverbal communication, (p. 72)	microexpressions, (p. 80)	noncommon effects, (p. 85)
attribution, (p. 72)	channel, (p. 81)	consensus, (p. 86)
impression formation, (p. 72)	linguistic style, (p. 81)	consistency, (p. 86)
impression management, (p. 72)	correspondent inference, (p. 83)	distinctiveness, (p. 86)
nonverbal cues, (p. 76)	fundamental attribution error, (p. 89)	action identification, (p. 89)
staring, (p. 78)	actor observer bias, (p. 93)	correspondence bias, (p. 89)
body language, (p. 78)	self serving bias, (p. 93)	implicit personality theories, (p. 100)

As You Read...Practice Activities

NONVERBAL COMMUNICATION: THE UNSPOKEN LANGUAGE OF EXPRESSIONS, GAZES AND GESTURES

Do Not Change the Channel...
(Nonverbal Communication: The Basic Channels, pages 76-78)

1. There are **five** channels through which nonverbal communication takes place. Name and describe the **five** channels.

    1. _____

    _____

    2. _____

    _____

    3. _____

    _____

    4. _____

    _____

    5. _____

    _____

Your Emotions are Showing...
(Unmasking the Face: Facial Expressions as Clues to Others' Emotions, pages 76-78)

2. Research has shown there are **five** basic emotions. Name each of them.

    1. _____

    2. _____

    3. _____

    4. _____

    5. _____

I Beg Your Pardon…Are You Staring?
(Gazes and Stares: Eye Contact as a Nonverbal Cue, page 78)

3.   According to Kleinke (1986), a high level of gazing is a sign of what?

_____

Also, there is an exception to this rule. Elaborate on this exception.

_____

_____

_____

Ballet and Social Psychology?? Of Course!
(Body Language: Gestures, Posture, and Movements, pages 78-79)

4.   Aronoff, Woike and Hyman (1992) conducted an exciting study investigating the idea that body
        movements and postures can be indicative of one's emotional state. Discuss the findings of this
        study.

_____

_____

_____

_____

_____

How Rude!
(Body Language: Gestures, Posture, and Movements, pages 78-79)

5.   The gesture that represents the okay sign in the United States (touching the first finger to the
        thumb to form a circle with the other three fingers upright) is considered an extremely foul
        gesture in Brazil. Define the term, *gesture*. Name a gesture we tend to use in the United States
        and define its meaning. By the way…the okay sign in the United States is interpreted as giving
        someone "the finger" in Brazil.

_____

_____

_____

_____

Are You Touching Me?
(Touching: Is a Firm Handshake Really a "Plus?" pages 79-80)

6.   Lynn has just given Marilyn pat on the hand. Why did Lynn touch Marilyn? The answer to this question depends on several factors. What are they? What are some of the things that a touch can represent?

_____

_____

_____

_____

Shake My Hand Like You "Mean It"!
(Touching: Is a Firm Handshake Really a "Plus?" pages 79-80)

7.   Terry's father has always been told he that whenever he shakes someone's hand, he should shake it firmly and with conviction. Terry's father must have known of the research of Chaplin et al. (2000). What exactly did Chaplin et al. find?

_____

_____

_____

The Greatest Deception Men Suffer is from Their own Opinions - Quote by Leonardo Di Vinci...
(Deception: Recognizing It Through Nonverbal Cues and Its Effects on Social Relations, pages 80-81)

8.   You have the sense that your lab partner is not being completely truthful with you and you would like to know if your feelings are correct. You have read research on deception; in particular, you have read the research conducted by Ekman (2001) and Etcoff et al (2000).

You have read the research conducted by Ekman (2001) and Etcoff et al (2000).

How would these researchers advise you in this situation? That is, is it possible to conclusively determine if your partner is lying to you?

_____

_____

_____

_____

How Needful are You?
(Deception: Recognizing It Through Nonverbal Cues and Its Effects on Social Relations, pages 80-81)

9.　　Who would be better at reading nonverbal cues: someone who is high in the need to belong or someone who is low in the need to belong? How do we know?

_____

_____

_____

_____

Helpful Hints...
(Deception: Recognizing It Through Nonverbal Cues and Its Effects on Social Relations, pages 80-81)

10.　　There are four cues that have been found to be helpful in determining if someone is attempting to deceive you. Answer the following in relation to these cues.

　　A.　　Carla has just made her first cake. She has a few of her friends over and asks them to sample the cake. Carla is paying careful attention to any cues as to whether or not her friends are enjoying the cake. She notices that one of her friends kind of narrows her eyes and raises her nose – what one might call "squinshing" her face. Then her friend gets a broad smile on her face. Carla assumes that her friend does not find the cake particularly appetizing. Which of the four cues is Carla using?

　　　　_____

　　B.　　Carla's friend, Bradford, will not look her in the eye; but, is stating that he absolutely "loves" the cake. In addition, Carla notes that Bradford is blinking more than usual and that his pupils are slightly over-dilated for the light in the room. Which of the four cues is Carla observing?

　　　　_____

　　C.　　Carla's friend from her psychology class, Helen, is smiling brightly, but is not looking at Carla when she states how great the cake is. Which of the four cues is Carla observing?

　　　　_____

　　D.　　The last person, Markus, has a HUGE smile on his face and is even making the "yum" sound. Unfortunately, Markus' smile appears to be forced and quite fake. Which of the four cues is Carla observing?

　　　　_____

The Great Debate – Women versus Men…Hmmm…
(Making Sense of Common Sense, pages 83-84)

11.   Provide a summary of the section entitled, *Are Men Really "Clueless" When It Comes to Nonverbal Cues? Fiction – and Fact – About Gender Differences in Nonverbal Communication.* Make sure you cite the research studies that add support to the answer to the question – are men really "clueless?"

_____

_____

_____

_____

_____

Why – Oh – Why??
(Making Sense of Common Sense, pages 83-84)

12.   Why are there differences in the interpretation of nonverbal clues in women versus men?

_____

_____

_____

ATTRIBUTION: UNDERSTANDING THE CAUSES OF OTHERS' BEHAVIOR

To What Do You Attribute That Behavior??
(From Acts to Disposition: Using Others' Behavior as a Guide to Their Lasting Traits, pages 85-86)

13.   Define the term *attribution*.

_____

_____

_____

Exactly What Can I Infer From Your Behavior?
(From Acts to Disposition: Using Others' Behavior as a Guide to Their Lasting Traits, pages 85-86)

14.   You and your new spouse are going to buy your first home. The two of you have narrowed the decision down to two choices.

Exactly What Can I Infer From Your Behavior?...Continued

Characteristics of each house are listed below.

House 1	House 2
Pool	Near a Playground
Two Story	Two Story
Fenced Yard	Fenced Yard
On 1 Acre of Land	On 1 Acre of Land

If you and your spouse decide to buy house 1, a home with a pool is something that is important to you. If you decide to buy house 2, being near a playground if important to you. That is, the two of you will have made this decision based on the existence of the pool or the playground and not on the fact that the house has two stories, has a fenced yard, or is on one acre of land.

This is an example of which theoretical perspective?

_____

Next, in an effort to elaborate on this perspective, provide your own example.

_____

_____

_____

_____

_____

Summarize...
(From Acts to Disposition: Using Others' Behavior as a Guide to Their Lasting Traits, pages 85-86)

15.   Summarize the theory proposed by Jones and Davis (1965).

_____

_____

_____

_____

To What Can You Attribute the Cause?
(Kelley's Theory of Causal Attributions: How We Answer the Question "Why"? pages 86-87)

16.   Harold Kelley (1972) proposed the *theory of causal attributions*. According to Kelley, we use this theory to determine the "why" of behavior. That is, we ask why someone performed a certain behavior. In determining the answer to the "why", we consider **three** types of information.

Name and describe the **three** types of information upon which we rely.

1. _____

_____

2. _____

_____

3. _____

_____

Which combination of the three items above results in an internal attribution for another's behavior? Which results in an external attribution for another's behavior?

_____

_____

_____

_____

Two Dimensional...
(Other Dimensions of Causal Attributions, pages 87-88)

17.   There are **two** dimensions of causal attributions. Name and discuss them.

1. _____

_____

2. _____

_____

Consider the two choices one has in each of the above dimensions and describe a factor that fits into each category. Then, using your examples, use your critical thinking skills to determine what would a stable/controllable and a stable/uncontrollable cause look like and what would an unstable/controllable and an unstable/uncontrollable cause look like.

Two Dimensional...Continued

You will have four answers to this. A chart is provided for your convenience.

Stability

Stable   **Unstable**

Controllable

Control

Uncontrollable

Is it Fate?
(Fate Versus Personal Actions, pages 88-89)

18.   If one states that an event is seen as due to fate, what are they saying?

_____

_____

_____

If someone states that an event is seen as a personal action, what are they saying?

_____

_____

_____

What is *construal*? How is construal related to fate?

_____

_____

I am Indeed Amazed When I Consider How Weak My Mind is and How Prone to Error. - Quote by Rene Descartes
(Attribution: Some Sources of Error, pages 89-96)

19.   Dr. Allister is having a rather tough day. He went out to his car this morning and realized that he had forgotten his keys in the house. Unfortunately, Dr. Allister had already locked the door to the house and had to wait for a locksmith to open the door for him. When he was finally able to retrieve his keys, he realized that he had missed a class and had forgotten to call the university to let them know that he would not be there. He got into his car and began driving to school, only to realize that he was very low on gas. As consistent with everything else that had transpired in Dr. Allister's life this morning, he was not able to make it to the gas station as he had thought he would and promptly ran out of gas. Dr. Allister called the auto club and they were able to bring him enough gas to get him to the local gas station. He filled his tank and finally made it to work 4 hours late. Though he was 30 minutes late, Dr. Allister was able to make it to his next class. When he explained his luck (or lack thereof) that morning, his class seemed sympathetic. After class, though, students were heard talking about how absent minded Dr. Allister is and how he needs to "get his head on straight."

The students are obviously overestimating the role of dispositional factors in Dr. Allister's behavior. When one has the tendency to overestimate the role of dispositional factors, (A) what type of error has he or she committed? (B) This error is also known as what kind of bias?

A.   The _____ Error

B.   The _____ Bias

We May Not Know Our Own Strength…
(Building the Science: Classics of Social Psychology – The Fundamental Attribution Error: Stronger Than You Might Guess! page 91)

20.   Fill in the following in an effort to summarize research conducted by Jones and Harris (1967) investigating the *fundamental attribution error*.

Hypothesis: _____

_____

_____

Task: _____

_____

_____

Independent Variable and Levels:

1. _____

2. _____

We May Not Know Our Own Strength…Continued

Dependent Variable: _____

Results: _____

_____

_____

Culture Matters…
(Cultural Factors in the Fundamental Attribution Error, pages 90-91)

21.   According to Triandis (1990), what is the difference between an *individualistic* and a *collectivistic* culture?

_____

_____

_____

Your textbook lists Western Europe, the United States, and Canada as individualistic cultures. Can you think of a culture that would be considered collectivistic? Why?

_____

_____

_____

Is it "Normal"?
(Cultural Factors in the Fundamental Attribution Error, pages 90-91)

22.   What is *the norm of internality*? How is this norm "played" out in both individualistic and collectivistic cultures?

_____

_____

_____

_____

_____

You Act – I Will Observe...
(The Actor-Observer Effect: "You Fell; I Was Pushed", pages 92-93)

23.   A recent divorcee, Belinda, has a court order that her ex-husband will pay $250.00 per month in child support for each of their two children. Unfortunately, Belinda's ex-husband has not paid child support for the last two months. Belinda spoke with her lawyer and told him that she was not surprised at her ex's response as he is an uncaring, callous man. The lawyer, in turn, called Belinda's ex who told the lawyer that he was behind on his support because he does not have a job and the job market is highly competitive at this time. When Belinda's lawyer spoke with Belinda again, she stated that she could not understand why her ex did not just get a job at McDonald's. She feels that he should do whatever it takes to pay the support.

First, explain *the actor-observer effect*. Then, summarize this scenario according to this effect.

_____

_____

_____

_____

_____

_____

Is This Self-Serve?
(The Self-Serving Bias: "I'm Good; You are Lucky", pages 93-94)

24.   You have had a 4.0 GPA for the past two semesters. According to the self-serving bias, to what do you attribute your GPA? To what would you attribute another's 4.0 GPA?

_____

_____

_____

_____

APPLICATIONS OF ATTRIBUTION THEORY: INSIGHTS AND INTERVENTIONS

Your Attributes can be Depressing...
(Attribution and Depression, pages 96-97)

25.   Marty is clinically depressed. He sleeps much of the day, has lost his appetite, feels worthless and hopeless. In addition, he no longer enjoys golfing, a sport in which he participated on almost a daily basis.

Your Attributes can be Depressing...Continued

According to the *self-defeating* pattern of attribution, to what would Marty attribute his triumphs?

_____

_____

Bruder et al (1997) have found that a new form of therapy has been successful helping depressed individuals change their attributional style. Discuss this new form of therapy.

_____

_____

_____

_____

IMPRESSION FORMATION AND IMPRESSION MANAGEMENT: COMBINING INFORMATION ABOUT OTHERS

Classics in the History of Psychology – Solomon Asch...
(The Beginnings of Research on First Impressions: Asch's Research on Central and Peripheral Traits, pages 98-99)

26.   Solomon Asch (1907 – 1996) was one of the classics in social psychology. Two of Dr. Asch's most memorable and referenced research studies include a study on conformity and a study on impression formation.

As delineated in your textbook, in your own words, discuss the research of Solomon Asch in relation to impression formation. Be sure to include the concept of *central traits*.

_____

_____

_____

_____

_____

Time is of the Essence...
(How Quickly are First Impressions Formed? Pages 99-100)

27.   Answer the question, "How quickly are first impressions formed?" Cite research evidence that support this claim.

_____

_____

_____

_____

_____

The Shaping of Your First Impressions...
(Implicit Personality Theories: Schemas That Shape First Impressions, pages 100-101)

28.   What is an *implicit* personality theory?

_____

_____

_____

Discuss the research of Nyman (1995) regarding how implicit personality theories can shape our first impressions of others.

_____

_____

_____

_____

_____

_____

One Piece of Information + One Piece of Information = A Unified Impression...
(Impression Formation: A Cognitive Perspective, pages 100-101)

29.   There are **two** suggestions as to how we combine information to form a unified impression of someone. What are they?

1. _____

_____

One Piece of Information + One Piece of Information = A Unified Impression…Continued

2. _____

_____

The Components of the First Impression…
(Impression Formation: A Cognitive Perspective, pages 100-101)

30.   Professor Sherriff is preparing a quiz for his class. He is planning to ask a question regarding which components contribute to the all important first impression. You are Dr. Sherriff's assistant and are asked to provide an answer to this question. In light of this, you provide the following:

Some models of impression formation stress the role of _____, which are often referred to as categorical judgments. Other models stress the role of _____.

IMPRESSION MANAGEMENT: THE FINE ART OF LOOKING GOOD

Are You Managing Your Impression?
(Tactics of Impression Management and Their Relative Success, pages 103-106)

31.   There are **two** strategies people use to enhance their image. Name and discuss these **two** strategies.

1. _____

_____

2. _____

_____

Give examples of how people engage in the first tactic.

_____

_____

_____

_____

Are You Managing Your Impression?...Continued

Give examples of how people engage in the second tactic.

_____

_____

_____

_____

Give an example of a time when you used the first tactic.

_____

_____

_____

Give an example of a time when you used the second tactic.

_____

_____

A Return to Cognitive Load...
(Impression Management: The Role of Cognitive Load, pages 105-106)

32.   Discuss the research of Pontari and Schlenker (2000) concerning the idea that some individuals sometimes feel discomfort when they are in social situations. Because of this, they tend to become anxious and worry about how others will perceive them. These people are much more comfortable when they are busy with other tasks that tend to distract them from the feelings of anxiety and this actually enhances their ability to present themselves in a favorable light.

_____

_____

_____

_____

_____

What Social Psychology Tells Us About …Speed Dating…
(Can We Really Choose the One We Might Love in a Few Minutes? Page 107)

33.   Summarize this section.

_____

_____

_____

_____

_____

_____

After You Read... MyPsychLab Connection

(1)   Do first impressions really carry as much "weight" as we tend to believe? The answer is YES! Try *Simulate: Impression Formation*. In this exercise you will find an activity based upon the work of noted psychologist, Solomon Asch (1946). Asch was interested in how we tend to form impressions of others.

(2)   Certainly motivation is important in the work environment. Those who are motivated are more productive than those who are not motivated. People who are highly motivated also have the tendency to like their jobs more as compared to those who are low in motivation. Check out *Watch: Work Setting and Motivation.*

(3)   What is the difference between an internal and an external attribution? To answer this question, listen to *External Attribution and Internal Attribution.*

After You Read... Practice Test #1

_____1.   Janice realizes that someone is looking intensely at her. In fact, they are staring.
According to your textbook, why might this person is staring?
- A.   They like Janice.
- B.   They are expressing positive feelings.
- C.   They are expressing negative feelings.
- D.   All of the above represent reasons as to why this person might be staring at Janice.

_____2.   According to Jones and Davis's Theory of Correspondent Inference (1965)
- A.   we have the tendency to make inferences on the basis others' actions about specific traits and dispositional factors they might possess.
- B.   we have the tendency to focus on certain types of actions; including those that are infrequent.
- C.   we have the tendency to focus on certain types of actions; including those that are freely chosen.
- D.   Both A and C are correct.

_____3.   You have asked your best friend, Rob, to meet you for dinner at his convenience over the weekend. He has your cell phone number and states that he will call when he is available. It is now Sunday evening and you have not heard from Rob. According to Kelley's Theory of Causal Attributions, when searching for an answer as to why Rob may have exhibited this behavior, we focus on **ALL** of the following, **EXCEPT**
- A.   consensus.
- B.   constancy.
- C.   consistency.
- D.   distinctiveness.

_____4.   The term *construal* is defined as
- A.   whether we exhibit the tendency to think about things in either a concrete or abstract way.
- B.   whether we exhibit the tendency to view others' behavior as due to internal or external events.
- C.   whether we exhibit the tendency to view our own behavior as due to internal or external events.
- D.   whether we exhibit the tendency to think about things in either a positive or negative way.

_____5.   Attributions can best be defined as
- A.   our efforts to define our behavior.
- B.   our efforts to define the behavior of others.
- C.   Both A and B are correct.
- D.   Neither A nor B are correct.

_____

6. _____ are concrete examples that are consistent with a given trait; whereas, _____ are mental summaries that are abstracted from repeated observations of others' behaviors.

A.	Exemplars; abstractions	C.	Attributes; abstractions
B.	Abstractions; exemplars	D.	Abstractions; attributes

7. Lula is trying to deal with a personal family issue, the deadline on a term paper, her social psychology final examination, and her calculus final examination all on the same day. It is likely that Lula is experiencing
   A.   cognitive extreme.
   B.   cognitive overload.
   C.   cognitive suppression.
   D.   None of the above is correct.

_____8. According to the theory of _____, we have the tendency to understand others' traits by observing their behavior – particularly behavior that is, among other things, freely chosen.
   A.   noncommon effects
   B.   social desirability
   C.   social observation
   D.   correspondent inference

_____9. Mario has failed his anthropology midterm; while George has passed with an A. According to the actor – observer effect, Mario is likely to explain the cause of his grade as being _____ and the cause of George's grade as being

_____.
   A.   internal; external
   B.   external; internal
   C.   personal; situational
   D.   Both A and C are correct.

_____10. Oftentimes we use _____ to make ourselves look more appealing to others.
   A.   other-enhancement
   B.   self regulation
   C.   self-enhancement
   D.   attributions

11. _____ is a form of communication in which no words are exchanged.

12. Wendy is staring at you. From your social psychology class you are aware that this can either mean one of two things: either she is likes you or is feeling some form of _____ towards you.

13.   You have just completed an interview and reach out to shake the interviewer's hand. You are demonstrating an _____, which can be defined as a body movement that carries an unambiguous meaning in the United States.

14.   There are a few ways in which one can tell if someone is lying to them. One of the ways is eye contact. If someone is lying the pupils in the eye often appear _____ dilated than they would if they were telling the truth.

15.   Research findings have shown that _____ are more sensitive to nonverbal cues than are _____.

After You Read... Practice Test #2

_____ 1.   According to your textbook, there are five basic emotions. They include all of the following **EXCEPT**
    A.   anger
    B.   disgust
    C.   fear
    D.   All of the above are among the five basic emotions.

_____ 2.   A(n) _____ is a difficult to suppress reaction that usually appears immediately after an emotion loaded event.
    A.   emotion
    B.   eye blink
    C.   microexpression
    D.   macroexpression

_____ 3.   The Theory of Causal Attributions states that we tend to focus our attention to three major types of information. The information includes consensus, consistency and distinctiveness. We are most likely to attribute someone else's behavior to internal causes if
    A.   consensus is high.
    B.   distinctiveness is high.
    C.   consistency is low.
    D.   None of the above is correct.

_____ 4.   Mrs. Houston is substituting for her son's high school history class. She appears to be very confused about what the class should be doing. After class, a few of the students are discussing how disorganized Mrs. Houston is and how she should not be allowed to substitute teach. Jones (1979) would refer to this as the _____ at work.
    A.   dispositional bias
    B.   situational bias
    C.   attitudinal bias
    D.   correspondence bias

_____ 5.   Jacque is meeting a blind date tonight. His friends have been telling him that he needs to have his hair cut and, since he wants to put his best foot forward, he gets a haircut prior to meeting the blind date. Jacque is engaging in _____.
    A.   impression management.
    B.   nonverbal communication.
    C.   attributional bias.
    D.   deception.

_____ 6.

Last night at his graduation party, Harry gave Lincoln, one of his best friends, a hug. Lincoln's reaction, according to your textbook, depended on
   A.   who did the touching.
   B.   the nature of the touch.
   C.   the length of the touch.
   D.   All of the above are correct.

_____7.   People who have a strong need to belong in a group tend to
   A.   read nonverbal with much less accuracy that verbal cues.
   B.   pay less attention to others.
   C.   want others to understand them.
   D.   want to understand others more than someone without a strong need to belong.

_____8.   Leon is smiling, but is failing to maintain eye contact with you. You assume Leon is lying because
   A.   it is difficult to smile and maintain eye contact at the same time.
   B.   of interchannel discrepancies.
   C.   you know Leon is not happy today.
   D.   Leon is normally not so shy

_____9.   Erin is not a person to be trusted. At least this is your opinion. You base this on the fact that she
   A.   has lied to you in the past.
   B.   blinks a lot when she speaks with you.
   C.   Both A and B are correct.
   D.   does not smile a lot around you.

_____10.   Hillary is in a class with James. Today, James made a total fool out of himself when answering the professor's question regarding how to find the square root of a number. Hillary is sure that James is as intelligent as the side of a barn. Hillary's assessment is known as the _____ and refers to our tendency to perceive others as acting they way they act because of internal factors, such as intelligence (or lack thereof).
   A.   classical ideal theory
   B.   interchannel discrepancy
   C.   fundamental attribution error
   D.   anchoring and adjustment theory

11.   Dr. Pontey's drama class is unhappy that their recent performance of *King Lear* was less than optimal. Many of the students are attributing their performance to lack of practice time due to the semester schedule. Dr. Pontey, though, is holding the class, itself, responsible. Dr. Pontey is using the _____.

12.   According to the _____, Rob believes that he won the art competition because he is a great artist; while last year when Wally won, it was because Emily, did not enter.

13. _____ theories state that when people exhibit certain traits they are also likely to have some closely related traits.

14. In an effort to increase her appeal to the sorority, Jennifer has started wearing conservative clothing, wearing less makeup and studying more. Jennifer is engaging in _____.

15. Solomon Asch (1949) defined _____ as those traits that powerfully influence our impressions of others.

After You Read... Practice Test #3

_____1.	We can often identify someone who is lying to us. We can do this by paying attention to **ALL** of the following **EXCEPT:**
A.	Microexpressions
B.	Interchannel Discrepancies
C.	Eye Contact
D.	All of the above are correct

_____2.	The evolutionary perspective:
A.	Explains that appearance is more important to women than men because appearance is closely related to the social status of women.
B.	Explains that eye contact is more important to women than men.
C.	Explains that women are more likely than men to perceive their world as "rosy".
D.	Explains that women are less likely to rely on appearance for understanding others

_____3.	Rachelle is trying to understand the behavior of Terry's behavior. In other words, Rachelle is trying to find a(n) _____ for Terry's behavior.
A.	Attribution.
B.	Negative option.
C.	Positive option.
D.	Interchannel Discrepancy.

_____4.	Mary believes that Ron is not contributing to the class discussion on the fundamental attribution error because he is stupid and unable to articulate his opinions. Mary is making a(n)
A.	Attribution for Ron's behavior.
B.	Correspondent Inference.
C.	Situational Attribution.
D.	Both A and B are correct.

_____5.	_____ is defined as the extent to which a person reacts in the same manner in different events or to different stimuli.
A.	Consensus.
B.	Consistency.
C.	Distinctiveness.
D.	Commonality.

_____6.	If an individual can influence factors, those factors are termed _____.
A.	Distinct.
B.	Consistent.
C.	Controllable.
D.	Uncommon.

_____7.   _____ is/are defined as forces outside of our control that predetermine our destiny.
A.   Environmental factors.
B.   Fate.
C.   Faith.
D.   Situational factors.

_____8.   Most people tend to display the _____ bias; while those who are depressed tend to display the _____ bias.
A.   Self-serving; Self-descriptive.
B   Self-descriptive; Self-determining.
C.   Self-serving; self-defeating.
D.   None of the above are correct.

_____9.   The basic principle of the Gestalt psychology is:
A.   Attributions are unjust.
B.   The whole is often greater than a sum of its parts.
C.   The sum of the parts is greater than the whole.
D.   A and C are correct.

_____10.   Wendy is very intelligent. Because of Wendy's intelligence, she is rarely asked out because it is also felt that she is not fun-loving. This is an example of a(n):
A.   Implicit Personality Theory.
B.   Self-serving error.
C.   Situational marginal.
D.   Other Descriptive Bias.

11.   _____ refers to our desire to present ourselves as we want others to

perceive us.

12.   Larry is explaining the behavior of Chris as being due to his laziness even though he has been out

of town for a week. Larry is committing the _____ bias.

13.   _____ is defined as specific traits.

14.   _____ is, simply, defined as communication without speech.
15.   A firm, welcoming _____ is often indicative of wanting to make a

positive first impression.

After You Read... Practice Test #4

_____1.   When someone is lying, they tend to:
   A.   Look directly at you.
   B.   Look away from you.
   C.   Have pupils that are more dilated than usual.
   D.   Both B and C are correct.

_____2.   Women find it necessary to pay particular attention to nonverbal behavior because they:
   A.   Have less power in society.
   B.   Have less status in society.
   C.   Have little else to do.
   D.   Both A and B are correct.

_____3.   Some internal causes of behavior tend to be quite stable overt time. These include:
   A.   Personality traits.
   B.   Temperament.
   C.   Both A and B are correct.
   D.   None of the above is correct.

_____4.   The _____ would explain the idea behind Mrs. Allen's view that Debbie should accept responsibility for hitting her car.
   A.   Norm of Internality.
   B.   Norm of Externality.
   C.   Norm of Responsibility.
   D.   Norm of Substantially Responsible Behavior.

_____5.   The United State is a(n) _____ culture.
   A.   Collectivistic.
   B.   Individualistic.
   C.   Moral.
   D.   Nativistic.

_____6.   Collectivistic cultures emphasize:
   A.   The individual in society.
   B.   The group in society.
   C.   Responsibility of others.
   D.   Consistency.

_____7.   _____ traits are those that strongly shape the impression others have concerning us.
   A.   Representative.
   B.   Bias.
   C.   Peripheral.
   D.   Central.

_____ 8.   We experience _____ when we are trying to handle more information
              than we can at any given moment.
              A.   The counterfactual error.
              B.   The counterproductive error
              C.   Cognitive Intrusion.
              D.   Cognitive Overload.

_____ 9.   The theory of correspondent inference states that we try to infer others' traits from
              observing certain aspects of the behavior. These aspects include all of the following
              except:
              A.   Is the behavior freely chosen.
              B.   Is the behavior low in social desirability.
              C.   Is the behavior common.
              D.   All of the above are true of the theory.

_____ 10.   The fact that there are five basic emotions suggests that:
              A.   There are only five emotions that can be shown by facial expressions.
              B.   Emotions can influence our productivity.
              C.   All emotions are universal.
              D.   All of the above are untrue.

11.   A high level of eye contact (or staring) is a sign of potential _____.

12.   A good way to make a good first impression is to shake someone's hand in a _____

        manner.

13   _____ are better at identifying nonverbal cues than _____.

14.   The extent to which a person reacts in the same manner in virtually all situations is considered a

        definition for _____.

15.   The _____ is described as our tendency to see our behavior as

        being due to internal causes and the behavior of others as being due to external causes.

When you have finished... Crossword Puzzle

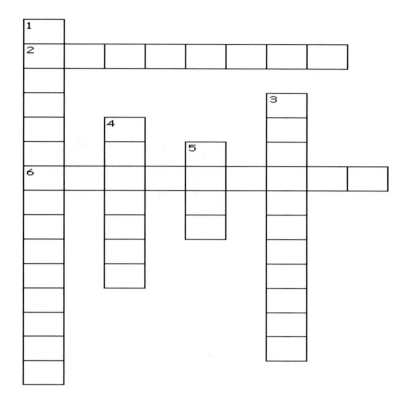

Across

2.   Personality theories that present the idea that certain traits go together
6.   Extent to which other people react to a given situation in the same manner as the person we are considering

Down

1.   Extent to which an individual reacts in the same manner to different stimuli
3.   Extent to which an individual reacts to an event in the same way over time
4.   Types of traits that strongly influence the overall impression of people
5.   Type of enhancement that is designed to increase our appeal to others

Created by Puzzlemaker at DiscoverySchool.com

When you have finished... You be the Researcher

Using the form on the next page, describe yourself based on the following traits on a scale from 1 – 5:

1 = poor
2 = fair
3 = neutral
4 = good
5 = excellent

Then, using copies of the same form, have 4 of your classmates, friends, or family (anyone that knows you well enough) rate you on the same traits. Percentage-wise, analyze your data. That is compare your self-concept to the how others' perceive you. For example, let us say that you rate yourself on the trait, intelligent, as a 4 - how many of your respondents also rated you a four. How many rated you higher than a 4? Lower than a four?

_____

_____

_____

_____

Answer the question, "According to the responses of your respondents, how accurate would you consider your self-concept?" In addition, if there are great discrepancies, what do you think can account for these?

_____

_____

_____

_____

_____

PLEASE PROVIDE A NUMBER (1 – 5) FOR EACH TRAIT USING THE FOLLOWING SCALE

1	2	3	4	5
Poor	Fair	Neutral	Good	Excellent

Trustworthy   _____

Intelligent   _____

Honest   _____

Caring   _____

Empathetic   _____

Dependable   _____

Determined   _____

Efficient   _____

Friendly   _____

Giving   _____

Thankful   _____

Cheerful   _____

Thoughtful   _____

Warm   _____

Wise   _____

Decisive   _____

Reliable   _____

Attentive   _____

Answers – After You Read…Practice Activities

1. Facial Expressions; Eye Contact; Body Movements; Posture; Touching

2. Anger; Fear; Happiness; Sadness; Disgust

    Face A. The hint is the smile.

3. Friendliness; Staring is an exception which can lead one to interpret anger and hostility.

4. Diagonal/angular posture = dangerous
    Rounded posture = warm

5. Gestures are body movements that carry specific meanings in any given culture. Students are to provide an example; but one such example would be the thumbs up sign. This is indicative of a job well done.

6. Lynn was most likely showing a caring interest in Marilyn. The answer depends on who did the touching, the nature of the contact, and the context in which the touch was given. Provide your own answer as to what you believe a particular touch can represent.

7. Chaplin et al (2000) found that the firmer, longer, and more enthusiastic the handshake, the higher we tend to rate the shaker in terms of extraversion and openness to experience. Also, the firmer the handshake, the more likely we are to rate the shaker favorably upon our first meeting.

8. Ekman (2001) found that we tend to do only a tiny bit better than chance in determining if someone is deceiving us. Also, according to Ekman (2001) we have the tendency to believe that all people are honest and, therefore, simply do not look for clues to deception.

Etcoff et al (2000) found that we like to be polite to others and this tends to make us hesitant to identify deception and we miss clues that would cue us to the fact that deception is being used.

In light of these findings, both Ekman and Etcoff et al would tend to tell us that it is difficult to determine definitively if someone is lying to us.

9. Pickett, Gardner and Knowles (2004) found that those who are high in the need to belong are better at reading nonverbal cues. This is because people high in this trait pay careful attention to other people and want to understand them.

10. A. Microexpressions
    B. Eye Contact
    C. Interchannel Discrepancies
    D. Exaggerated Facial Expressions

11. Basically, something should be said concerning the idea that the researchers cited in this section found that women are better at men in interpreting certain nonverbal cues. These include specific personality characteristics (Vogt and Colvin, 2003), identifying current mood state (Hall and Matsumoto, 2004), and in sending and interpreting nonverbal cues, in general (Mayo and Henley, 1981; Rosenthal and DePaulo, 1979). Women also tend to be superior in the interpretation of body movement and gestures (Rosenthal and DePaulo, 1979). Women also tend to remember one's appearance better than do men (Horgan et al., 2004).

    Student, though, will provide their own summary.

12. Women are more perceptive of another's appearance. Women also have less prestige in society and have to pay attention to nonverbal cues more than men, who tend to have a greater amount of prestige, do.

13. An attribution is an explanation for the causes behind someone else's behavior or for our own behavior.

14. Theory of Correspondent Inference. Provide an example similar to the one provided.

15. Jones and Davis (1965) proposed the theory of correspondent inference which, in summary, states that we have the tendency to attribute others' behavior to stable traits in three conditions: (1) The behavior is freely chosen. (2) The behavior results in noncommon effects. (3) The behavior is low in social desirability.

16. *Distinctiveness* - the extent to which a particular person reacts in a similar manner in a different situation.

    Consensus – the extent to which we all respond in a similar way.

    Consistency – the extent to which a particular person reacts in a similar manner most of the time.

    Low consensus, high consistency, and low distinctiveness = internal attributions.
    High consensus, high consistency, and high distinctiveness = external attributions.

17. Control = how much a person can influence factors. Factors are either controllable or uncontrollable.

    Stability = are the factors long-standing or do they change. Factors are either stable or unstable.

18. If an event occurred due to fate, the event occurred due to forces outside of our control. If an event occurred due to personal actions, the event occurred due to our own actions. That is, the events that occur due to personal actions are freely chosen.

The level of construal is defined as whether we tend to think about events concretely or in abstract terms. Construal is related to fate in thinking in abstract terms (high levels of construal) are more likely to accentuate the important of fate as a factor. Likewise, thinking in more concrete terms influences us to understate the importance of fate.

19. A. Fundamental Attribution Error
    B. Correspondence Bias

20. Hypothesis: The fundamental attribution error is so strong that even when people are told how to act (or, in this case, from what opinion to write), we can still ascertain that person's beliefs from what how they have acted or what they have written.

    Task: Read an essay in support of or in objection to Castro's rule in Cuba. IV and levels: Instructions given. In level one, participants were given the instructions that the essay writer chose to write the essay and that it reflects his or her true opinion. In level two, participants were told that the writer was told to write in agreement with either a pro or con position.

    DV: Estimation of the author's true beliefs.

    Results: In both conditions, the participants showed the tendency to believe that they could uncover the author's true beliefs from the essay.

21. Individualistic cultures emphasize individual freedom. On the other hand, collectivistic cultures emphasize the group.

    China could be considered a collectivistic culture. The reason for this is the Chinese show less emphasis on the individual in society and more

22. The norm of internality refers to the idea that people are responsible for their own actions and the subsequent outcomes. This norm is present and strong in individualistic cultures; while it is either weak or absent in collectivistic cultures.

23. The actor-observer effect is the tendency to explain our behavior as situational or external; while explaining the behavior of others as dispositional or internal.

   In summary, Belinda has determined that her ex's behavior is due to internal causes of lack of care. Belinda's ex has determined that his being behind in his support payments is due to the fact that he cannot get a job – an external cause.

24. You would tend to attribute your 4.0 GPA to internal causes. That is, you are intelligent and studious. You would attribute another's 4.0 GPA to external causes. That is, others are just lucky or they did well on their tests (which contributed to the 4.0) because they were just having exceptionally good days on the days tests were given.

25. Marty would attribute negative outcomes to internal causes and positive outcomes to external causes.

   The new form of therapy focuses on getting the person who is depressed to modify their attributional style. That is, help them see internal causes for good outcomes and external causes for negative outcomes.

26. Dr. Asch provided his participants with a list of traits describing a stranger. He, then, asked his participants to specify their impression of the stranger by checking the traits that were felt to "fit" into their impression of the stranger. Asch was attempting to find out if people tend to add traits together to form

emphasis on group membership, including that of the family.

an impression. He found that this was not the case, though. In the example of a list of traits supplied by the text, participants based their impressions on one word which was changed within the two lists. In this case, the words on the two lists were "warm" and "cold". Dr. Asch came to the conclusion that these two words, in this case, were "central" traits. That is, these two words were pivotal in forming our impression of the stranger.

27. According to research evidence, impressions are formed very rapidly. Research evidence that may be cited includes the research of Todorov, Mandisodza, Goren and Hall (2005) and the research of Willis and Todorov (2006).

28. An implicit personality theory is defined as beliefs that certain traits or characteristics tend to "go together."

   The research of Nyman (1995) investigates that use of traits commonly associated with being first-born, middle children, and only children.

29. One suggestion is that we tend to form unified impressions by adding together discrete pieces of information. Another suggestion is that we tend to average all available information.

30. Abstractions; behavioral exemplars.

31. Self-enhancement and impression management. Give your own examples.

32. Pontari and Schlenker (2000) has extraverts and introverts take part in a mock interview in which they presented themselves either as they are or opposite of what they are.

33. Student will summarize the section.

Answers – Cross Word Puzzle

Across

2.   implicit
6.   consensus

1.   distinctiveness
3.   consistency
4.   central
5.   self

Answers – Practice Test #1

1.   D
2.   A
3.   B
4.   A
5.   C
6.   A
7.   B
8.   D
9.   D
10.   C
11.   nonverbal communication
12.   anger
13.   gesture
14.   more
15.   women; men

Answers – Practice Test #3

1.   D
2.   A
3.   A
4.   D
5.   C
6.   C
7.   B
8.   C
9.   B
10.   A
11.   impression formation
12.   correspondence
13.   exemplars
14.   nonverbal communication
15.   handshake

Answers – Practice Test #2

1.   D
2.   C
3.   D
4.   D
5.   A
6.   D
7.   D
8.   B
9.   C
10.   C
11.   norm of internality
12.   fundamental attribution error
13.   implicit personality theory
14.   impression management
15.   central

Answers – Practice Test #4

1.   D
2.   D
3.   C
4.   A
5.   B
6.   B
7.   D
8.   D
9.   D
10.   D
11.   anger
12.   firm
13.   women/men
14.   distinctiveness
15.   actor observer effect

CHAPTER 4

THE SELF:
ANSWERING THE QUESTION, "WHO AM I?"

Before You Read...Chapter Summary

Chapter Four begins with an account of your author's journey through the clandestine world of the chat room. Though the journey is a bit (to say the least) strained and rough at first, your author soon settles into this covert world. The purpose of this journey is to introduce the concept of the self. The self can best and most simply be defined as "who we are." It involves our temperament, our personality and any individual traits associated with who we are and who we want to be. The self composes our unique individuality and identity as a human being. The self is not something to which only the beholder is privy. We present our self in the open for the world to see, to interpret and, yes, to scrutinize. Because the world is given the task of interpreting who we really are, it seems in our best interest to present our best and most capable of being liked self to the world. In section one, the concept of self-promotion is discussed. Self promotion can be equated to a kind of ad campaign for the self. We want to present a positive light so that people will "buy" into who we want others to think we are. Another way to present a favorable picture is to use the strategy of ingratiation, which includes making our self look good by making those around us also look good.

After the rather enlightening discussion of the self and our presentation of who we are and who we want others to think we are, the focus of Chapter Four shifts to the search for the answer to the question; "How do we know who we are?" One central method is through introspection. In section two, we learn what introspection is, how it is helpful and how it also might be misleading. We also learn that, rather than looking inwardly, we can gain knowledge of the self by taking an observer's view – that is, seeing ourselves as others tend to see us. The next item presented in your textbook is the personal versus social identity continuum. This continuum represents two distinct sides of the self: the personal identity self is an individualized self while the social identity self is a self interacting with others in specific social groups.

No discussion of the self would be complete without a discussion of the concept of self-esteem. In this section, the focus is three-fold: the measurement of self-esteem, the desirability of high degree of self-esteem and differences seen in men and women in reference to their level of self-esteem. Chapter Four comes to an end with explanations of how we tend to evaluate the self, including an explanation of the self-serving bias, and the emotional, cognitive and behavior consequences of the self as a target of prejudice.

Before You Read…Learning Objectives

After reading this chapter, you should be able to:

- Discuss the strategies we use to present ourselves to others in the best possible light.
- Define and elaborate upon the concepts of *self promotion, self verification, ingratiation,* and *self depreciating.*
- Explain how we tend to present ourselves online and the concept of asynchronous communication.
- Elaborate on the concept of self-knowledge, including ways in which we gain self-knowledge.
- Define the concept of *introspection.*
- Explain the ideas concerned with the actor versus the observers in self-knowledge.
- Elaborate on the personal versus the social identify continuum.
- Compare and contrast the terms intragroup and intergroup.
- Explain how the situation is important in the self we present to the world.
- Discuss how we tend to manage any conflicts among our identities.
- Explain the term *self -efficacy* and delineate between people who are high in self-efficacy and those who are low in self-efficacy.
- Define the terms *self control* and *self construal.*
- Discuss the concept of self *esteem* including how it is measured, how being high in self-esteem can be both elevating and hindering, and how women and men differ in the concept.
- Elaborate on the idea of social comparison – both downward and upward.
- Discuss *Festinger's social comparison theory.*
- Describe the *self serving bias.*
- Explain the concept of *unrealistic optimism.*
- Elaborate on the self as a target for prejudice – including the idea of *stereotype threat.*

As You Read…Term Identification

Important Terms to Know
Below is a list of some of the key terms and concepts from this chapter. Make flashcards in order to enhance your recall ability of these terms. Refer to the definitions that are either in boldface or in the margins of this chapter for help. You may also want to include additional terms from this chapter as you deem necessary.

stigma consciousness (p. 113)	intragroup (p. 120)	upward/downward social comparisons (p. 133)
self-promotion (p. 114)	personal-versus-social identity continuum (p. 120)	social comparison theory (p. 134)
self-verification perspective (p. 114)	salience (p. 120)	self-evaluation maintenance model (p. 135)
ingratiation (p. 114)	intragroup comparisons (p. 121)	above average effect (p. 136)
self-depreciating (p. 115)	autobiographical memory (p. 126)	positive illusions (p. 136)
asynchronous forms of communication (p. 117)	possible selves (p. 126)	devalued group (p. 138)
introspection (p. 117)	self-control (p. 127)	stereotype threat (p. 140)
observer (p. 117)	self- efficacy (p. 127)	
social identity theory (p. 120)	self-esteem (p. 129)	

As You Read...Practice Activities

SELF – PRESENTATION: MANAGING THE SELF IN DIFFERENT SOCIAL CONTEXTS

Harvey for President...
(Self-Presentation Tactics, page 114)

1. Harvey is running for student body president and has recently developed posters announcing his candidacy. A copy of his flyer can be found below. By displaying this flyer, Harvey is engaging in the phenomenon of what?

_____

According to the self-verification perspective, has Harvey included the proper information in his flyer? Why or why not?

_____

_____

_____

California Girl...
(Self-Presentation Tactics, page 114)

2.   Janice is a California native and a freshman at I Can Do It University in Florida. At present, Janice does not know anyone at the school and plans to attend a social gathering tonight so that she will have the chance to get to know others who attend the school.

According to Chen, Chen and Shaw (2004), what type of people will Janice prefer?

_____

_____

_____

Anything I Can Do To Make YOU Look Better...
(Self-Presentation Tactics, page 114)

3.   Define the term *ingratiation*.

_____

_____

_____

Put your critical thinking skills to work in answering the following: You have a new girlfriend and want to make your best impression on her. According to the phenomenon of ingratiation, what would you do to impress her? Provide concrete examples; for example, you would tell her over and over again how beautiful she is. Now it is your turn...

_____

_____

_____

Okay, Maybe I Am a Loser...
(Self-Presentation Tactics, page 114)

4.   Angela has a boyfriend who feels threatened by the fact that she was raised in a very affluent family, while he was raised in a low income environment. In order to present herself to him in a way that he will accept her, she is constantly putting herself down and making herself look bad. What type of self-presentation tactic is Angela displaying?

_____

Is That Truly Honest??
(Self-Presentation Tactics, page 114)

5.   According to Kashy and DePaulo (1996), are our presentations of who we are always honest?

    _____

    How is this correlated (related) to the amount of friends one might have?

    _____

    _____

    _____

The "Online Self"...
(Making Sense of Common Sense, page 115)

6.   When an individual is on the internet, does he or she have the tendency to apply different rules to his or her mode of self-presentation? Does someone present an impression much like someone would have in person? These questions are answered in this section of your textbook. Read the section entitled, *The Internet: Presenting Your Online Identity* and, using research evidence, answer the questions at the end. Make sure in your answer you provide a definition for *paralinguistic cues* and *asynchronous forms of communication.*

    _____

    _____

    _____

    _____

    _____

    _____

SELF-KNOWLEDGE: HOW DO WE KNOW WHO WE ARE?

William Godwin, a 18th century English author, wrote: "The philosophy of the wisest man that ever existed is mainly derived from the act of introspection..."
(Introspection: Looking Inward to Discover the Causes of Our Own Behavior, page 117)

7.   The phenomenon of introspection has long been the topic of many thoughtful writings – psychological as well as philosophical. Philosophers such as Wittgenstein, Aristotle and Renee Descartes, who believed that it is through introspection that we have complete access to all contents of the mind, all wrote of the phenomenon. The term *introspection* quite literally means "looking within" (from the Latin "spicere" meaning "to look" and "intra" meaning "within").

William Godwin, a 18ᵗʰ century English author, wrote: "The philosophy of the wisest man that ever existed is mainly derived from the act of introspection…"…Continued

Is introspection all that it is truly "cracked up" to be? Support your answer by elaborating on the text provided.

_____

_____

_____

_____

_____

The Future Self…
(Introspection: Looking Inward to Discover the Causes of Our Own Behavior, page 117)

8.   Introspection might be misleading when we are attempting to predict our future feelings in response to a given event. Describe the research of Gilbert and Wilson (2000) which investigated our predictions of how we will feel one year after an event.

_____

_____

_____

_____

How Others See Us…
(The Self from the Other's Standpoint, page 119)

9.   If you remember from Chapter Three, actors exhibit the tendency to make situational attributions for their behavior, while observers exhibit the tendency to cite dispositional factors as attributional causes for their behavior.

If we use the observer's perspective in describing ourselves we are more likely to characterize ourselves in _____ factors.

How Would You Describe Yourself as You Were Five Years Ago?
(The Self from the Other's Standpoint, page 119)

10.   Describe the research of Pronin and Ross (2006) regarding how we tend to describe ourselves when using the observer's perspective.

_____

How Would You Describe Yourself as You Were Five Years Ago?...Continued

_____

_____

_____

THINKING ABOUT THE SELF: PERSONAL VERSUS SOCIAL IDENTITY

Isn't Life Just a Continuum?
(Page 120)

11.   Describe _social identity theory_ (Taifel & Turner, 1986).

_____

_____

Below is a pictorial representation of the Personal Identity – Social Continuum. Under each end of the continuum, on the lines provides, place the letter of the characteristic that is associated with that particular identity.

A.	Involves contrast between individuals	G.	Importance is placed on how we differ from other individuals
B.	We think of ourselves as members of specific groups	H.	Intragroup
C.	Emphasis is group description	I.	Involves contrast between groups
D.	We think of ourselves as individuals	J.	Importance is placed on how our groups differs from other groups
E.	Emphasis is self description		
F.	Intergroup		

PERSONAL IDENTITY   **SOCIAL IDENTITY**

Isn't Life Just a Continuum?...Continued

1._____   1._____

2._____   2._____

3._____   3._____

4._____   4._____

5._____   5._____

Are You Truly Who You Say You Are???
(Page 121)

12.   Can we truly say that one of our "selves" represented on the personal/social identity continuum is our "true" or "real" self? Answer this question and provide research findings as found within the textbook to support your answer.

_____

_____

_____

Yes, Virginia, We Do Change With Age...
(Who I Am Depends on the Situation, pages 121 – 123)

13.   The way we tend to see ourselves has been shown to change with age. Describe the types of changes as addressed within this section.

_____

_____

_____

_____

Another Side of the Issue –Culture...
(Pages 121 – 123)

14.   Trafimow, Silverman, Fan & Law, 1997, conducted a fascinating study investigating the idea that people who are "bi-cultural" tend to possess **two** separate identities – one for each cultural background. Provide the following information in your discussion of this study:

Hypothesis: _____

_____

_____

Another Side of the Issue –Culture…Continued

Procedure: _____

_____

_____

_____

Participants:

Group I _____

Group II _____

Results: _____

_____

_____

_____

_____

Which Self is Most Important to Us?
(Pages 121 – 123)

15.   There are **three** things that help determine which self is most important to us at **any particular** moment. Describe each of these.

1. _____

_____

2. _____

_____

3. _____

_____

What Social Psychology Tells us About...
(How We Manage When There is Conflict Among Our Identities, page 124)

16.   Provide a summary on this section. As always, make sure you include research findings within your summary.

_____

_____

_____

_____

_____

_____

_____

_____

And...Just What is *Your* Opinion?
(Who I Am Depends on Others' Treatment, pages 123, 125)

17.   People who are high *self-monitors* tend to care very much what other people think of them. Let's say you have a student in a social psychology class. Today, the professor is discussing prejudice and discrimination. This particular student, a male, is from planet Boppie and feels extremely negative towards people from the planet Loppie. In other words, this student has prejudicial attitudes towards the inhabitants of Loppie. The professor is praising the inhabitants of Loppie as highly intelligent, honest, trustworthy, and undyingly committed to their families. This student strongly disagrees with this interpretation. Instead of arguing the point, though, this student keeps his opinions to himself. This scenario illustrates the results of a study conducted by Tajfel in 1978.

        Explain the findings of this research and address the statement, "We can't always hide certain aspects of the self."

_____

_____

_____

_____

_____

_____

Does Our Self Perception Change or Is It Relatively Stable?
(Possible Selves: The Self Over Time, page 126)

18.   Wilson and Ross (2003) addressed the question presented above in a series of studies. The researchers were mainly interested in how the *distant self* was perceived in relation to the *near distant self.*

Discuss the results of the Wilson and Ross studies.

_____

_____

_____

_____

What about our *future self* or *possible self*? Discuss the findings of Markus & Nurius (1986).

_____

_____

_____

How is the *possible self* related to *role models*? That is, what effect do *role models* have on the *possible self*? In addition, address the role of *self-efficacy* in the *possible self.*

_____

_____

_____

_____

_____

Control Thyself…
(Self-Control, page 127)

19.   Define the term *self-control.*

_____

_____

It is Not Unlimited...
(Self-Control, page 128)

20. The ability to control oneself is not without limit. Explain this statement.

_____

_____

_____

SELF-ESTEEM: ATTITUDES TOWARD OURSELVES

How do You Feel About Yourself?
(Page 129)

21. What is your attitude towards yourself? Do you "like" yourself? Do you perceive yourself in negative terms? Do you tend to view yourself in a manner that is consistent in <u>all</u> situations or is your view subject to the environment in which you find yourself? If a psychologist were to ask you these questions, what *self construct* would the psychologist be trying to access? Provide a definition for this construct.

_____

_____

_____

High versus low...
(The Measurement of Self-Esteem, pages 129 - 130)

22. Eisenstadt and Leippe (1994) and DeHart and Pelham (2007) conducted research into self-esteem. According to these research studies, what are some of the reasons for high and low self-esteem?

_____

_____

_____

_____

I Think High Self-Esteem is Overrated. A Little Low Self-Esteem is Actually Quite Good. Maybe You're Not the Best, So You Should Work a Little Harder. - Jay Leno
(Is High Self-Esteem Always Beneficial? page 131)

23.   Give examples as to why high self-esteem may be both harmful and beneficial. Why does it appear that high self-esteem may be an impediment?

_____

_____

_____

_____

A Long Time Ago...
(Do Women and Men Differ in Their Level of Self-Esteem? Pages 131 - 133)

24.   How was gender difference in self-esteem conceptualized by George Herbert Mead in 1934?

_____

_____

_____

The World Over...
(Do Women and Men Differ in Their Level of Self-Esteem? Pages 131 - 133)

25.   Describe the cross-cultural findings of Williams and Best (1990) regarding self-esteem in women.

_____

_____

_____

_____

_____

SOCIAL COMPARISON: HOW WE EVALUATE THE SELF

To Whom Are You Comparing Yourself?
(page 133)

26.   Elaborate on *self-comparison theory*.

The Artist...

(page 134)

27.   Britt is a very accomplished artist. To whom would it be better for him to compare himself?
        Pablo Picasso? Rembrandt? Hillary, the ten year old, who is taking beginning painting classes
        at the YMCA? Or another accomplished artist who is similar to him in talent?

        _____

        Explain your answer.

        _____

        _____

        _____

Are You Biased Toward Yourself? Probably not...
(Self-Serving Biases, page 136)

28.   Sally sees herself as being intelligent, honest, trustworthy, and empathetic towards others. She
        exemplifies the concept of high self-esteem.

        How might Sally's opinion of herself be demonstrative of the *above average effect*? How does
        the *above average effect* influence one's self-esteem?

        _____

        _____

        _____

Are You Biased Toward Yourself? Probably not...Continued...

If one is provided with information that refutes one's "golden" image, what might the response be?

_____

_____

_____

_____

_____

Building The Science: Classics of Social Psychology...
(Is Being Unrealistic Good For You? Can That be Realistic? page 137)

29.   Provide a summary of this section. Within your synopsis, be sure to include a definition for the term _unrealistic optimism_.

_____

_____

_____

_____

_____

_____

_____

THE SELF AS TARGET OF PREJUDICES

There are Consequences for Everything...
(Emotional Consequences: How Well-Being Can Suffer, page 138)

30.   As discussed in an earlier chapter, we have the tendency to attribute our own as well as others' behavior as due to internal or external causes. This section provides a progression of the conception of the self from the worst possible form of attribution for one's psychological well-being to the most protective form of attribution.

    With the first rectangle being the worst form and the third rectangle being the best, fill out the following chart representing this progression.

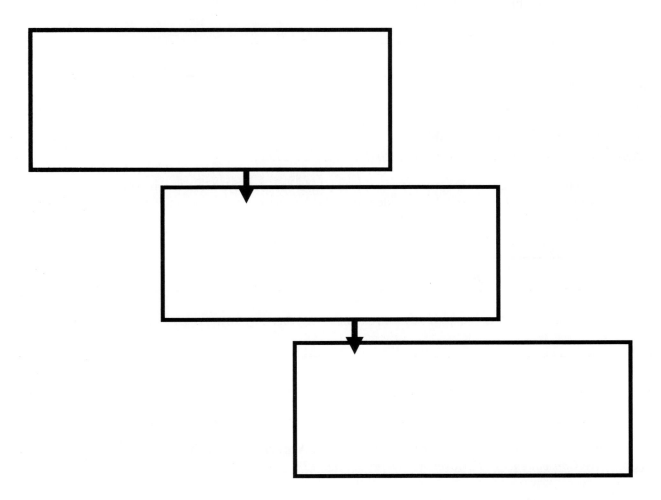

Prejudice in Women
(Emotional Consequences: How Well-Being Can Suffer, page 139)

31.   Schmidt, Branscombe and Postmes (2003) conducted an attention demanding investigation regarding prejudice towards women. In the study, the participants were all female. Participants were all exposed to identical negative criticism from one of 20 male interviewers. The difference between the participants was that some were given the pre-feedback condition where they were told, in supposed confidence, that the interviewer was a "jerk" and is known to give everyone the same evaluation (the non-sexist condition). Another group was told, post-feedback, that their interviewer was sexist against women, but is positive towards men (lone sexist condition). The final group was told that all of the interviewers were sexist (pervasive sexist condition).

Discuss the findings of this study.

_____

_____

_____

The Clandestine Identity...Shhh!
(Cognitive Consequences: Performance Deficits, page 139 - 140)

32.   There are times, for whatever reason, we may hide our identity. Give two reasons (1 & 2 below) why one would want to hide their identity and (3) explain why hiding one's identity may actually be detrimental.

1. _____

_____

2. _____

_____

3. _____

_____

Valuation (or is it Devaluation) of The Elderly in American Society...
(Cognitive Consequences: Performance Deficits, page 139 - 140)

33.   Being an individualistic nation, the United States has long demonstrated the devaluation of elderly in our society. Oppositely, in China, the elderly have a long-standing history of being revered almost to the point that one might consider Chinese elders on a plane just short of a "god-like" status.

Levy and Langer used the suggestion given above as the basis for a research investigation they conducted in 1994.

Valuation (or is it Devaluation) of The Elderly in American Society...Continued...

Describe Levy and Langer's findings.

_____

_____

_____

A Stereotype can be a Threat...
(Behavioral Consequences: Stereotype Threat, page 140)

34.   Define _stereotype threat._

_____

_____

_____

A Stereotype can be a Threat...Continued

Tilman, a white male, decided to take a course on cultural diversity this semester. During a lecture, the professor was discussing the thinking processes of a white supremacist. Tilman, a "southern" boy – born and bred – knew quite a bit about this subject, having both an uncle and a grandfather who – right or wrong – believed that whites were, indeed, supreme to all other races. Though Tilman had numerous comments on the subject, he sat in silence.

Why might Tilman have remained silent?

_____

_____

_____

Assuming Tilman was trying to hide his connection with white supremacists, according to research, how easy might this be for Tilman? Substantiate your claim.

_____

_____

_____

Give Me Three Reasons...
(Behavioral Consequences: Stereotype Threat, page 141)

35.   Your textbook lists **three** response options for those members of a devalued group who find themselves in situations in which they may experience stereotype threat. Delineate upon each.

   1. _____

   _____

   2. _____

   _____

   3. _____

   _____

Decrements are Inevitable...
(Behavioral Consequences: Stereotype Threat, pages 140 - 142)

36.   Give research evidence as to why decrements due to stereotype threat tend to occur when the anxiety associated with the stereotype threat is induced in women, African Americans, and Latinos.

   _____

   _____

   _____

Oftentimes, there is contradictory evidence found in research. Such is the case in the discrepancies found between the research of Aronson et al (1999) and that of Osborne (2001). Discuss the research of Aronson et al in this regard.

   _____

   _____

   _____

And the Question is…
(Behavioral Consequences: Stereotype Threat, page 142)

37.   Your author asked the question, "*Is it only for groups that are historically devalued in the culture as a whole that stereotype threat effects have been observed?*" This question has been addressed by numerous researchers, including Leyens, Désert, Croizet and Darcis (2000), Stone, Lynch, Sjomeling and Darley (1999) and Aronson et al (1999).

Match the researchers to their research findings.

_____1.   Aronson et al. (1999)

_____2.   Stone, Lynch, Sjomeling and Darley (1999)

_____3.   Leyens, Désert, Croizet and Darcis (2000),

A.   Stereotype threat effects are seen in men who are not a devalued group (as a whole), but who are stereotypically seen as being less emotional than women.

B.   Whites show deficits in math performance when they are threatened by a negative comparison to Asians who are typically stereotyped as being superior in math skills.

A.   Stereotype threats can occur in dominant group members when their group performance is expected to be less favorable than a comparison group.

After You Read... MyPsychLab Connection

(1)   You can take on the world!! Well...possibly. Are you overconfident? If so, is this a good thing or a not so good thing? *LISTEN* to *Overconfidence* for answers.

(2)   Shyness is rampant in adolescence, especially for adolescent girls. *LISTEN* to *Adolescent Shyness* as renowned psychologist, Phillip Zimbardo, discusses why shyness is so pervasive in this population.

(3)   Are ALL homosexual (gay) men feminine? Are ALL homosexual (lesbian) women masculine? Go to *LISTEN: Sexual Orientation and Gender*. Michael Bailey of Northwestern University discusses some of the stereotypes of gay men and women.

After You Read... Practice Test #1

_____1.   _____ is defined as a readiness to consider negative outcomes to be due to discrimination.
   A.   Discriminatory responsibility
   B.   Stigma consciousness
   C.   Self deference
   D.   Prejudice

_____2.   Mary is applying for a job and wants to put her best foot forward by presenting her most favorable self-aspects. Mary is engaging in
   A.   self-esteem.
   B.   self-aspect formation.
   C.   self-promotion.
   D.   self-defeating.

_____3.   It is a beautiful day outside. You go sit under a large tree and begin to think about your life and what you have accomplished. In other words, you are attempting to directly analyze yourself. You are engaging in
   A.   self-description.
   B.   self-thought.
   C.   introspection.
   D.   extraspection.

_____4.   Taifel and Turner (1986) divide how people perceive themselves at a given time into a continuum. On one side is the _____ identity and on the other is the _____ identity.
   A.   self; group
   B.   image; emotional
   C.   negative; positive
   D.   personal; social

_____5.   The possible self is the _____ self.
   A.   negative
   B.   positive
   C.   regulatory
   D.   future

_____6.   A high level of self-construal means that one thinks in _____ terms.
   A.   concrete.
   B.   abstract.
   C.   both concrete and abstract
   D.   biased

_____7.   If we were to make an intragroup comparison, we would be comparing ourselves to
   A.   others in our group.
   B.   other groups.
   C.   one individual in the other group.
   D.   None of the above is correct.

_____8.   One's overall attitude towards themselves is termed
            A.   self-identity.
            B.   self-attitude.
            C.   self-efficacy.
            D.   self-esteem.

_____9.   In India women have more _____ self-concepts than those in the US.
            A.   negative
            B.   positive
            C.   Neither, they are about equal.
            D.   neutral

_____10.   William is comparing his grades to his brother who has an IQ of 200. William's IQ is
            125. What type of comparison is William making?
            A.   Downward
            B.   Inward
            C.   Upward
            D.   Outward

11.   The _____ occurs when we accept credit for positive

       outcomes.

12.   A stereotypic threat is _____ to control.

13.   Ron is a member of the RRS Society and they are all aggressive. This is an example of

       _____.

14.   _____ is a tactic in which we belittle ourselves to convey our respect for

       others.

15.   Debbie feels sure that she will make an "A" on her next exam. This is an example of Debbie's

       high _____.

After You Read... Practice Test #2

_____ 1.   Todd thinks that he is better than the average person in his ability to play football. This is referred to as the _____ effect.
A.   intentional ability
B.   above average
C.   achievement orientation
D.   goal driven

_____ 2.   If we want others to think of us as being as capable as we perceive ourselves to be, we need to employ
A.   self-representation.
B.   self-ingratiation.
C.   self-promotion.
D.   self-advertisement.

_____ 3.   Alex is applying for an engineering position and wants to portray himself as intelligent, hard working, and highly capable. He is applying the
A.   self-verification perspective.
B.   self-efficacy perspective.
C.   employment rule.
D.   relevant information hypothesis.

_____ 4.   Research has shown that people prefer to be with
A.   people who verify our self views.
B.   people who flatter us.
C.   people who have a self view matches our own.
D.   people who have a positive self-image.

_____ 5.   _____ is defined as implying that we are not as good as others.
A.   Self-monitoring
B.   Self-esteem
C.   Self-depreciating
D.   Self-motivation

_____ 6.   People who tell many lies tend to have _____ friends.
A.   few
B.   many
C.   no more – no less
D.   less than three

_____ 7.   When we speak with the use of gestures and differing tones of voice, we are using
A.   language emphasizers.
B.   paralinguistic cues.
C.   speaking accentuators
D.   None of the above is correct.

_____8.   Asynchronous is to synchronous as
            A.   indirect is to direct.
            B.   separate is to face to face.
            C.   text is to voice.
            D.   All of the above are correct.

_____9.   To privately think about yourself is to employ
            A.   shallow processing.
            B.   introspection.
            C.   inward thought.
            D.   Both B and C are correct.

_____10.   On the Tajfel and Turner (1986) continuum, if we think of ourselves primarily as
            individuals, we are on the _____ side of the spectrum.
            A.   social.
            B.   identity.
            C.   personal.
            D.   intrapersonal.

11.   If a man were to make a self judgment in an intragroup context, he would be comparing
        himself to _____.

12.   When we try to hide aspects of ourselves from others we tend to do this because we fear
        _____ from them.

13.   Studies of _____ memory show that when we compare our past self with
        our present self and see improvement over time, we feel good about ourselves.

14.   Our future self is our _____ self.

15.   Wendell is very down on himself. He feels that he is no good and will never make anything of his
        life. Apparently, Wendell has low _____.

After You Read... Practice Test #3

_____1. When we compare ourselves to others we usually gauge our abilities by comparing ourselves based on similarities in such categories as **ALL** of the following **EXCEPT**
   A.   age.
   B.   gender.
   C.   race.
   D.   experience on a particular task.

_____2. In China, the most important basis for self-esteem is
   A.   group adherence.
   B.   honesty.
   C.   modesty.
   D.   aggression.

_____3. Chinese students are likely to see their failures as their
   A.   parents' fault.
   B.   teacher's fault.
   C.   own fault.
   D.   None of the above is correct.

_____4. Zack sees his future as very rosy. In fact, he sees his chances as much higher than those of his peers because he is a genius. This phenomenon is called
   A.   arrogant thinking.
   B.   future prediction.
   C.   above average bias.
   D.   unrealistic optimism.

_____5. Discrimination is to prejudice as _____ is to _____.
   A.   action; thought.
   B.   thought; feeling.
   C.   action; desire.
   D.   None of the above is correct.

_____6. Cognitive deficits that are based upon concerns about one's social identity are seen when it is an identity that is _____ by the larger culture.
   A.   valued.
   B.   devalued.
   C.   revered.
   D.   appreciated.

_____7. _____ is a dimension at which white men are believed to excel, according to Leyens, Desert, Croizet and Darcis (2000).
   A.   Natural athletic ability
   B.   Social identifying
   C.   Sports intelligence
   D.   Undermining ability

_____8.   A _____ effect can occur when people are reminded of their devaluation as a group.
    A.   stereotype threat
    B.   stereotype influence
    C.   prejudice
    D.   discrimination

_____9.   The US military's "don't ask – don't tell" policy is an attempt to hide aspect of the self for fear of _____ by others.
    A.   disapproval
    B.   sympathy
    C.   Both A and B are correct.
    D.   Neither A nor B are correct.

_____10.   According to DeHart, Pelham, and Tennen (2006), young adults whose parents were nurturing tend to have higher _____ self-esteem.
    A.   explicit
    B.   implicit
    C.   emotional
    D.   intellectual

11.   Low self-esteem can lead to _____, poor _____ and _____.

12.   High self esteem can lead to _____, _____ and interpersonal _____.

13.   A low level of self-construal involves thinking in _____ terms.

14.   Alois is a high achiever. He is smart and he knows it. The probability that Alois has high _____ is very high.

15.   _____ is a powerful social category in that we use it most of the time.

After You Read... Practice Test #4

_____1.   Paralinguistic cues include
A.   facial expressions.
B.   gestures.
C.   tone of voice.
D.   All of the above are correct.

_____2.   The more we engage in introspection, the greater _____ we tend
to have.
A.   self-esteem
B.   self-concept
C.   self-knowledge
D.   self-depreciation

_____3.   "We always know why we feel how we feel." This statement
A.   is false.
B.   is true.
C.   has not been determined.
D.   is not quite accurate since we know approximately 99.9% of the time.

_____4.   The Rosenberg Scale (1965) measures _____.
A.   self-concept.
B.   self-promotion.
C.   self-esteem.
D.   self-knowledge.

_____5.   In England, men and women tend to perceive themselves
A.   equally favorably.
B.   as having many positive attributes.
C.   as having many negative attributes.
D.   differently with men perceiving themselves more favorably than women.

_____6.   The worst attribution for psychological well-being is when outcomes are seen as
A.   internal.
B.   stable.
C.   external.
D.   Both A and B are correct.

_____7.   _____ are the least likely to protect our well-being.
A.   Internal attributions
B.   External attributions
C.   Contradictory attributions
D.   Neutral attributions

_____8.   _____ is defined as occurring when we think we might be judged by a negative stereotype.
   A.   Stereotype rule
   B.   Stereotype variance
   C.   Stereotype threat
   D.   Stereotype judgment

_____9.   When different aspect of ourselves is in conflict, it can be
   A.   emotionally difficult.
   B.   enlightening.
   C.   satisfying.
   D.   None of the above is correct.

_____10.   Turner and Onorato (1999) found that aspects of the self referred to with verbvs or adjectives are likely to elicit self perceptions
   A.   at the personal identity level.
   B.   at the social identity level.
   C.   at both the personal and the social identity levels.
   D.   at the interpersonal level.

11.   When people with low self-esteem receive negative feedback, their self-esteem tends to

       _____.

12.   _____ was the first to suggest that our self-esteem is affected by how others see us.

13.   _____ investigated self-concept in women in 14 nations.

14.   Among whites, _____ are the most likely candidates to be discriminated against.

15.   High self-esteem is associated with violence when one's _____ view of themselves is threatened.

Answers – After You Read…Practice Activities

1. Harvey is engaging in self-promotion. He, however, is not going about it the right way. According to the self-verification perspective, he should have emphasized the qualities that would make him a good president; not the qualities that would tend to characterize him as a party-animal and anti-establishment.

2. Janice will tend to prefer people who see her as consistent with how she sees herself. She will also prefer people who tend verify her self-view.

3. Ingratiation refers to the tendency to try to make others like us by flattering them.

4. Angela is engaging in self-depreciating activity.

5. No, we are not always honest. In fact, we tend to tell lies to others approximately two times per day.

   People who tend to tell more lies, tend to have a greater number of friends

6. Paralinguistic cues refer to gestures and tone of voice. Asynchronous forms of communication include e-mail and text messaging.

7. Though a useful tool in self-discovery, introspection is not as useful as one might think. Cite evidence through the research of Wilson and Kraft (1993) regarding use of introspection about their feelings for their romantic partners and how introspection led to their regrettably changing their minds about their partners.

8. Gilbert and Wilson (2000) found that when we think of something awful that has happened to us and attempt to predict how we will feel about the situation one year later, we tend to focus on the negativity of the event and neglect any other factors that may have contributed towards an increase in the level of happiness a year later.

9. Internal factors.

10. Pronin and Ross (2006) found that the present self appears to have more situational variability and was less likely to be characterized in terms of dispositional factors than was the self in the past

11. People tend to perceive themselves differently at one time than another. This depends on where they are on the personal-versus-social identity continuum.

    Personal Identity = A, D, E, H, G

    Social Identity = B, C, F, I, J

12. We can not definitively say that one of the selves is our true self. Oakes and Reynolds (1997) found that all of the selves are portraits of our true self, but which ones accurately predict our behavior depends on the context and comparison dimension. That is, people tend to display different selves depending on the situation.

13. Our tendency to see the self in terms of what aspects are important to us in terms of our self-concept.

14. Hypothesis: The participants who had experience with both the Asian and the Western cultural traditions would express their Asian-ness in contexts that prompt that aspect of themselves and express their Western-ness in contexts that prompt that aspect of themselves.

    Procedure: Participants were asked to answer the question, "Who am I?" in either Chinese or English.

Group I: Answers in Chinese.
Group II: Answers in English.

Results:

Group I described themselves in vocabulary reflective of group memberships.

Group II described themselves in vocabulary reflective of personal traits.

15.   1. One aspect of the self might be more important to us in a particular context than in another.

2. The context, itself, can make certain aspects more distinctive than in other contexts.

3. People may have the tendency to classify themselves as having a particular personality trait of group identity due to the importance of these traits/identities to the self.

16.   Provide a summary in your own words

17.   According to Tajfel (1978), there are some aspects of the self that, no matter how hard we try, we cannot hide from others. We cannot hide our gender, sometimes our age, our skin color. At times, when we do try to hide any aspect of our self, we may come in contact with others who would reject us if they knew that certain aspect of our self. This can lead us to emphasize that particular aspect as a means of contrasting our self from those who would reject us and this, in turn, communicates that aspect of our self.

18.   Wilson and Ross (2001) found that people who sense they are close to some type of self-failure, view their current self as less positive than those who see failure as in the far distant past.

Markus and Nurius (1986) found that if one has a positive possible self it can inspire the individual to strive towards an established goal state.

The possible self is motivated by role models. Self-efficacy adds motivation to achieve the possible self.

19.   Self-control involves establishing limits on the self.

20.   If one has recently been involved in some of self-control, they have limited resources to engage in a second task involving self-control.

21.   Self-esteem.

22.   Self-esteem increases when we have achieved an important goal. Failure can harm self-esteem. When individuals are reminded of failures, self-esteem decreases. When people with an already low self-esteem receive negative feedback, their self-esteem decreases further. Being excluded can lower self-esteem.

23.   Low self-esteem is implicated in dangerous behaviors such as drug abuse. It is also implicated in poor school performance, depression, and violence. In addition, low self-esteem can cause aggression and general negativity towards others.

24.   Mead believed that women should have lower self-esteem than men because the self-esteem is influenced by the treatment we receive from others.

25.   In India and Malaysia women have very negative self-concepts because they are expected to stay at home and be wives and mothers. In England and Finland, women tend to perceive themselves more favorably because they are active in the labor force.

26. It is believed that all human judgment is relative to some form of comparison.

27. It depends on his motivation. If he wants to feel very good about his ability, he should compare himself to the child. If he wants to feel (for whatever reason) that he is beneath others in his ability, he should compare himself to the famous painters. If he wants an accurate assessment, he should compare himself to some like him.

28. The above average effect allows us to think that we are better than the average person on certain dimensions. The more one exhibits this effect, the higher the self-esteem. When we receive information that refutes our golden image we tend to forget such instances and, instead, focus on the positive.

29. Student will provide a summary.

30. Worst = Outcome is seen as internal and stable
Next = Making an attribution to prejudice
Best = External attributions

31. Feelings of self-esteem and mood were worse when the prejudicial outcome was seen as reflecting discrimination. When discrimination was seen as due to one lone person, self-esteem was no worse than in the non-sexist jerk condition.

32. 1. People do not want to be associated with their devalued group.
2. People want to present their best possible image.
3. Hiding identity can affect our ability to learn because it can be distracting when you allocate resources to this task and do not have enough resources to learn left.

33. Levy and Langer found that since the elderly in the US were more likely than those in China to be perceived as having little value, American elders showed deficits in memory that were not seen in the Chinese elders.

34. A stereotype threat occurs when individuals believe that they will be perceived in a negative light due to their social identity or that they may unintentionally act in a way as to confirm a negative stereotype of their group.

Tilman apparently is afraid that he will be perceived as harboring white supremacist attitudes because he is from the south. Hiding this connection, though, may not be easy for Tilman, especially if he has been indoctrinated with the principles long-held by white supremacists.

35. 1. Disidentify themselves from situations in which they are vulnerable.
2. Attempt to distance the self from the group identity.
3. Distance themselves from stereotypic dimensions that represent a threat to their performance in a particular domain.

36. Osborne (2001) found that anxiety is evoked in women, African Americans, and Latinos when their group membership is depicted as indicative of poor performance.

Aronson (1999) found no increase in self-reported anxiety among stigmatized group members in stereotype threat conditions. The theory behind why this was found was that they may have been reluctant to report the feelings of anxiety.

37. B, C, A

Answers – Cross-Word Puzzle

Across

7.   social comparison

Down

1.   self-efficacy
2.   self-verification
3.   introspection
4.   ingratiation
5.   self-promotion
6.   social identity

Answers – Practice Test #1

1.   B
2.   C
3.   C
4.   D
5.   D
6.   B
7.   A
8.   D
9.   A
10.   C
11.   self-serving bias
12.   difficult
13.   prejudice
14.   ingratiation
15.   self-efficacy

Answers – Practice Test #2

1.   B
2.   C
3.   A
4.   A
5.   C
6.   B
7.   B
8.   D
9.   D
10.   C
11.   other men
12.   disapproval
13.   autobiographical
14.   possible
15.   self-esteem

Answers – Practice Test #3

1.   A
2.   C
3.   C
4.   D
5.   A
6.   B
7.   C
8.   A
9.   A
10.   B
11.   drug abuse, school performance, violence
12.   bullying, narcissism, aggression
13.   concrete
14.   self-esteem
15.   gender

After You Read... Practice Test #4

1.   D
2.   C
3.   A
4.   C
5.   A
6.   D
7.   A
8.   C
9.   A
10.   D
11.   decrease
12.   Mead
13.   Williams and Best
14.   women
15.   superior

CHAPTER 5

ATTITUDES:
EVALUATING AND RESPONDING TO THE SOCIAL WORLD

Before You Read…Chapter Summary

An attitude can be most appropriately defined as a personal evaluation (feeling/belief) of the social world that influences the way one responds to people, objects and events. More simply, an attitude is indicative of whether we tend to "like" or "dislike" something. For example: how do you "feel" about a particular presidential candidate? Do you "like" him/her? Do you "dislike" him/her? What is your opinion on gun control? What do you think about the legalization of marijuana? In the beginning of Chapter Five the topic of how attitudes are formed is discussed. If you think back to your introductory psychology class, you probably remember Pavlov and the principles of classical conditioning; likewise, you may remember the ideas espoused by B.F. Skinner regarding instrumental conditioning. You probably will also recall that we also learn, as advocated by Albert Bandura, through the process of observation. It is through these three processes – classical conditioning, instrumental conditioning, and observational learning – that our attitudes are often formed.

Next, you will have the opportunity to read of a study conducted by Richard LaPiere (1934). This is a study of which every social psychology student should be aware. In this study, LaPiere investigated the extent to which negative attitudes are reflective of our actions. This is an interesting, attention-grabbing study that fits in as well when it was originally conducted in the early 1930's as it does today. Next, you will learn of the role social context plays in the formation of a link between our attitudes and our behaviors. By the way, social context plays a rather important role in the formation of or the actual continuance of the link once it is established. Your author also presents for your consideration a discussion of the strength of attitudes, including the extremity of an attitude and the degree of certainty with which an attitude is retained.

If you have ever wondered how our attitudes guide our behavior, you are in the right chapter. Within Chapter Five you will find an in-depth description of the *attitude to behavior model* (Fazio, 1990; Fazio & Roskos-Ewoldsen, 1994) which explains the ways in which our attitudes can direct our behavior. You will also become privy to the "fine art" of persuasion; including the role of the communicator, the message, itself, and the audience. Since persuasion can be insidious at times, you will also read a discussion of how one can resist persuasive techniques. Finally, in Chapter Five, you will be introduced to the topic of cognitive dissonance which is defined as a state where there is a discrepancy between an attitude and a behavior. The end result of cognitive dissonance can be a state of tension very similar to anxiety.

Before You Read...Learning Objectives

After reading this chapter, you should be able to:

- Define the term *attitude.*
- Explain the difference between someone who is prevention focused and promotion focused.
- Know the difference between *explicit attitudes* and *implicit attitudes.*
- Elaborate on the social learning processes through which attitudes are acquired; these include classical conditioning, instrumental conditioning, and observational learning.
- Explain the concepts of subliminal *conditioning* and *mere exposure.,*
- Discuss the role of social comparison in determining if our views regarding social reality are correct or not.
- Explain the sentence "attitudes towards groups, issues or objects do not always predict behavior."
- Define *situational constraint* and delineate upon the idea.
- Define *pluralistic ignorance* and discuss how it tends to limit the extent to which we can express our attitudes in public.
- Elaborate upon the factors that are related to attitude strength: extremity, certainty and degree of personal experience.
- Discuss the two ways in which attitudes tend to influence our behavior.
- Discuss the *art of persuasion.*
- Explain two theories of *persuasion – the elaboration - likelihood model* and *the heuristic – systematic model.*
- Elaborate upon the two routes that can be used to process persuasive messages.
- Describe the influence of caffeine in persuasion.
- Discuss factors that contribute to our ability to resist persuasion.
- Define and discuss the terms *forewarning* and *selective avoidance.*
- Explain the role of individual differences in our ability to resist persuasion.
- Define *ego-depletion* and *self-regulation.*
- Discuss the phenomenon of *cognitive dissonance.*
- Define *forced compliance.*
- Explain the *less leads to more effect.*
- Elaborate upon how dissonance can be reduced.
- Discuss *hypocrisy.*

As You Read…Term Identification

Important Terms to Know

Below are a list of some of the key terms and concepts from this chapter. Make flashcards in order to enhance your recall ability of these terms. Refer to the definitions that are either in boldface or in the margins of this chapter for help. You may also want to include additional terms from this chapter as you deem necessary.

attitude, (p. 148)	observational learning, (p. 154)	heuristic processing, (p. 168)
explicit attitude, (p. 148)	social comparison, (p. 154)	elaborative likelihood model, (p. 169)
implicit attitude, (p. 148)	reference group, (p. 154)	cognitive dissonance, (p. 176)
prevention focused, (p. 149)	pluralistic ignorance, (p. 154)	less-leads-to-more effect, (p. 175)
promotion focused, (p. 149)	theory of planned behavior, (p. 162)	hypocrisy, (p. 180)
conditioned stimulus, (p. 150)	implementation plan, (p. 163)	reactance, (p. 172)
social learning, (p. 151)	attitude-to-behavior model, (p. 164)	forewarning, (p. 172)
classical conditioning, (p. 151)	habit, (p. 165)	selective avoidance, (p. 172)
subliminal conditioning, (p. 152)	persuasion, (p. 165)	ego-depletion, (p. 175)
mere exposure, (p, 152)	fear appeals, (p. 167)	self-regulation, (p. 175)
instrumental conditioning, (p, 153)	systematic processing, (p. 168)	

As You Read...Practice Activities

ATTITUDE FORMATION: HOW ATTITUDES DEVELOP

What is Your Attitude Towards...
(Introduction, page 148)

1.   Define the term *attitude*. Assess your own attitudes towards the legalization of marijuana, homosexual marriage, and illegal immigration. Are you pro or con?

_____

_____

_____

_____

_____

_____

Implicit versus Explicit...
(Introduction, page 148)

2.   What is an *implicit attitude*? What is an *explicit attitude*? How are implicit attitudes measured?

_____

_____

_____

_____

_____

_____

Is It Really Important?
(Introduction, pages 148-149)

3.   Why are attitudes important? Give **three** reasons.

1. _____

_____

Is It Really Important?...Continued

2. _____

_____

3. _____

_____

The New Baby...
(Introduction, pages 150-155)

4. Ashley has a new baby. Having knowledge of learning theory, she realizes that her baby will learn many of his views through interaction with others and by observing the behavior of others. This type of learning is often referred to as what mode of learning?

_____

What are the **three** processes through which social learning occurs?

1. _____

2. _____

3. _____

Ivan Pavlov and His Dog...
(Classical Conditioning: Learning Based on Association, pages 150-151)

5. *Ivan Pavlov*, a Nobel Prize winning physiologist, literally stumbled into the phenomenon of classical conditioning. You may recall from your introductory psychology class, classical conditioning involves pairing an unconditioned stimulus (unlearned) with a conditioned stimulus (learned) repeatedly until an association is formed.

According to your textbook, how can classical conditioning lead or contribute to attitude formation? You may use the example in your textbook on attitude formation in children to provide supporting research.

_____

_____

_____

_____

_____

Subliminally speaking…
(Classical Conditioning: Learning Based on Association, pages 150 151)

6.   Explain *subliminal conditioning* and *mere exposure.*

_____

_____

_____

How can subliminal conditioning and mere exposure influence attitude formation? In your
answer, discuss the research of Krosnick et al (1992).

_____

_____

_____

_____

_____

Your Mind will be Instrumental in Completing This Question…
(Instrumental Conditioning: Rewards for the Right View, pages 154-155)

7.   What is meant by *instrumental conditioning?*

_____

_____

_____

Why do children tend to have views that are the same or very similar to their parents? How
might this tend to change as an individual approaches adulthood?

_____

_____

_____

_____

_____

Adaptation is good...
(Instrumental Conditioning: Rewards for the Right View, pages 153- 154)

8.   How might our attitudes change or adapt to different audiences?

_____

_____

_____

Let us say you are highly religious and believe abortion to be wrong regardless of the circumstances. You, though, join a sorority. This weekend your sorority is going to participate in a pro-choice rally. You are left with making a choice. Do you stick to your religious beliefs and not attend? Or, do you follow your fellow "sisters" and attend the rally? According to the research of Noel, Wann & Branscombe (1995) how do you think you would react? Why?

_____

_____

_____

_____

I Observe That You are Learning...
(Observational Learning: Learning by Exposure to Others, pages 154-155)

9.   What is *observational learning?*

_____

_____

Why does *observational learning* occur?

_____

•   _____

_____

Does *observational learning* occur even when we compare our views to the views of anyone such as a complete stranger?

_____

_____

_____

Researcher to Research...
(Observational Learning: Learning by Exposure to Others, pages 154-155)

10. Match the researcher to the research findings:

_____1.   Terry and Hogg (1996)

_____2.   Maio, Esses and Bell (1994)

_____3.   Turner (1991)

_____4.   Fleming and Petty (2000)

A.   People who show high identity with their group show more favorability towards products that are introduced in terms of their group liking the product.

B.   Hearing others who are similar to us expressing negative views about a group can stir us towards negative attitudes

C.   We develop discomfort when our attitudes differ from those we see as similar to us

D.   The extent to which we will adopt change depends on the extent to which the individual identifies with the group advocating the change.

How are Your Marketing Skills?
(Observational Learning: Learning by Exposure to Others, page 154-155)

11.   Using the research of Fleming and Petty (2000) as a background, let us pretend that you are a highly successful marketing executive in charge of marketing a new brand of shampoo. Develop a marketing plan designed to market the product to its target group – teenage girls.

_____

_____

_____

_____

_____

_____

When And Why Do Attitudes Influence Behavior?

Once Again, We are Making Common Sense...
(Making Sense of Common Sense, page 157)

12. Summarize *"Making Sense of Common Sense: Are Attitudes Consistently Related to Behavior?"* Provide within your summary a discussion of the 1934 LaPiere study.

_____

_____

_____

_____

_____

_____

The Marriage of Attitudes and Behavior...
(Role of Social Context in the Link Between Attitudes and Behavior, pages 156-158)

13. What are some of the factors that help determine the extent to which attitude and behavior relate?

_____

_____

Can Ignorance by Plural? Would that be Ignorances??
(Situational Constraints That Affect Attitude Expression, page 158)

14. Define *pluralistic ignorance.*

_____

_____

Discuss the research of Miller, Monin and Prentice (2000). How does the phenomenon of pluralistic ignorance come into play in this study?

_____

_____

_____

_____

How Strong is Your Attitude?
(Strength of Attitudes, pages 158-159)

15.   What are the **four** components that determine the extent to which attitudes drive our behaviors?

    1. _____

    _____

    2. _____

    _____

    3. _____

    _____

    4. _____

    _____

By the Power Vested In Me...
(Attitude Extremity: Role of Vested Interest, pages 159-160)

16.   Define *vested interest*.

    _____

    _____

    _____

Now, complete the following diagram:

Greater Vested Interest ➡ _____ **Impact of Attitude on Behavior**

Diminished Vested Interest ➡ _____ **Impact of Attitude on Behavior**

Change in the Legal Drinking Age – What Do You Think?
(Attitude Extremity: Role of Vested Interest, pages 159-160)

17.   Discuss the research of Crano and Sivacek (1982) in which participants were asked if they would participate in a campaign against an increase in the legal drinking age from 18 – 21. What was the hypothesis of this study?

Change in the Legal Drinking Age – What Do You Think?...Continued

What were the findings?

_____

_____

_____

_____

Certainty of Attitudes...
(Attitude Certainty: Importance of Clarity and Correctness, pages 160-161)

18.　　There are **two** components to attitude certainty, discuss each of them.

1. _____

_____

2. _____

_____

Provide the following information from the Petrocelli et al (2007) study:

Part I:

IV and Levels: _____

_____

_____

Results: _____

_____

Part II:

IV and Levels: _____

_____

_____

Certainty of Attitudes...Continued

    Results: _____

_____

The Reliability of Our Predictions...
(Attitude Certainty: Importance of Clarity and Correctness, pages 160-161)

19.   Finish the following sentence:

    An attitude that is high in _____and _____ is most

likely to predict behavior in public as well as in private.

This is Personally Relevant to Me...
(Role of Personal Experience, page 161)

20.   Expand upon the statement, "**Attitudes based on personal experience can exert strong effects on behavior**"; by citing the research of Tormala, Perry and Brinol (2002) and Wegener, Petty, Smoak and Fabrigar (2004).

_____

_____

_____

_____

_____

HOW DO ATTITUDES GUIDE OUR BEHAVIOR?

Planning Behavior?
(Attitudes Arrived At Through Reasoned Thought, pages 162-164

21.   Explain *the theory of planned behavior.*

_____

_____

_____

_____

An Early Class...Yawn!
(Attitudes Arrived At Through Reasoned Thought, pages 162-164)

22.   The theory of planned behavior is stronger when we have a plan to follow. Consider the following scenario: You are going to have to sign up for an 8:00 AM class. What plan might you establish to make sure you show up at your class on time?

_____

_____

_____

Good Intentions...
(Attitudes Arrived At Through Reasoned Thought, pages 262-164)

23.   Intentions are determined by **three** factors. Name and discuss each.

        1. _____

        _____

        2. _____

        _____

        3. _____

        _____

        Apply the **three** factors to the following scenario: You want to joint the military.

        _____

        _____

        _____

        _____

Ecstatic Opinion...
(Attitudes Arrived At Through Reasoned Thought, pages 162-164)

24.   Discuss Orbell et al's (2001) study investigating the use of the drug, Ecstasy.

        _____

        _____

Ecstatic Opinion…Continued

_____

_____

_____

Make Haste…
(Attitudes and Spontaneous Behavioral Reactions, pages 164-165)

25.   Individuals often act in haste – without much thought. Fazio (1990) and Fazio and Roskos-Ewoldsen (1994) described a theoretical view as to how oftentimes attitudes appear more automatic and intentions play a lesser role in the determination of attitudes.

        Name the theoretical view and explain the process.

_____

_____

_____

_____

_____

THE FINE ART OF PERSUASION: HOW ATTITUDES ARE CHANGED

Persuasion is Persuasive…
(Introduction, page 165)

26.   Define the term _persuasion._

_____

_____

_____

Elements of Persuasion…
(Persuasion, Communicators, Messages, and Audiences, pages 165-168)

27.   Hovland, Janis and Kelley (1953) sum up the key elements of persuasion within one question. What is the question? Explain the various components.

_____

Elements of Persuasion...Continued

_____

_____

_____

Are You Credible?
(Persuasion, Communicators, Messages, and Audiences, pages 165-168)

28.   According to your textbook, communicators are more persuasive if they are credible. Describe the research of Hovland and Weiss (1951) regarding the credibility of the communicator.

_____

_____

_____

_____

_____

The Role of Attractiveness...
(Persuasion, Communicators, Messages, and Audiences, pages 165-168)

29.   Communicators are also seen as more credible if they are perceived as being attractive.

Explain how the media often portrays this.

_____

_____

_____

Don't Blame the Messenger...
(Persuasion, Communicators, Messages, and Audiences, pages165-168)

30.   The message is as important as the messenger. Relying on the research of Walter and Festinger (1962) explain this statement. That is, what type of message would be most persuasive?

_____

_____

Can You be Persuaded to Feel Fear?
(Persuasion, Communicators, Messages, and Audiences, pages165-168)

31.   Define *fear appeal*. Is mildly induced fear worse or better for changing behavior?

_____

_____

_____

Processing Persuasion...
(The Cognitive Processes Underlying Persuasion, pages 168-170)

32.   We can process persuasive messages in **two** ways. Identify and describe both ways.

_____

_____

_____

Timing is Everything...
(The Cognitive Processes Underlying Persuasion, pages 168-170)

33.   When do we tend to engage in *systematic processing? Heuristic processing?*

_____

_____

_____

_____

Does Caffeine Really Affect Persuasion?
(The Effects of Caffeine on Persuasion, pages 171-172)

34.   Summarize this section – in your own words.

_____

_____

_____

Does Caffeine Really Affect Persuasion?...Continued

_____

_____

_____

RESISTING PERSUASION ATTEMPTS

Try to Resist…It May Be Harder Than You Think…
(Reactance: Protecting our Personal Freedom, pages 170-172)

35.   Explain _reactance_ as a way of enhancing our ability to resist persuasion.

_____

_____

If You Cannot Resist, Maybe Forewarning Will Help…
(Forewarning: Prior Knowledge of Persuasive Intent, pages 172-173)

36.   Define _forewarnings_ a way of enhancing our ability to resist persuasive techniques.

_____

_____

_____

Be Forewarned…
(Forewarning: Prior Knowledge of Persuasive Intent, pages 172-173)

37.   Forewarning influences factors that influence resistance to persuasion. One such factor is that it provides us with the opportunity to produce _counterarguments_. What is a _counterargument?_

_____

_____

Selectively Avoid The Attempt...
(Selective Avoidance of Persuasion Attempts, page 173)

38.   One way of resisting attempts aimed at persuading us is *selective avoidance*.
        Give an example of how one might selectively avoid information designed to persuade.

        _____

        _____

        _____

        _____

Counterarguing Revisited...
(Actively Defending our Attitudes: Counterarguing Against the Competition, pages 173-174)

39.   When we actively engage in *counterarguing* against views that are unlike our own, it makes
        opposing views more memorable and reduces their influence on our attitudes. Early et al (2001)
        investigated this phenomenon. Describe the research.

        _____

        _____

        _____

        _____

        _____

        _____

        _____

Individual Differences...
(Individual Differences in Resistance to Persuasion, page 174)

40.   Barry was a participant in the 2004 study conducted by Bristol et al. This study was designed to
        measure the thought processes that people employ to increase their ability to resist persuasion.
        As a participant, Barry was given an advertisement for "Brown's Department Store". The
        researchers found that scores that are indicative of the two thought processes were successful in
        predicting resistance to persuasion to the message in the advertisement.

        What are the **two** measures on which the scores were determined?
        1. _____

        _____

        _____

Individual Differences…Continued

2. _____

_____

_____

Undermining Opposition…
(Ego Depletion Can Undermine Resistance, page 175)

41.   There are issues that make it an arduous task to resist persuasion due to the fact that they challenge our ability to *self-regulate*. Define the term *self-regulate*.

_____

_____

_____

When you are overly-stressed and unable to self-regulate you are said to be in a state of *ego-depletion*. Define *ego-depletion*.

_____

_____

_____

What effect does *ego-depletion* have on our ability to resist persuasion?

_____

_____

_____

COGNITIVE DISSONANCE: WHAT IS IT AND HOW DO WE MANAGE IT?

Cognitive Conflict...
(Introduction, pages 176-177)

42.   Theresa is a very intelligent young woman. In fact, she is intelligent enough to have earned a full scholarship to an "ivy-league" university. In addition, Theresa has been told that should she maintain a "B" or above average during her pre-med curriculum, she will also be awarded entrance into the medical school with another full scholarship.

Recently, Theresa began dating Michael, another pre-med student. Michael is struggling to maintain his "D" average and feels intimidated by Theresa. In light of this, Theresa has begun to slip in her grades and, though she is more than capable, she is having a difficult time maintaining the "B" average. Theresa has decided that she is going to quit dating Michael and continue to move towards her goal of med school.

Theresa is experiencing a phenomenon known as *cognitive dissonance*. This theory was espoused by Leon Festinger in 1957.

What is *cognitive dissonance?*

_____

_____

_____

How is the scenario above indicative of this phenomenon?

_____

_____

_____

Let's Sum It Up...
(Building The Science: Classic Contributions, page 178)

43.   Provide a synopsis of this section.

_____

_____

_____

_____

_____

The Management of Dissonance...
(Introduction, pages 176-177)

44.   There are **two** ways that we can manage cognitive dissonance. Some of these strategies are *direct* and some are *indirect*.

        What is the difference between *direct* strategies and *indirect* strategies?

        _____

        _____

        _____

        _____

        _____

        _____

        Your textbook presents **three** *direct* methods. Discuss each of these.

        1. _____

        _____

        2. _____

        _____

        3. _____

        _____

        In addition, your textbook presents **one** *indirect* method. Discuss this method.

        _____

        _____

        _____

Does Less Really Lead to More?
(Dissonance and Attitude Change: The Effects of Induced Compliance, pages 178-179)

45.   What is *the less leads to more effect?*

        _____

        _____

A Hypocrite??
(When Dissonance is a Tool for Beneficial Changes in Behavior, pages 179-180)

46.   You would probably agree with the statement that driving over the speed limit in a school zone provides an unsafe environment for the children arriving at or leaving the school. Unfortunately, there are people who simply refuse to slow down.

Your author states that there is a growing body of evidence that dissonance can be used to promote positive behavioral changes.

When is this particularly true?

_____

_____

_____

After You Read... MyPsychLab Connection

(1)   *WATCH: Self-Concept* for a discussion of how and when we form our self-concept. Also, you will hear of some of the beliefs of a prominent theorist, Erik Erikson, regarding the formation the self-concept.

(2)   Have you ever wondered if gay men are always feminine and lesbian women are always masculine? Well, here is your answer. *WATCH: Sexual Orientation and Gender* for a discussion of stereotypes of sexual orientation and gender.

(3)   *LISTEN* to *Overconfidence* for a discussion of the concept and how it is applicable to our understanding of our self.

After You Read... Practice Test #1

_____1.   Which if the following is a method used in the assessment of implicit attitudes?
- A.   Implicit/Explicit Associations Test.
- B.   Implicit Association Test.
- C.   Implicit Attitudes Test.
- D.   Explicit Attitudes Test.

_____2.   Attitudes are important for **ALL** of the following reasons, **EXCEPT**
- A.   they are building blocks of social thought.
- B.   they affect our behavior.
- C.   they are incapable of being a product of deception.
- D.   the help us predict the actions of others.

_____3.   Prevention focused individuals are
- A.   concerned with loss avoidance.
- B.   concerned with not missing opportunities to benefit from a persuasive argument.
- C.   primarily focused on comfort.
- D.   primarily focused on the acceptance of the persuasive argument.

_____4.   When we learn on basis of association, we are employing
- A.   instrumental conditioning.
- B.   observational learning.
- C.   classical conditioning.
- D.   comparative learning.

_____5.   Alice is trying to diet. She is invited to a party in which she finds a lavish display of deserts. Though she is on a diet, Alice samples the cheese cake; only later to feel bad about her action. She, though, seeks to make herself feel better and decides that she will go back on her diet the next morning.
- A.   Alice experienced forced compliance.
- B.   Alice experienced cognitive dissonance.
- C.   Alice experienced the use of the availability heuristic.
- D.   Both A and B are correct.

_____6.   When we compare ourselves to others to determine if we have views that are correct, we are
- A.   assessing our reactance.
- B.   doing a social comparison.
- C.   experiencing cognitive dissonance.
- D.   implementing the theory of planned determination.

_____7.   According to your textbook, in particular the discussion of the research of Weinberg and Bealer (2002), caffeine does **ALL** of the following **EXCEPT**
- A.   activates the brain.
- B.   activates the central nervous system.
- C.   affects an individual's ability to focus their attention on a particular task.
- D.   affects an individual's ability to focus their attention on numerous tasks at one time.

_____8.   _____ is defined as efforts to change attitudes through the use of messages.
    A.   Stereotyping
    B.   Rational thought
    C.   Persuasion
    D.   Heuristic processing

_____9.   Instrumental conditioning involves
    A.   rewards and punishment.
    B.   punishment and self-reinforcement.
    C.   association between two things.
    D.   careful observation.

_____10.   _____ can best be defined as the erroneous belief that others have different attitudes than we do.
    A.   Automatic processing
    B.   Insidious processing
    C.   Subtle ignorance
    D.   Pluralistic ignorance

11.   _____ characteristically occurs when we have attitudes and behaviors that are inconsistent.

12.   The _____ of an attitude denotes both the _____ of an attitude and the degree of _____ with which an attitude is held.

13.   When attempting to persuade someone, it is important that the communicator be _____ or someone who knows what they are talking about or is an expert.

14.   _____ are defined as messages that arouse fear in the recipient of the audience exposed to the persuasive tactic.

15.   An argument that refutes a persuasive message is called a (n) _____.

After You Read... Practice Test #2

_____1.   When people are experiencing cognitive dissonance, they often engage in
_____ to restore their positive self-evaluation that has been
threatened by the dissonance.
  A.   introspection
  B.   self-reliance
  C.   self-reassurance
  D.   self-affirmation

_____2.   Conditioning that occurs in the absence of conscious awareness is called
  A.   unconscious learning.
  B.   absence of cues.
  C.   subliminal conditioning.
  D.   subliminal cuing.

_____3.   Virginia is trying to persuade a group of teenagers that it is best to practice safe sex in
light of the risk of sexually transmitted diseases. The teenagers are Virginia's
_____.
  A.   sources of persuasion.
  B.   audience.
  C.   messengers.
  D.   None of the above is correct.

_____4.   We tend to engage in _____ processing when we have little time to
process information slowly.
  A.   expedited
  B.   heuristic
  C.   reduced
  D.   elaborate

_____5.   High clarity is predictive of behavior
  A.   in private.
  B.   in public.
  C.   with a significant amount of ambiguity.
  D.   that is unlike the behavior of others.

_____6.   The extremity of an attitude refers to
  A.   the sense that you know what your attitude is.
  B.   the feeling that your attitude is correct.
  C.   how strong an attitude is.
  D.   the dissonance produced by an attitude.

_____7.   The effects of _____ on attitudes are stronger when the stimulus is
presented subliminally.
  A.   mere exposure
  B.   maximum exposure
  C.   negative feelings
  D.   positive feelings

_____8.   An unconditioned stimulus _____ a neutral stimulus in classical conditioning.
     A.   is presented after
     B.   precedes
     C.   cancels out
     D.   converts into

_____9.   Selective avoidance refers to
     A.   the tendency to disregard information that challenges our existing views.
     B.   the tendency to give much credence to information that is consistent with our views.
     C.   the tendency to decide which views are important and which are not.
     D.   None of the above is correct.

_____10.   When someone has great interest in the importance of an attitude, they are said to have
     A.   a generalized concern.
     B.   a central interest.
     C.   a reasoned interest.
     D.   a vested interest.

11.   When we are exposed to a message we consider to be of great importance we tend to process the information using the _____ route.

12.   Sean asks his girlfriend for her views on the Iraq War so that he can assess his own opinion. The process of _____ is at work here.

13.   In addressing health messages, _____ messages are most effective.

14.   Renee is a gymnast. This weekend she is participating in a competition and is very sure that she has a real chance of winning. This scenario represents Renee's degree of

_____.

15.   Marianne, a strong believer in pro-life, recently had an abortion for an unplanned pregnancy. Without a doubt, Marianne experienced some degree of _____.

After You Read... Practice Test #3

_____1.   Attitude certainty is made up of two components. One of the components is attitude clarity. What is the other?
A.   Attitude validity.
B.   Attitude identification.
C.   Attitude specificity.
D.   Attitude correctness.

_____2.   **ALL** of the following are related to the theory of planned behavior **EXCEPT**
A.   theory of reasoned action.
B.   behavioral intentions.
C.   irrational processing.
D.   Martin Fishbein and Icek Ajzen.

_____3.   _____ can be defined as an individual's perception of whether or not others will approve or disapprove of a behavior.
A.   Subjective norms
B.   Objective norms
C.   Persuasion
D.   Social context theory

_____4.   Systematic processing is also known as the _____ route to persuasion.
A.   heuristic
B.   peripheral
C.   central
D.   evaluative

_____5.   Martin et al (2007) found that those participants in their study who changed their attitudes due to caffeine consumption were _____ able to resist subsequent persuasion attempts.
A.   less
B.   more
C.   equally
D.   Martin et al found no relationship between caffeine consumption and resistance to persuasion.

_____6.   When individuals are ego depleted, they experience great difficulty with _____.
A.   self-regulation
B.   determining attitudinal correctness
C.   being able to convey attitudes.
D.   None of the above is correct.

_____7. Festinger and Carlsmith (1959) found that _____ rewards produce less attitudinal change; while _____ rewards produce more attitudinal change.
A. small; large
B. large; small
C. persuasive; nonpersuasive
D. nonpersuasive; persuasive

_____8. When one has experienced cognitive dissonance, they will frequently engage in this to restore their positive self-evaluation.
A. Self-reflection.
B. Self-safety.
C. Self-regulation.
D. Self-affirmation.

_____9. The process of persuasion involves three basic steps. Which of the following does **NOT** belong?
A. Source directs the message.
B. The type of message is determined by the source.
C. The message is transferred to the audience by the communicator.
D. All of the above belong.

_____10. Oliver has recently been selected as a juror in a murder case. While he has not been sequestered, he has been asked not to watch any news reports on the case. Tonight, Oliver is watching the news. He hears that after the next commercial they will have a report on the trial in which he is participating as a juror. Oliver quickly changes the channel. This is an example of _____.
A. selective avoidance.
B. forewarning.
C. attitude formation.
D. heuristic processing.

11. In their classic study, Hovland and Weiss (1951) found that those participants who thought the message presented was from a _____ in-group member showed greater attitude change than those who thought the message was from an out-group member.

12. _____ are determined by one's attitude toward a certain behavior, subjective norms, and perceived behavioral control.

13. Attitudes that are formed on the basis of _____ experience are likely to be more likely to come to mind when in the presence of the attitude object.

14. Tina has been given an antibiotic to help fight her sinus infection. In this instance, the antibiotic functions as a _____.

15. _____, the founder of the type of conditioning that involves making associations was not a psychologist; rather he was a physiologist interested in processes of digestion.

After You Read... Practice Test #4

_____1. Orbell et al (2001) conducted a study investigating the use of the drug, Ecstasy. In this study, the researchers had the participants complete a questionnaire measuring, among other things, whether or not the participants had friends who would approve of their using the drug. Formally defined, this measure was designed to evaluate
_____.
A.   objective opinions.
B.   attitudes towards the drug, itself.
C.   perceived control.
D.   subjective norms.

_____2. The _____ delineates the process through which an attitude along with previously stored information influences our definition of an initiating event.
A.   behavior to attitude process model
B.   behavioral model of thought
C.   attitude to behavior process model
D.   attitudinal model of thought

_____3. If communicators of a persuasive message lose their credibility, their ability to persuade is _____.
A.   increased.
B.   reduced.
C.   not changed.
D.   enhanced.

_____4. _____ are more effective when they are used to address potentially fatal health issues.
A.   Negative messages
B.   Positive messages
C.   Fear inducing messages
D.   Self-regulatory messages

_____5. The _____ model is involved when we have a lot of knowledge about the topic and a lot of time to carefully consider any arguments.
A.   heuristic systematic
B.   capacity
C.   elaborative likelihood
D.   cognitive task

_____6. _____ have been shown to lessen a message's impact on the individual.
A.   Counter-arguments
B.   Forewarning
C.   Self-regulatory behavior
D.   None of the above is correct.

_____7.   _____ is defined as being provoked by external forces to say or do things that are contradictory to our actual attitudes.
    A.   Cognitive dissonance
    B.   Forewarning
    C.   Forced compliance
    D.   Self-regulation

_____8.   One of the issues involved in persuasion is the source. Research has shown that one is more likely to be persuaded if the source is _____ and _____.
    A.   reliable; attractive
    B.   attractive; credible
    C.   reliable; credible
    D.   credible; dedicated to the reason for the persuasion

_____9.   Regarding fear appeals, it has been found that _____ fear induction results in a greater change in behavior.
    A.   powerful
    B.   mild
    C.   verifiable
    D.   constant

_____10.   We tend to use heuristic processing when the issue is _____ to us.
    A.   important
    B.   imperative
    C.   critical
    D.   unimportant

11.   When the capacity to process information in a persuasive message is limited we tend to adopt the _____ mode of thought.

12.   We can lessen _____ by acquiring new information that defends our behavior.

13.   _____, which is defined as erroneously believing that others have different attitudes than we do, is a situational constraint that prevents us from expressing our attitudes openly.

14.   People that tend to hold our values and with whom we identify are often called our _____.

15.   One reason children tend to express views that are similar to their parents is _____.

When you have finished... Crossword Puzzle

Across

5.   Efforts to change attitudes through the use of messages
6.   Not consciously accessible

Down

1.   Erroneously believing that others have different attitudes than we do
2.   Evaluation of any aspect of the social world
3.   Negative reactions to efforts by others to reduce or limit our personal freedom
4.   Tendency to compare ourselves with others to determine whether our views are correct or not

Created by Puzzlemaker at DiscoverySchool.com

> ## *When you have finished... You be the Researcher*

Library Time!!!

The self is an important concept throughout the psychological realm. You will find it in almost every branch!

You are to find three articles in peer-reviewed psychological journals in which "self" is in the title. Then, do three things. **First**, look at the name of the journal. Which branch of psychology does this journal represent? **Second**, you are to use your thinking skills to determine why this particular branch of psychology is interested in the self. **Finally**, you are to analyze one of the articles, thoroughly by identifying the type of study, the variables, the participants, the procedure(s), and the results.

Answers – After You Read…Practice Activities

8. It depends on who the audience is and what you perceive their expected value may be of your opinion.

    If you want to remain in the sorority and not have others know of your beliefs, you will participate. On the other hand, if you want to risk being ostracized you will tell your "sisters" that you cannot participate due to your religious convictions.

9. When people gain specific behaviors or attitudes by observing others.

    Due to social comparison which is defined as the tendency of comparing ourselves to others to determine if our views are consistent with those of others and therefore are accurate.

    No, it only occurs when we make the comparison to those we value and identity with such as our reference group.

10. D, B, C, A

11. You may state something like – show teenage girls using the shampoo and enjoying the benefits of it – possibly even getting the guy because of its use.

12. Student will provide his or her own summary, making sure to include information about the LaPiere study.

13. Two factors that help determine the extent to which attitude and behavior relate are the situation and the features of the attitudes, themselves.

14. Pluralistic ignorance refers to the idea that we mistakenly believe that others are not in agreement with out attitudes.

Miller, Monin and Prentice (2000) found that students' private attitudes towards alcohol consumption were relatively negative; but the students tended to believe that other students' attitudes towards alcohol consumption were much more positive than their own.

15. Extremity = how strong the emotional reaction is.
    Certainty = you know what your attitude is and feel it is correct.
    Personal Experience = how much experience you have had with the attitude object.

    Accessibility = how easily the attitude comes to mind.

16. Vested interest is defined as now much the attitude is relevant to the concerns of the individual who holds it.

    Strong
    Weak

17. Hypothesis: First group (those less than 21 years of age) would be more likely to join the rally.

    Findings: Forty-seven percent with a high vested interest (those 21 and over) agreed to take part in the rally.

18. Attitude Clarity = how clear on is about their attitude.

    Attitude Correctness = feeling that one's attitudes are valid or proper.

    Part I: Attitudes toward carrying an ID card at all times

    IV and Levels: Manipulate consensus concerning attitude position towards having to carry an ID card at all times. Clarity in both conditions was equal.
        Level 1: Most students agree (89%)

Level 2: Most disagree (only 11% agreed)

Results: Perceived correctness was greater when consensus was high (89%) as compared to low (11%)

Part II: Attitudes toward gun control

IV and Levels: How many times asked to express attitude.

Level 1: Many times
Level 2: One time

Results: Group I had increased certainty and Group II had a decreased amount of certainty

19. Clarity and Correctness.

20. Tormala, Petty and Brinol (2002) found that attitudes are more likely to come to mind when formed by direct experience.

Wegener, Petty, Smoak and Fabrigar (2004) found that attitudes based on personal experience are less likely to succumb to change.

21. The decision to engage in a particular behavior is the result of a rational process. The options for the behavior are evaluated. The decision is reflected in behavioral intentions which are strong indicators as to whether we will act on our attitudes.

22. Develop a plan on how your intention will lead to action. You might include: set the alarm, have homework ready, and, if alarm fails, have a friend wake you up.

23. 1. Attitudes toward behavior = negative or positive evaluations of performing behavior.
2. Subjective norms = will others approve.
3. Perceived behavioral control = appraisal of ability to perform behavior.

24. Participants were young people.

Procedure involved a questionnaire asking (1) attitude towards drug; (2) intentions to use in next three months; (3) whether friends use it; (4) two aspects of perceived control (obtain it and resist it).

Two months later participants were contact and asked if they had used the drug during those two months.

Results: Positive attitude towards drug seen in those seeing use as normative and having perceived control. These were both predictors of use.

25. The theoretical perspective is known as the attitudes to behavior process model.

The process is as follows:

Event leads to attitude which, in turn, influences how we perceive the attitude object. At the same time, knowledge of what would be appropriate behavior is activated. Attitude and knowledge of what is appropriate shape our definition of the initiating event. This event then influences our behavior.

26. Persuasion is defined as a phenomenon in which efforts are made to change our attitudes through the use of various kinds of messages.

27. "Who says what to whom with what effect?" "What" is the message. "Whom" is the audience, and "effect" is the source.

28. Participants read communications dealing with various issues (automatic submarines, future of movie theatres). The source was varied according to credibility (high/in group versus low/out group). One week before the study participants were asked their opinions on the issues and were again asked their opinions immediately after receiving the

communications. Results showed that the high credibility/in group displayed a significantly greater attitude change.

29.   Attractive models are used in advertising. If we buy the product being marketed, we are led to believe that we will be attractive. Also, media will often use someone who is perceived as "attractive" as a spokesperson.

30.   A message is most persuasive when it is not designed to change our attitudes.

31.   Fear appeal is defined as a message that arouses fear. Mildly induced fear is better for changing behavior.

32.   Systematic processing = central route to persuasion; careful consideration of message and the ideas it contains. Heuristic processing = peripheral route; simple rules of thumb, requires less effort.

33.   According to the elaboration likelihood model, we engage in systematic processing when motivation and capacity to process is high. According to the heuristics systematic model, we tend to engage in heuristic processing when we lack the ability or capacity to carefully process information.

34.   Student will summarize the section on his or her own.

35.   Reactance is defined as a negative reaction to efforts by others to reduce our freedom by getting us to believe or do what they want.

36.   Forewarning involves having prior knowledge of the persuasive intent behind the message.

37.   A counterargument is an argument that refutes the message and limits its impact.

38.   Your example may by similar to turning the TV off during commercials, not

looking at the advertisements in magazines, etc. Provide some of your own.

39.   Students were participants. They were either pro-life or pro-choice. They each heard a persuasive message which was either consistent or contrary to their views. The strength of their attitudes and all arguments that could be recalled from the message were reported. They also listed the thoughts they had during the message.

40.   1. Actively engaging in counter-arguing. A person, who scores high in on this assessment, would say something like, "If my beliefs are challenged, I welcome the chance for debate."

    2. Actively resisting persuasion by reinforcing their own beliefs when they meet with counter-attitudinal messages.

41.   Self-regulation = to engage one's willpower to control their own thinking process.

    Ego-depletion = state of failure to self-regulate your behavior due to taxing emotional or physical inability.

    When someone is in a state of ego-depletion, they are unable to adequately resist temptation and tend to concede.

42.   Cognitive dissonance = a state of anxiety that occurs when our attitudes and our behaviors do not match.

    Theresa's admittance to med school is very important to her. When she began dating Michael, she put her attitudes away and began to make less than acceptable grades. This was inconsistent with her goals.

43.   Student will provide their own synopsis.

44.   Direct methods = focus on the attitude-behavior discrepancy that is the cause of the dissonance.

Indirect methods = the discrepancy between the attitude and the behavior is intact, but the feelings of uneasiness are reduced.
Direct:

1.   Alter either our attitude or behavior to make the two consistent.
2.   Acquire additional information to support our behavior.
3.   Determine that the inconsistency really does not matter.

Indirect:

1.   Self-affirmation = re-establishing positive self-evaluations that have been threatened by the dissonance. What this means is focus on good things about yourself.

45.   Less reasons for an action or less rewards for an action can lead to an increased attitude change.

46.   This is particularly true when feelings of hypocrisy are induced. What this means is that the attitude that driving at the reduced speed limit through a school zone is advocated. This makes it salient that anyone who speeds through a school zone is acting in a way that is inconsistent with their own attitudes.

Answers – Cross Word Puzzle

Across

5.   persuasion
6.   implicit

Down

1.   pluralisticignorance
2.   socialcomparison
3.   attitude
4.   reactance

Answers – Practice Test #1

1.   B
2.   C
3.   A
4.   C
5.   D
6.   B
7.   D
8.   C
9.   A
10.   D
11.   cognitive dissonance
12.   strength, extremity, certainty
13.   credible
14.   fear appeals
15.   counter-argument

Answers – Practice Test #2

1.   D
2.   C
3.   B
4.   B
5.   A
6.   C
7.   A
8.   B
9.   A
10.   D
11.   central
12.   social comparison
13.   positive
14.   perceived behavioral control
15.   cognitive dissonance

Answers – Practice Test #3

1.   D
2.   C
3.   A
4.   C
5.   B
6.   A
7.   B
8.   D
9.   D
10.   A
11.   credible
12.   intentions
13.   direct
14.   reward
15.   Ivan Pavlov

Answers – Practice Test #4

1.   D
2.   A
3.   B
4.   B
5.   C
6.   A
7.   C
8.   B
9.   B
10.   D
11.   heuristic
12.   cognitive dissonance
13.   pluralistic ignorance
14.   reference group
15.   peer influence

CHAPTER 6

THE CAUSES, EFFECTS, AND CURES OF STEREOTYPING, PREJUDICE AND DISCRIMINATION

Before You Read...Chapter Summary

Following September 11, 2001, the issues of stereotyping, prejudice and discrimination against Muslims came to the forefront very similarly to the way comparable issues against African Americans came to the forefront in the 60's. Again, in 2007, we were faced with the massive killing of students at Virginia Tech and, once again, our sights were set on a specific group of people – those of Asian descent. Chapter Six begins with a discussion of the discrepancy between groups in the perception of inequality in our society. It seems that White Americans tend to perceive stereotyping, prejudice and discrimination to be not as pervasive an issue as do African Americans. This is followed by a rather in-depth dialogue of the nature and origins of stereotyping. Within this section, the reader is also becomes privy to the definitions of and the differences between the concepts of stereotyping, prejudice and discrimination. A discussion of gender stereotypes and the "glass ceiling" is also offered. A discussion of stereotyping, prejudice and discrimination cannot be complete without addressing the idea of "tokenism" which is defined as hiring people simply on the basis of a certain characteristic or characteristics rather than by their merit.

In today's society, the proverbial gender and race cards are used with an ever-increasing frequency. The section entitled, *"Making Sense of Common Sense"* addresses this issue and answers the question, *"Are these cards too easy to play or is playing them much more difficult than one would think?"* Gender and race are certainly two mitigating factors that explain the existence of stereotypes and Chapter Six addresses eloquently the topic of why we form and use stereotypes and if stereotypes, once formed, are capable of being modified.

Chapter Six also tackles the topic of prejudice by investigating the origins of prejudice, how prejudice can threaten one's self-esteem, and the suggestion that one of the sources of prejudice may be competition for resources. The latter idea is considered within realistic conflict theory. In *"Building the Science: Classics in Social Psychology,"* the causes of prejudice and the potential inevitability of prejudice are discussed. Later in the chapter, that author returns to the inevitability of prejudice, along with some research-driven techniques designed to counter the effects of prejudice. The final issue presented in this chapter is that of discrimination. A rather thought-provoking example of an extreme in discrimination is given through the brief recounting of the story of Matthew Shepard, a college student who was brutally murdered in 1998 due to his sexual orientation. Finally, as stated above, the Chapter Six ends with a return to the subject of prejudice. This time the author provides some note-worthy research evidence concerning how attitudes towards those who are different from can us can be influenced by others, including our parents. Here the author presents the contact hypothesis, the concept of re-categorization, and the benefit of guilt as three ways of potentially reducing the hatred associated with stereotyping, prejudice, and discrimination towards others.

Before You Read...Learning Objectives

After reading this chapter, you should be able to:

- Discuss the discrepancy between different groups in the perception of inequality in our society.
- Explain what *gender stereotypes* are and elaborate on the idea of the *glass-ceiling*.
- Describe *tokenism*.
- Explain the two types of evaluations – *subjective and objective* - used to measure stereotypes.
- Discuss *singlism* as a form of stereotyping.
- Define *prejudice* and explain *social identity theory*.
- Relate the topic of discrimination to stereotyping and prejudice.
- Discuss the idea of *collective guilt.*
- Elucidate upon several ways that social psychologists believe that we can reduce prejudice.

As You Read...Term Identification

Important Terms to Know
Below are a list of some of the key terms and concepts from this chapter. Make flashcards in order to enhance your recall ability of these terms. Refer to the definitions that are either in boldface or in the margins of this chapter for help. You may also want to include additional terms from this chapter as you deem necessary.

prejudice, (p. 187)	subjective, (p. 197)	superordinate goals, (p. 206)
stereotyping, (p. 188)	singlism, (p. 198)	modern racism, (p. 211)
discrimination, (p. 188)	subtype, (p. 200)	bona fide pipeline, (p. 212)
risk averse, (p. 188)	essences, (p. 202)	collective guilt, (p. 212)
gender stereotypes, (p. 191)	minimal groups, (p. 203)	social learning view, (p. 215)
glass ceiling, (p. 192)	incidental feelings, (p. 203)	contact hypothesis, (p. 215)
tokenism, (p. 194)	implicit associations, (p. 203)	recategorizations, (p. 216)
shifting standards, (p. 196)	threat, (p. 204)	common in-group identity model, (p. 261)
objective, (p. 197)	realistic conflict theory, (p. 206)	

As You Read...Practice Activities

HOW MEMBERS OF DIFFERENT GROUPS PERCEIVE INEQUALITY

Group Differences...
(Pages 188-190)

1. There is abundant research evidence concerning the perception of inequality. Your author addresses this topic through **two** different groups – whites and non-whites (particularly blacks). Your task is to match the researcher(s) with the research.

   ___A___ 1.   Kahnmen and Tversky (1984)

   ___B___ 2.   Sigelman and Welch (1991)

   ___D___ 3.   Johnson, Simmons, Trawalter, Ferguson, and Reed (2003)

   ___C___ 4.   Branscombe, Schmitt, and Schiffhauer (2007)

   ___F___ 5.   Eibach and Keegan (2006)

   ___E___ 6.   Crosby (2004)

   ___G___ 7.   Lowery, Unzueta, Goff, and Knowles (2006)

        A.   Developed the prospect theory that states people are *risk averse.*

        B.   Found that Blacks and Whites differ in opinion as to the degree of discrimination they perceive to be operating in *housing and employment situations.*

        C.   Whites are the recipients of certain privileges in society and become defensive when faced with the possibility that these privileges may be in jeopardy. This defensiveness is seen in the guise of increased racism.

        D.   Whites perceive less racism in everyday activities and events than do Blacks.

        E.   People tend to perceive *Affirmative Action* as a measure against Whites and a gain for minorities.

        F.   The *racial divide* stems in part from Whites viewing social change as involving loss of status.

        G.   Whites show the propensity towards opposing *Affirmative Action* regardless of the impact on minority groups.

THE NATURE AND ORIGINS OF STEREOTYPING

The Terms can Often be Confusing..
(Introduction, pages 190-191)

2.   The terms *stereotype, prejudice* and *discrimination* are often confused as being one in the same. This is incorrect. Show that the terms are not interchangeable by defining each.

Prejudice: _____

_____

Stereotype: _____

_____

Discrimination: _____

_____

The Cognitive Component...
(Stereotyping: Beliefs about Social Groups, pages 191-192)

3.   Most people believe that stereotypes are strictly negative. This, though, is untrue. Stereotypes can be positive or even neutral. For example, take the stereotype that **ALL** bikers dress in leather. This is a neutral stereotype. The stereotype that **ALL** Asians are highly intelligent is a positive stereotype.

Use your thinking skills to come up with **two** positive stereotypes for any social group.

1. _____

_____

2. _____

_____

Stereotypes Concerning Characteristics of Men and Women...
(Stereotyping: Beliefs about Social Groups, pages 191-192)

4.   Define *gender stereotype*. Discuss the gender stereotypes (both negative and positive) of women as delineated by Fiske, Cuddly, Glick and Xu (2002)

Positive: _____

Negative: _____

Women Appear "More" Positive Than Men...
(Stereotyping: Beliefs about Social Groups, page 192)

5.   Your textbook refers to the *women are wonderful* effect in its discussion of gender stereotyping. Elaborate on this sentence by citing the research findings of Eagly and Mladinic (1994).

_____

_____

_____

_____

The Secretary...
(Stereotyping: Beliefs about Social Groups, pages 192-193)

6.   Though the traits of *warmth* and *kindness* are two admirable traits, they, unfortunately, are sometimes a hindrance to women. Discuss how two such admirable traits can produce a deficit for women.

_____

_____

_____

_____

Be Careful – It Can Hurt...
(Stereotypes and the "Glass Ceiling, pages 192-193)

7.   Define the term *glass ceiling*. How are women who violate stereotypic expectations fair in the male dominated corporate world?

_____

_____

_____

_____

It, Though, Can be Broken…
(Stereotypes and the "Glass Ceiling, pages 192-193)

8.   When women are successful in breaking the *glass ceiling*, they often come in contact with less than favorable outcomes. Explain some of these outcomes.

_____

_____

_____

_____

Is it a Glass Ceiling or a Glass Elevator?
(Stereotypes and the "Glass Ceiling, pages 192-193)

9.   Larry has made it to the "top." Just six short months ago he was hired as a cook in the local bistro, he was recently made head cook, given an increase in responsibilities and a substantial raise. According to Williams (1992), Larry has ridden *the glass elevator* to the top. Explain this concept.

_____

_____

_____

_____

R-E-S-P-E-C-T…Find Out What it Means to Me…
(Gender Stereotypes and Differential Respect, page 193)

10.   Patrice has recently been named CEO of a large corporation. While she worked very hard to achieve her status, she feels that she is not respected in her position of authority. Jackson, Esses, and Burris (2001) proposed that the *glass ceiling* is not the only issue that women in the workplace face. According to the researchers, women also face differential respect issues. Describe what Patrice might be experiencing and why.

_____

_____

_____

_____

_____

_____

Tokenism – One of the Many "Isms"...
(Consequences of Token Women in High Places, pages 194-195)

11.   *Tokenism* refers to the practice of hiring people from underrepresented groups often in accordance with standards as set forth by entities such as Affirmative Action. This practice, though, often leads to feelings that members of certain groups are hired more on their physical and cultural characteristics than on merit. It also leads to feelings that the positions to which certain people are hired are simply given to them rather than earned.

This certainly appears to be the case with the employment of women in positions of status. According to your textbook, few women are employed in positions of status. This is frequently interpreted as evidence that women lack the qualities that are necessary for attainment of employment in these positions.

What are some of the *negative* consequences of tokenism?

_____

_____

_____

Other Manifestations of Tokenism...
(Consequences of Token Women in High Places, pages 194-195)

12.   *Tokenism* can be exhibited in forms than the hiring of someone being hired due to their group membership. It also includes the performance of small positive actions towards people who are potential targets of prejudice. According to your textbook, the performance of these positive acts toward people who are potential targets of discrimination serves a function in the person performing these acts. What is the function?

_____

_____

_____

The Negative Effects of Tokenism...
(Consequences of Token Women in High Places, pages 194-195)

13.   There are **two** negative effects of tokenism listed in your textbook. Discuss each of them.

1. _____

_____

2. _____

_____

Summarize…
(Making Sense of Common Sense: "The Gender or Race-Card: Too Easy to Play, or Harder than You Think? Pages 195-196)

14.   Summarize this section, make sure that you provide research evidence for ideas found within the segment.

_____

_____

_____

_____

_____

_____

The Answer is "NO"…
(Can we Conclude that Stereotyping is Absent When Members of Different Groups are Rated the Same? Pages 196-197)

15.   This section evaluates the idea that stereotypes may exert and influence evaluation ratings. There are **two** standards that are used in our evaluations of others. One of the standards is *subjective* and the other is *objective*. Explain each standard.

_____

_____

_____

_____

Here Comes the Bride…
(Can we Conclude that Stereotyping is Absent When Members of Different Groups are Rated the Same? Pages 196-197)

16.   You are getting married and have an appointment with the baker this afternoon to decide on a design for your wedding cake. You have searched the internet for designs and know that you want a white cake with cream colored icing. You also want a cake that has a minimal amount of sugar because your husband-to-be is a diabetic and you, certainly, want him to be able to eat the cake.

        When you arrive at the bakery you are first given the chance to taste test several types of cake – vanilla, lemon-flavored, and almond-flavored. You decide that the almond –flavored cake has an excellent flavor.

Here Comes the Bride...Continued

Here, you are applying what type of *standard (subjective or objective)?*

_____

You, then, begin talking with the baker regarding the sugar issue. The baker tells you that he can bake a cake using a mixture of a product and sugar that will greatly reduce the amount of sugar in the cake. The amount of sugar in the cake – whether 1 cup or 10 cups – is the same no matter who will make the cake. In this case, what is the *standard of evaluation* being applied?

_____

Singlism...
(Can We be Victims of Stereotyping and Not Even Recognize it: The Case of Single People, pages 198-199)

17.   Define *singlism.*

Singlism - _____

_____

_____

Now, provide a detailed discussion of the research of DePaulo (2006).

Interest of Investigation: _____

_____

_____

Participants: _____

Findings: _____

_____

_____

_____

_____

The Glorification of the Institution of Marriage...
(Can We be Victims of Stereotyping and Not Even Recognize it: The Case of Single People, pages 198-199)

18.   In 2006, DePaulo and Morris suggested that the negative stereotyping of singles has a function in our society. What is that function?

_____

_____

Sticks and Stones May Break My Bones – But, Words Will Never Harm Me – Unfortunately, they will...
(Why do People Form and Use Stereotypes? Pages 200-201)

19.   There are **three** reasons that answer the question presented above – *"Why do people form and use stereotypes?"* Elaborate on each of these reasons.

1. _____

_____

2. _____

_____

3. _____

_____

We are Going to Operate on Your Stereotype...
(Stereotypes: How They Operate, page 200)

20.   Though Ellen has never had contact with a person who has AIDS, she has some definite opinions about them and is comfortable discussing these opinions. According to Judd, Ryan and Park (1991), why can Ellen so easily speak of her opinions towards AIDS patients?

_____

_____

_____

_____

Making the Inconsistent Consistent...
(Stereotypes: How They Operate, page 200)

21.   When we are presented with information that is inconsistent with our stereotype of a group, what tendency do we display?

_____

_____

_____

_____

She Just Does Not Seem to Fit...
(Stereotypes: How They Operate, page 200)

22.   What happens when we come in contact with a person who, according to their group membership, should "fit" within a particular category; but, for whatever reason, does not "fit"? For that matter, what happens when we come in contact with a cat that does not "fit" in with your pre-conceived stereotypes of what a cat should be?

For example, you are a "dog person" and hold the stereotype that all cats are lazy, do nothing but sit around and sleep, and are, for lack of better words, judgmental. Your next door neighbor gets a cat for her children and, after trying desperately to avoid the cat, one day the cat comes over to your home and cuddles next to you. In opposition to your stereotype of cats, you notice that this cat is playful and very full of life. In addition, the cat seems to like you very much. According to research findings, does this encounter change your mind? That is, are you now prone to changing your mind when it comes to all cats? Why or why not?

_____

_____

_____

_____

_____

Stereotypical Change...
(Do Stereotypes Ever Change? PageS 200-201)

23.   According to Eagly (1987), Oakes, Haslam and Turner (1994), Pettigrew (1980), and Tajfel (1981), can stereotypes change?

_____

_____

Stereotypical Change…Continued

Haslam (2001) addresses the issue of changing one's stereotypical opinions. What did Haslam find in 2001?

_____

_____

_____

PREJUDICE AND DISCRIMINATION: FEELINGS AND ACTIONS TOWARD SOCIAL GROUPS

Word Search Puzzle…
(pages 202-204)

24.   **Find the Following Words in the Puzzle Found Below**

DISCRIMINATION   GENDER
GROUP   MARITALSTATUS
PREJUDICE   RACE
SEX   STEREOTYPE
TOKENISM

```
Q  R  U  R  U  Y  Y  S  N  J  X  N  J  H  G
E  D  H  I  H  R  X  B  J  Q  E  O  Y  Q  Z
Z  M  N  P  B  S  Y  L  G  Y  C  I  D  P  M
B  M  A  R  I  T  A  L  S  T  A  T  U  S  E
V  P  C  E  F  E  M  P  H  M  R  A  I  O  W
Z  U  L  J  W  R  I  X  T  H  O  N  I  V  O
N  H  N  U  E  E  P  Q  T  I  E  I  I  W  Q
J  E  K  D  Y  O  F  U  Q  K  M  M  R  K  B
R  G  N  I  P  T  X  R  O  O  X  I  S  L  W
E  E  I  C  T  Y  A  T  Y  R  Q  R  B  M  L
G  Q  V  E  F  P  X  T  O  Q  G  C  G  M  I
C  Y  H  F  O  E  H  F  X  J  J  S  R  Q  E
I  C  Q  N  S  J  S  V  Z  C  N  I  V  A  C
N  D  N  U  H  N  J  L  U  U  M  D  P  G  U
R  P  N  M  L  J  P  L  D  N  J  R  I  U  O
```

It is Nothing Personal...
(Pages 202-204)

25.   Address the following: "Prejudice is **not** personal."

_____

_____

_____

Information Processing and Prejudice...
(Pages 202-204)

26.   William is an introductory psychology student. This past Tuesday, while studying the chapter on social psychology, William's professor discussed the concept of *prejudice*. During class, the professor gave the class a test designed to measure prejudice in individuals. William scored very high on the test which is indicative of some strong-held prejudicial attitudes. The professor informs the class that those who score high in prejudice tend to process information about groups in a different manner than do those who score low in the measure. What are some of the **differences** discussed in your textbook?

_____

_____

_____

The Emotional Causes Behind the Behavior...
(Pages 202-204)

27.   Prejudice is the result of an emotional response towards a group of people. Because of this, it is important to note which emotions serve as bases for the actions associated with the prejudice. When anger is the primary emotion underlying the prejudicial attitudes, the behavior might possibly be an attempt to harm a member of the group against whom the attitudes are targeted. When prejudice is **based on pity or guilt**, what might be the behavior in response?

_____

_____

How might the connection between the emotion and the behavior be something important to know when attempting to reduce prejudice?

_____

_____

_____

Anger Yields Negativity...
(Pages 202-204)

28.   Using the following rubric, describe the research of DeSteno, Dasgupta, Bartlett, and Cajdric (2004) in which negative emotions were induced to determine if they lead to prejudicial attitudes.

Participants: _____

Group I: _____

_____

Group II: _____

_____

Tasks:

1: _____

_____

2: _____

_____

Measure: _____

_____

Results: _____

_____

_____

_____

_____

Findings are NOT Culturally Specific...
(The Origins of Prejudice: Contrasting Perspectives, pages 204-205)

29.   What did Cohen, Montoya and Insko (2006) find regarding **cross-cultural similarities** between loyalty to one's in-group and prejudice towards an out-group?

_____

_____

_____

That is Threatening to My Self-Esteem…
(Threats to Self-Esteem, pages 205-206)

30.   Branscombe and Wann (1994) conducted a study designed to investigate what particular research question? Also, provide the answer as presented by Branscombe and Wann.

_____

_____

_____

A Competitive Player…
(Competition for Resources as a Source of Prejudice, page 206)

31.   Explain *realistic conflict theory*. How does this theory "play out" in prejudice towards others? Give an example of a situation in which realistic conflict theory may be at play.

_____

_____

_____

_____

_____

The Thief's Cavern…
(Building The Science: Classics in Social Psychology - What Causes Groups to Be Prejudicial toward Other Groups and Is Prejudice Inevitable? Page 207)

32.   The *"Robber's Cave"* camp study (Sherif et al, 1961) is an excellent example of a type of research known as the ***field experiment***. Field experiments are experiments conducted in everyday settings, but with situations that are artificially established. The reason this type of study is still considered an experiment is that the experimenters still manipulate the independent variable.

Using 22 fifth grade Caucasian boys as their participants, Sherif and his cohorts conducted one of the most cited and fascinating studies in psychology. Sherif et al's hypotheses were as follows:

(1) When individuals who don't know each other are exposed to one another and required to achieve a common goal, they will put aside differences and be able to work on and complete the task as one group.

(2) When two in-groups are formed and they are brought together for competition, hostility will arise and prejudicial attitudes will be formed and expressed.

The Thief's Cavern...Continued

The study took place in three separate steps or phases – each of which is delineated in your textbook. Describe each of the three phases and provide an explanation of the results of this famous experiment.

Phase 1: _____

_____

_____

Phase II: _____

_____

_____

Phase III: _____

_____

_____

Results: _____

_____

_____

_____

_____

_____

You Versus Me – or Us Versus Them...
(Role of Social Categorization: The US – vs – Them Effect, pages 208-211)

33.   Answer the following questions regarding the study performed by Tajfel, Billig, Bundy, and Flament (1971): How did the researchers divide their participants into groups?

_____

_____

What was the required task?

_____

You Versus Me – or Us Versus Them…Continued

What were the results?

_____

_____

_____

How does this study demonstrate the ideas found within *social identity theory?*

_____

_____

_____

WHY PREJUDICE IS NOT INEVITABLE: TECHNIQUES FOR COUNTERING ITS EFFECTS

Teach Your Children Well…
(On Learning Not to Hate, page 215)

34.   The *social learning view* suggests that children learn negative attitudes towards others by interacting with their significant others. Describe **two** ways in which this learning can occur.

1. _____

_____

2. _____

_____

An Identity Crisis???
(On Learning Not to Hate, page 215)

35.   What is a determining factor in the extent to which a child's negative attitudes develop?

_____

_____

"If You Judge People, You Have No Time to Love Them." – Mother Teresa
(On Learning Not to Hate, page 215)

36.   Research findings have shown a *correlation* between degree of prejudice embodied by an individual and satisfaction/enjoyment with life. After interpreting the findings of Feagin and McKinney (2003) and Harris et al (1991), what type of correlation did they find? How do you know?

_____

_____

_____

Contact Me…
(The Potential Benefits of Contact, pages 215-216)

37.   Explain the *contact hypothesis* and give **two** reasons why using having contact with others can be effective in reducing hate.

_____

_____

_____

_____

_____

You May Want to Adjust Your Categories…
(Recategorization: Changing the Boundaries, pages 216-217)

38.   Define *recategorization*. Then, explain the *common in-group identity model.*

_____

_____

_____

_____

_____

Communal Guilt??
(The Benefits of Guilt for Prejudice Reduction, pages 217-218)

39.　Explain the idea of *collective guilt*. How can *collective guilt* reduce prejudice?

_____

_____

_____

_____

_____

Stop It!
(Can We Learn to "Just Say No" to Stereotypes? Pages 218-219)

40.　According to the research of Kawakami et al (2000), it may be just that easy to **stop or ease** our reliance on stereotypes. What type of **training** did Kawakami et al, find that would **weaken** stereotypes, in particular implicit stereotypes? What does this training involve?

_____

_____

_____

_____

_____

Finish The Sentence...
(Social. Influences as a Means of Reducing Prejudice, pages 219-220)

41.　"Providing people with evidence that members of their own group _____

persons belonging to another group that is typically the target of prejudice can

_____ serve to weaken such negative reactions (Pettigrew, 1997;

Wright et al, 1997)."

After You Read... MyPsychLab Connection

(1)   Go to *EXPLORE: Reducing Prejudice*. This activity provides four examples of ways to reduce prejudice which include *cooperation, contact, critical thinking,* and *empathy*. The term *cooperation* refers to the practice of individuals working together as opposed to working separately in a competitive nature. The term *contact* can be defined as close interaction which might be as close as physical touching. *Critical thinking* is a cognitive process that involves looking and evaluating all sides of an issue and *empathy* can best be defined as a feeling of concern and understanding for another person's feelings. It is very similar to putting yourself in another's shoes.

(2)   What do you, personally, consider attractive? Is it someone who is financially secure and independent? Or – is it someone who is physically eye-catching? *WATCH: Attraction.* Here you will find a short film clip narrated by Dr. Don Straussberg who discusses his research activities investigating the construct of attraction. You might find some very surprising information in this one!

(3)   In *WATCH: Girls Will Be Girls and Boys Will Be Boys*, Patricia Bower, a child development specialist, discusses research conducted on both boys and girls investigating factors in the development of gender. In this short video clip, there is discussion of a study in which it was found that boys typically choose male gender-appropriate toys; while girls typically choose female gender-appropriate toys. This is even found in a family in which two lesbians are raising two boys conceived by artificial insemination.

(4)   If you only visit one of the cites discussed in this section, make it this one! *WATCH: Nappy Hair Controversy* is about a book entitled, "Nappy Hair." This book was read by a teacher to her class and resulted in her dismissal from the school for what amounts to racism. Ironically, her class consisted mainly of African American and Latino students. There are views on both sides – should the teacher be reinstated or should she remain dismissed? This is really thought-provoking!

After You Read… Practice Test #1

_____1. Michael, a 12 year devoted employee of Sun Shipping, was recently passed over for a promotion. The job was given to a woman, Lisa, who had worked for the shipping company for just 2 ½ years. According to Michael, Lisa was promoted because of her status as a woman and the company had failed to promote a woman for the past 6 years. To Michael, this represented a form of _____.
   A.   credential impairment.
   B.   identity assessment.
   C.   tokenism.
   D.   race discrimination.

_____2. Singlism refers to
   A.   the negative stereotyping of people who are **not** married.
   B.   the positive stereotyping of people who are **not** married.
   C.   the fact that single people tend to live shorter lives than do married people.
   D.   stereotyping single people as overwhelmingly positive.

_____3. Stereotypes can be
   A.   positive.
   B.   negative.
   C.   neutral.
   D.   All of the above are correct.

_____4. Prejudice is defined as
   A.   the action component of attitudes.
   B.   the behavioral component of attitudes.
   C.   the feeling component of attitudes.
   D.   the sensing component of attitudes.

_____5. Marti is a member of Joan's in-group; Peter is a member of Joan's out-group. Therefore
   A.   Marti and Joan are in the same group.
   B.   Marti and Peter are in the same group.
   C.   Joan and Peter are in different groups.
   D.   Both A and C are correct.

_____6. In the Robber's Cave experiment, negative feelings between the boys were the result of _____.
   A.   the activities enjoyed by the boys.
   B.   the names of the groups as chosen by the boys.
   C.   direct competition between the boys.
   D.   long standing rivalries between the boys.

_____7.   There is a strict division between liberals and conservatives. Drew is a conservative.
           Therefore, _____ would be considered his out-group(s). <u>Be careful on
           this one</u>.
           A.   liberals
           B.   females
           C.   other conservatives.
           D.   females and liberals

_____8.   According to your textbook, in recent years, discrimination has
           A.   increased.
           B.   decreased.
           C.   remained relatively the same.
           D.   increased only in certain portions of the country.

_____9.   "Old fashioned racism" as compared to "modern racism"
           A.   is more negative.
           B.   resulted in more out in the open racism.
           C.   resulted in more discrete racism.
           D.   was very subtle and under the table.

_____10.   The bona fide pipeline can best be defined as
           A.   a priming method used to automatically activate negative attitudes.
           B.   a procedure in which participants see various pictures and have to indicate if the
                 picture is of a good or a bad event.
           C.   a procedure in which participants are asked to verbalize negative attitudes
                 towards what they would consider to be one of their out-groups.
           D.   a priming method used to automatically activate positive attitudes.

11.   The idea that women are inferior to men is an example of a _____.

12.   _____ states that prejudice stems from our tendency to separate the
       world into "them" and "us."

13.   Children tend to acquire negative attitudes towards out-groups due to views expressed by
       significant others, in particular, their _____.

14.   Increased contact between different groups is the content of the _____.

15.   Allen is a white male who participated in the civil rights movement. In fact, he was a participant
       in one of the marches with Dr. Martin Luther King. Today, he feels very guilty for his in-group's
       history of perpetrating acts of discrimination against Blacks. This is a form of

       _____.

After You Read... Practice Test #2

_____1.   Prejudice is best defined as
A.   dislike based on one's gender.
B.   dislike based on one's sexual orientation.
C.   dislike based on one's age.
D.   All of the above are definitions of types of prejudice.

_____2.   Kahneman and Tversky (1984) presented the _____ which states that
people tend to be "risk averse" which means they tend to weigh losses more heavily than
they weigh their gains.
A.   gains advantage theory
B.   loss aversion theory
C.   gain benefit theory
D.   prospect theory

_____3.   The _____ is an obstacle that prevents women from
obtaining top positions in the workplace.
A.   final solution
B.   glass ceiling
C.   feminine mystique
D.   brick wall

_____4.   When someone "plays" the race-card or the gender-card, members of the dominant group
see this person as
A.   blaming themselves for their negative outcomes.
B.   blaming others for their negative outcomes.
C.   lazy and unwilling to stand up for themselves.
D.   a poor example of his or her group.

_____5.   Standards for evaluation that have the same meaning regardless of to whom they are
applied are called
A.   objective.
B.   subjective.
C.   normative.
D.   evaluative.

_____6.   DePaulo and Morris (2006) suggested that negative stereotyping and discrimination
against single people serves to
A.   protect the stereotypes.
B.   force them to get married.
C.   reinforce the idea that married people are happier than unmarried people.
D.   protect the institution of marriage as a social institution.

_____7.   Stereotypes can also serve as
A.   discrimination.
B.   schemas.
C.   negative behaviors against others.
D.   positive attitudes.

_____8.　　　When we are faced with an individual or group of individuals who do not "fit" into a stereotypical category, we tend to place this person/these people in special categories known as _____.
A.　subtypes.
B.　schemas.
C.　typicality groups.
D.　activation subsets.

_____9.　　　Regarding information processing in those who score high on measures of prejudice versus those who score low on these measures, those who score high tend to
A.　process information in the same way as those low on these measures.
B.　process information differently than those low on these measures.
C.　process information slower than those low on these measures.
D.　None of the above is correct.

_____10.　　　_____ contact between persons of differing groups often results in _____ prejudice.
A.　Increased; decreased
B.　Decreased; increased
C.　Decreased; decreased
D.　Increased; increased

11.　　Shifting the boundary between "us" and "them" thus making the former out-groups into members of the "us" category is referred to as _____.

12.　　_____ is defined as hiring someone solely on the foundation of racial and/or ethnic categories rather than due to the individual's merit.

13.　　One of the primary issues contained in this chapter is that prejudice is not inborn; rather it is

_____.

14.　　The _____ theory states that the main source of prejudice is competition over resources.

15.　　Thought is to action as _____ is to discrimination.

After You Read… Practice Test #3

_____1.   Overt is to covert as _____ is to _____.
A. old fashioned racism; modern racism
B. modern racism; old fashioned racism
C. modern prejudice; past prejudice
D. past prejudice; modern prejudice

_____2.   In Sherif et al's Robber's Cave study, it was found that competition tends to
A. decrease negative attitudes between groups.
B. increase negative attitudes between groups.
C. in no way changes the amount of negative attitudes between groups.
D. None of the above is correct.

_____3.   The participants in the Robber's Cave study were
A. girls between the ages of 10 and 13.
B. fifth grade boys.
C. a group of former mental patients.
D. a group of highly religious individuals.

_____4.   Regarding how much progress has been made towards equality, it has been consistently found that Whites tend to perceive that there has been _____ progress; whereas Blacks tend to believe that there has been _____ progress.
A. not much; quite a bit
B. little; some
C. quite a bit; not much
D. some; little

_____5.   Stereotypes are beliefs that can be related to ALL of the following, EXCEPT
A. appearance.
B. sexual orientation.
C. gender.
D. All of the above are correct.

_____6.   The representation of women is that they are high in warmth but low in
_____.
A. caring.
B. competence.
C. intelligence.
D. consideration.

_____7.   Research has found that when women are given leadership roles, they tend to receive _____ evaluations from their subordinates than are males.
A. lower
B. higher
C. equal
D. substantially higher

_____8.   Branscombe and Wann (1994) conducted a study to investigate the extent to which an event must threaten a group's identity for prejudice responses to occur. College students who served as participants in the study were shown one of two video clips from the movie, *Rocky IV*. In the nonthreatening condition, Rocky won the fight against Ivan, the Russian contender. In the threatening condition, Rocky lost the fight against Ivan. What were the findings of this study?
   A. Those who saw Rocky lose showed increased prejudice towards Russians.
   B. Those who saw Rocky win showed increased prejudice towards Russians.
   C. Those who saw Rocky win showed equal prejudice towards Russians as those who saw Rocky lose.
   D. Those who saw Rocky lose showed equal prejudice towards Russians as did those who saw Rocky win.

_____9.   Criticism of the Robber's Cave study include
   A. Sherif did not show whether competition is necessary for prejudice to develop.
   B. the boys in the study may have actually had some psychological adjustment issues.
   C. some of the boys were from affluent homes and others were from poor homes.
   D. the friendships between the boys that developed due to the cooperative behavior task were not long-standing.

_____10.   It is noted in your textbook that prejudice appears to have decreased in recent years. One reason why this might be the case is that
   A. people are, simply, less prejudice.
   B. prejudice is now expressed more openly than in the past.
   C. the prejudice we see today is more subtle.
   D. people are too consumed with their own lives which allows little time for prejudicial feelings.

11.   When people are faced with the knowledge that members of their own group have imposed prejudicial actions against members of other groups, they sometimes react by denying the possibility of _____ responsibility.

12.   _____ involves individuals accepting that their actions resulted in harmful outcomes; but, it was necessary to achieve "larger" moral purposes.

13.   The _____ view states that children acquire negative attitudes because of exposure to negative views expressed by significant others in their lives.

14.   Children are influenced by their parents' racial attitudes to a certain degree that is comparable to the extent with which the children _____ with their parents.

15.   _____ seems to affect all humans at some time during their lives.

After You Read… Practice Test #4

_____1. Research has shown that when White Americans who are highly identified with their racial group, are threatened with loss of their privileged state, they tend to respond
A. positively with decreased racism.
B. negatively with increased old fashioned racism.
C. negatively with increased modern racism.
D. positively with increased racism.

_____2. Regarding Affirmative Action, Whites who view Affirmative Action as negatively affecting their chance to get a job are prone to _____ Affirmative Action.
A. oppose
B. be in favor of Affirmative Action, but only for Blacks
C. oppose Affirmative Action for all except women
D. be in favor of Affirmative Action, but only for women

_____3. _____ are considered to be the cognitive component of attitudes towards a social group.
A. prejudice
B. discrimination
C. negative attitudes
D. stereotypes

_____4. Stereotypes can be either positive or negative. They can also be
A. agreed with or rejected.
B. accurate or inaccurate.
C. Both A and B are correct.
D. None of the above is correct.

_____5. One problem with the stereotypes of women is that
A. the traits that are supposed to possess are often viewed as inappropriate for high status positions.
B. more than half of the US population is made up of women.
C. people tend to feel more negatively about women as compared to feelings about men.
D. the vast majority of women are employed in high status positions.

_____6. The "think manager – think male" mentality helps preserve the _____.
A. brick wall.
B. glass ceiling.
C. hollowed box.
D. glass railing.

_____7. Men tend to rise very quickly to the top on the _____.
A. glass ceiling.
B. concrete floor.
C. glass elevator.
D. None of the above.

_____ 8.   This model suggests that recategorization can reduce prejudice. It states that when "them" turns into "us" prejudice has the potential of being reduced or even eliminated.
A. Recategorization of others model.
B. Common in-group identity model.
C. Prejudice reduction model.
D. Discriminatory discounting model.

_____ 9.   A study conducted using Jewish Americans as participants investigated the idea of recategorization. The participants were induced to think either of Jews and Germans as separate groups or as one single group. Participants were then asked to indicate the degree to which they would be willing to forgive the Germans for past events towards the Jews. Which group showed the least forgiveness towards the Germans?
A. Those in the group that was induced to think of the two as a single group.
B. Those in the group that was induced to think of the two as separate entities.
C. Both groups were equally negative about the Germans due to the horrible acts that were perpetrated against the Jews.
D. Both groups were equally positive about the Germans due to the time lapse between the atrocities and the present.

_____ 10.   Elise has been investigating her lineage. She found that her great-grandmother on her father's side was an African American. Elise, though, has always classified herself as a Caucasian. According to the _____, though, she would be considered an African American just like her great-grandmother.
A. lineage determination model
B. categorization classification model
C. one drop rule
D. racial classification rule

11.   I am going to deny you apartment rental because of your ethnicity. This is an example of

_____.

12.   I believe Yaholala, a Soponian (a fictional race), to be lazy, rude, and unintelligent because of her attachment to the Soponian group.. This is an example of _____.

13.   All Justonians (my fictional out-group) should not be allowed to work in fast food restaurants because they tend to sample the food prior to giving it to the patron. This is an example of

_____.

14.   Rose is a 34 year old female. She is kind, nurturant, and considerate. Therefore, Rose is an excellent example of the positive side of the female _____.

15.   The _____ theory suggests that in incidences where competition is intensifying, the members of the groups involved will see each other in increasingly negative characterizations.

When you have finished... Crossword Puzzle

Across

4.   Attitude toward members of a social group
6.   Stereotyping and discrimination against people who are not married

Down

1.   Belief about the different attributes that others possess
2.   The invisible mechanism that holds qualified women back from attaining high-level positions in the workplace
3.   The hiring or acceptance of only a few members of a particular group
5.   Actions that deny certain things to members of certain groups

Created by Puzzlemaker at DiscoverySchool.com

When you have finished… You be the Researcher

A method of research that is sometimes used in social psychology is the **content analysis**. A researcher conducting a content analysis relies on written or auditory communication for his or her data. The written or auditory communication may consist of magazines, books (including fiction, non-fiction, children's books, adult books; novels, dictionaries, cookbooks, comic books, etc.), newspapers, television, radio, songs (including rap, blues, jazz, new-age, pop, classical, etc.), poems, instruction manuals, movies – the list is almost inexhaustible!

The data that is collected is normally based on counts. That is, let's say you are investigating the question, "Do movies show African Americans in high-prestige positions within the workplace as often as they tend to show Caucasians in such positions?" You may choose comedy movies as the communication form from which you will obtain your data. The procedure would consist of your watching a number of comedy movies and simply recording the number of African Americans you see in high-prestige positions and the number of Caucasians you see in the same positions. The numbers could then be converted to percentages and then compared to see which group is seen most often in these positions.

Your task here it to examine a form of written communication to determine how gender stereotypes are portrayed (and you can be certain that they will be). The procedure you will follow is as follows:

(1)   Determine what your hypothesis (es) will be.

       For example, do you think you will see more male typical behavior than female typical behavior portrayed in psychology textbooks?

(2)   Determine which type of communication you will rely upon for your data collection.

       You may choose one type of communication from the following: Children's books, magazines or textbooks.

(3)   You will use **three (3)** books, magazines or textbooks to acquire your data.

(4)   Decide what behaviors you will be counting as typically male and which you will be counting as typically female. These behaviors will need to be defined – so you will need to provide an in-depth **operational definition**. **An operational definition is a very clear and concise definition.** The reason that these operational definitions are so important is that they provide for a smooth replication of the study, if this is desired by another researcher.

       An example of an operational definition of a behavior (let's say – buying a snack out of the snack machine) is as follows:

       The person approaches the snack machine. He or she then puts money into the machine and chooses the numbers and/or letters that correspond to the snack he or she desires. The snack then falls into an area that is accessible by pushing a door-like area open. The person pushes the door area open and retrieves the snack.

This may seem almost kindergarten-like to you, but it is necessary for an adequate replication.

(5)   Collect your data – recording the number of times you see both female typical behavior and male typical behavior being displayed.

(6)   Convert your data to percentages.

(7)   Compare percentages and produce your conclusions.

Did you support your hypothesis?

Answers – After You Read…Practice Activities

1.   A, B, D, C, F, E, G

2.   Prejudice = thoughts or feelings about a particular group; affective component.

   Stereotype = beliefs as to what a particular group is like; cognitive component.

   Discrimination = actions taken towards a particular group; behavioral component.

3.   Student will provide two examples of positive stereotypes.

4.   Positive = Kind, nurturant, considerate.

   Negative = Dependent, weak, overly emotional.

5.   Society stresses the idea that women are warm and, in light of this, people tend to perceive women as more positive than men. This is what Eagly and Mladinic (1994) refer to as the "women are wonderful" effect.

6.   The traits of warmth and kindness are seen as being less appropriate for people in high status – such a corporate CEO. In light of this, women have been traditionally been employed in lower supporting positions such as secretaries. This is quite unfortunate in that positions such as this provide less monetary compensation and less prestige.

7.   The glass ceiling is an obstacle for women. It prevents them from reaching the most prestigious positions within the workplace. In the corporate world, women who violate the expected norms are seen as atypical. Those who do not violate or personify the expected norms are left out. They appear to be less fit for the higher, more prestigious positions.

8.   Women who serve in the higher prestige positions often receive less than optimal evaluations. They also receive more gender discrimination than those women who are employed in "typical" female occupations such as clerical work.

9.   The glass elevator is the reverse of the glass ceiling. Men who are in typically female jobs, such as a cook at a restaurant, often "ride" the glass elevator to the top in their occupations. They also acquire these positions much faster than women and with a greater frequency.

10.   This is often seen when women are in high power positions – such as CEO. The idea is that men are seen as more deserving of such positions. Also women being in such prestigious positions is a violation of female norms and can lead to rejection.

11.   One of the negative consequences of tokenism is that people who are hired as "token" employees are often perceived negatively. The token people are often unpopular with their coworkers which can make for a negative work environment for everyone. A second negative consequence is that "token" employees are often perceived as less competent than those who obtained their jobs through traditional means. Women who are hired as "tokens" are also undermined in their performance whenever they are chosen to lead a group

12.   These acts are often used for a means of rationalization for later discriminatory behavior.

13. Tokenism allows people to get "off the hook." When someone hires another person as a "token" it makes them and the system of hiring appear to be legitimate and fair. Tokenism also can be damaging to the self-esteem of the "tokens." They may feel that although they did, indeed, get the job; they got the job through the process of tokenism, rather than through their competence and merit.

14. Provide your own summary, remember to include research evidence in support of the claims within your summary.

15. Subjective standard = standard that can take on different meaning, depending on to whom they are applied.

    Objective standard = standard that has the same meaning – no matter what.

16. Subjective; objective.

17. Singlism = Negative stereotyping and potential discrimination towards people who are unmarried.

    Interest of Investigation: The characterization of single and married people.

    Participants: One thousand undergraduate students.

    Findings: Descriptors of single people were shown to be relatively negative when compared to how married people were characterized. In addition, 50% of the time people who were married were depicted as kind, giving and caring. These three attributes were only attributed to single people 2% of the time. These differences were even more pronounced when the people described were over 40 years of age as compared to 25.

18. DePaulo and Morris (2006) suggested that the function of the negative stereotyping of singles serves the function of protecting and venerating the institution of marriage.

19. 1. Stereotypes operate as schemas.

    2. Stereotypes are quick and readily available because they are considered pre-conceived ideas.

    3. Stereotypes also serve a motivational function. They can make us feel better about our own group memberships.

20. Once characteristics of a certain group or person are activated, they come to mind automatically. This occurs even in light of the fact that the person harboring the stereotypical notions has never had direct contact with the group or person they are considering.

21. We try to make the inconsistent information into information that is consistent with our stereotypes. This is done by refuting the inconsistent information or by changing the information into forms that more closely match our own stereotypes.

22. No, you are probably not going to change your ideas about all cats. According to research, you will, rather, construct a subtype for this cat. This subtyping acts to guard our stereotypes of cats.

23. The researchers found that stereotypes tend to remain stable as long as the nature of the relationship between groups remains stable.

    Haslam (2001) found that stereotypes can change only at the point where values change and the categories through which we classify people also change.

24.

```
+ + + + + + + + + + + N + + +
+ + + + + + + + + + E O + + +
+ + + P + S + + + C I + + M
+ M A R I T A L S T A T U S +
+ + + E + E + + + R A I + +
+ + + J + R + + + + N + + +
+ + + U E E P + + + E I + + +
+ + + D + O + U + K + M + + +
+ + N I + T + + O + + I + + +
+ E + C + Y + T + R + R + + +
G + + E + P X + + + G C + + +
+ + + + + E + + + + + S + + +
+ + + S + + + + + + I + + +
+ + + + + + + + + + D + + +
+ + + + + + + + + + + + + +
```

(Over,Down,Direction)

DISCRIMINATION(12,14,N)
GENDER(1,11,NE)
GROUP(11,11,NW)
MARITALSTATUS(2,4,E)
PREJUDICE(4,3,S)
RACE(11,5,N)
SEX(5,13,NE)
STEREOTYPE(6,3,S)
TOKENISM(8,10,NE)

25. Prejudice is not based on personal attributions; rather, it is based on group membership. Members are disliked not on the basis of their personal characteristics.

26. Information about the groups that are targets of the prejudice is given increased attention. This information may also be processed in a more careful fashion. People who score high in prejudice are very interested in finding out what group or groups with which a person is associated.

27. Prejudice that is based on the emotions of pity or guilt may lead to the avoidance of the group at which the prejudicial attitudes are aimed.

    The connection between the emotion and the behavior is important to the reduction of prejudice because in order to reduce the prejudice, the emotional portion should be addressed.

28. Participants:
    Group I: Over-estimators
    Group II: Under-estimators

Tasks:

    1. Negative emotion inducing writing task – write of a time when they felt very angry, sad or neutral)

    2. Evaluated other members of their in-group or the out-group

Results:

    Reaction time to associate both negative and positive words with in and out groups varied according to what type of negative emotion that the participant experienced. When angry, out group was more quickly associated with negative

evaluations and the in-group was more quickly associated with positive evaluations. When feeling neutral or sad, there existed no difference between association with the in-group and the out-group. In summary, the results showed that anger tended to produce automatic prejudice toward members of out-groups.

29. In 186 different societies, the more importance one displays towards their own group, the more support there is for prejudice towards other groups.

30. The research question addressed was, "Can exposure to a minor threat to one's identity result in prejudice?" In a nutshell, the answer was "yes".

31. Realistic conflict theory states that when there are limited resources, including territory as in the example in the textbook, conflict is a very viable reaction. This conflict can, in turn, lead to prejudice between groups or individuals who seek the same resource.

    You, now, are to provide your own example of the theory at play.

32. Phase I = The boys arrived at the camp and were assigned to two different groups. At this point, neither of the two groups of boys were unaware that other boys were at the camp, but in cabins that were far from them in proximity. The boys formed attachments to members of their group. The groups chose names for their group and made flags reflecting their membership

    Phase II = The two groups were brought together and a sequence of competitions began. The winning team, they were told, would receive a trophy as well as various other prizes. This established fertile ground for competition. As the boys competed for the prizes and the trophy, tension rose between the two groups. The tension consisted of, at first, verbal banter. It, though, quickly increased into "direct acts." There were increasingly negative taunts thrown from both groups. These taunts drew strong approval from members of their own group. Prejudice was, most certainly, at work.

Phase III = Groups were exposed to increased contact with the other. This, though, only increased feelings of hostility. The condition was, then, introduced in which the boys were required to work together on a task. The circumstances took a 180 degree turn. The boys began working in a cooperative fashion, the tension decreased, and friendships developed between members of the two groups.

Results = Prejudice between groups could be induced, especially under the competitive conditions that were set up.

In a cooperative task in which both groups needed to equally participate in order to reach the goal state, both groups could come together and even establish friendships with members of the other group.

33. Participants were shown a group of dots and were to estimate the amount of dots they saw. They were also shown a set of pictures by Klee and Kandinsky. They were, then, divided randomly, but were told that they have been put into a certain group because they had either over-estimated or under-estimated the number of dots or because of their preference for either Klee or Kandinsky paintings.

The task was to allocate money between one other participant who was an in-group member and one participant who was an out-group member.

The results were that participants awarded members of their own group with more money.

The social identity theory states that individuals tend to feel more positive towards their own groups than they do to other groups. Since the person gave more money to their in-group member than the out-group member, this study is demonstrative of the ideas behind the theory.

34. Children learn negative attitude by listening to views expressed by their significant others and through direct experience with people who belong to other groups.

35. The extent to which the child develops a negative attitude towards a particular group depends on how closely the child identifies with the parent.

36. They found a negative correlation – that is, when one variable increases (prejudicial attitudes), the other decreases (enjoyment with life).

37. The contact hypothesis states that prejudice can be diminished by an increase in contact between differing groups. Reasons why this may work include: The contact can lead to recognition of similarities between groups. The contact can also lead us to see that the out-group is not as "out" group as they may appear.

38. Recategorization refers to shifting our view of the differences between "us" and "them."

The common in-group identity model states that recategorization can, indeed, change our attitudes and reduce prejudice. Simply, the model states that as members of one group start to view their own group as well as another group as a "single social entity",

attitudes towards the other group
become more positive.

39. Collective guilt occurs when people
belonging to one group feel guilty for
the actions of other members of their
group. This can reduce prejudice by
framing attitudes towards another group
in a different way. That is, rather than
looking at the negatives, there may be
the tendency to focus on the positives

40. Negation training was used to lessen
implicit stereotypes. This form of
training involves learning to say no to
stereotypes.

41. "Providing people with evidence
that members of their own group
like persons belonging to another
group that is typically the target of
prejudice can **sometimes** serve
to weaken such negative
reactions (Pettigrew, 1997;
Wright et al, 1997)."

Answers – Cross Word Puzzle

Across

4. Singlism
6. Prejudice

Down

1. Stereotype
2. Glassceiling
3. Tokenism
5. Discrimination

Answers – Practice Test #1

1. C
2. A
3. D
4. C
5. D
6. C
7. D
8. B
9. B
10. A
11. Gender Stereotype
12. Social Identity Theory
13. Parents
14. Contact Hypothesis
15. Collective Guilt

Answers – Practice Test #2

1. D
2. D
3. B
4. B
5. A
6. D
7. B
8. A
9. B
10. A

11. Recategorization
12. Tokenism
13. Learned
14. Realistic Conflict
15. Prejudice

Answers – Practice Test #3

1. A
2. B
3. B
4. C
5. D
6. B
7. A
8. A
9. A
10. C
11. Collective
12. Legitimization
13. Social Learning
14. Identify
15. Prejudice

Answers – Practice Test #4

1. C
2. A
3. D
4. C
5. A
6. B
7. C
8. B
9. B
10. C
11. Discrimination
12. Stereotyping
13. Prejudice
14. Gender Stereotype
15. Realistic Conflict

CHAPTER 7

INTERPERSONAL ATTRACTION AND CLOSE RELATIONSHIPS

Before You Read...Chapter Summary

As human beings, we all have the need for some form of social contact. Chapter Seven begins with a discussion of the need for affiliation. This need is discussed as being highly individualized. That is, the need for affiliation varies from person to person. Some individuals have a very high need to affiliate and some have a low need to affiliate. The point is, though, that we all need others. This idea is not a contemporary idea. As a matter of fact, the need for affiliation goes far back and is noted to have an evolutionary purpose. Our ancestors had to interact with others in the acquisition of food products and for protective measures. The human species would not have continued if it had not been for the need for affiliation. Affiliation, though, is not a static process. It leads to interpersonal attraction, which is defined as the evaluations (both positive and negative) that we make about others. Attraction is determined by proximity to others and as well as by other factors, including physical attractiveness. Attractiveness is a relative term. What one finds attractive, someone else may and, in reality, will, find distasteful. Upon reading the section of this chapter that discusses attractiveness, you will find out what men tend to find attractive in a woman and what women tend to find attractive in a woman. Incidentally, what a man finds attractive about a woman and what a woman finds attractive about a man, serves the same evolutionary purpose as affiliation– the continuance of the species.

One of the topics addressed in chapter seven is the involvement of similarities in attraction. Do we tend to be attracted to those who are similar to us or do we tend to be attracted to those who are dissimilar to us? You will find the answer in this chapter. In addition to affiliation and attraction, close relationships are discussed. In particular, close relationships with family, friends, lovers, and marriage partners are discussed. As is noted in your textbook, there is one common characteristic that all close relationships share – interdependence. Going one step further there are some close relationships that involve the emotion of love. You will learn that there are different categories of love – including possessive love, companionate love, game playing love, logical love, and selfless love. Of these categories, companionate love and selfless love are the most desirable; while game playing love is the least desirable.

If one were to look at this chapter as a kind of continuum, it would start on one end with affiliation, then move to attraction, then on to love, to the institution of marriage (kind of like the "ultimate" affiliation), and, finally, to the failure of the marriage. At the end of Chapter Seven, you will read of the factors involved in marital happiness as well as the factors involved in marital disharmony – which may go all the way to complete failure of the marriage – divorce. You will learn the consequences of a failed marriage and how it tends to affect those involved.

Before You Read... Learning Objectives

After reading this chapter, you should be able to:

- Define the term *affiliate* and recognize the importance of affiliation in the human evolutionary process.
- Discuss individual differences in the need for affiliation.
- Elaborate upon the idea that affect and attraction are strongly related.
- Discuss the influence of external factors, including exposure to others, as determinants of attraction.
- Expand upon the idea that the observable characteristics of others, including physical attractiveness and behavior, can influence our level of attraction.
- Explain the role of similarity in our attraction to others.
- Discuss the idea of *reciprocity* in a relationship.
- Understand the cultural foundations of close relationships with family, friends, lovers, and spouses.
- Expand upon the idea of interdependence in a relationship.
- Elaborate upon the role of attachment style in the development of a close relationship.
- Discuss the various forms of attachment style.
- Explain some of the consequences of life in the absence of close relationships.
- Understand the similarities and differences between a friendship and a romantic relationship.
- Expand upon the criteria we tend to used in our selection of a potential mate.
- Delineate the different types of love – including *passionate love, unrequited love, companionate love, game playing love, possessive love, logical love,* and *selfless love.*
- Explain why we have the tendency to experience jealousy when we are in a caring relationship.
- Discuss the factors that can affect marital happiness.
- Understand why marriages fail and the consequences of a failed marriage.

As You Read...Term Identification

Important Terms to Know
Below are a list of some of the key terms and concepts from this chapter. Make flashcards in order to enhance your recall ability of these terms. Refer to the definitions that are either in boldface or in the margins of this chapter for help. You may also want to include additional terms from this chapter as you deem necessary.

interpersonal trust, (p. 246)	similarity-dissimilarity effect, (p. 240)	attachment style, (p. 246)
need for affiliation, (p. 227)	proportion of similarity, (p. 240)	unrequited love, (p. 256)
social comparison, (p. 241)	repulsion hypothesis, (p. 241)	companionate love, (p. 256)
dismissing avoidant attachment, (p. 247)	balance theory, (p. 241)	intimacy, (p. 257)
proximity, (p. 231)	adaptive response, (p. 242)	passion, (p. 257)
repeated exposure, (p. 232)	rule of reciprocity, (p.	assumed similarity, (p. 262)
physical attraction, (p. 233)	enemyship, (p. 245)	narcissism, (p. 262)
appearance-rejection sensitivity, (p. 237)	interdependence, (p. 245)	

As You Read...Practice Activities

DETERMINANTS OF ATTRACTION: THE NEED TO AFFILIATE AND THE BASIC ROLE OF AFFECT

A Basic Human Need...
(The Importance of Affiliation for Human Existence, pages 226-228)

1.   Defined *affiliation*.

_____

_____

As human beings, we have an innate need to interact with others. From an evolutionary perspective – why might this be true?

_____

_____

_____

_____

There are Those Who Need Others and Those Who, Well, Don't...
(Individual Differences in the Need to Affiliate, pages 227-228)

2.   The degree of our need to be with others is highly individualized. Some individuals thrive on being with others; while there are those who prefer to be alone much of the time. Let me introduce you to Ethel. Ethel is a lovely 88 year old lady who has lived alone since her husband died 5 years ago. Ethel loves to be with others and, for some unknown reason, her friends have begun to ignore her. She is unable to understand why this is occurring.

In this scenario, there are two issues that Ethel is finding frustrating: (1) It is her "friends" who are treating her this way and "friends", certainly do not treat other "friends" that way. (2) She is a very social person and being ignored is taking her social life away.

According to research findings, how might Ethel be feeling right now?

_____

_____

_____

_____

Hurricane Katrina and Social Psychology...
(Situational Influences on the Need to Affiliate, page 227)

3.   Hurricane Katrina devastated states along the Gulf coast of the United States. After Hurricane Katrina, people from all over the country, in fact, all over the world, came to the aid of those displaced by the storm. People opened their homes to complete strangers and provided refuge for those who, virtually, had nothing left.

The phenomenon of responding to a stressful situation/event, such as a hurricane, with friendliness and caring was first described by Schachter (1959). Describe Schachter's research.

_____

_____

_____

_____

_____

_____

A Common Need?
(Individual Differences in the Need to Affiliate: Are There People who Don't Need Other People? Pages 227-228)

4.   According to Koole, Greenberg and Pyszczynski (2006), the need to affiliate with other is

_____

_____.

You Show Me Your Information and I will Show You Mine...
(Individual Differences in the Need to Affiliate: Are There People who Don't Need Other People? Pages 227-228)

5.   Describe the research of Carvallo and Gabriel (2006) which was designed to gain evidence regarding whether or not people have the need to affiliate with others.

_____

_____

_____

_____

_____

We Like You...You Make Me Feel Good...
(The Direct Effect of Emotions on Attraction, pages 228-229)

6.   We have the tendency to like those who make us feel good and dislike those who make us feel bad. You strongly dislike your professor. You know the one - Dr. Roberts, the professor who "gave" you an "F" in his class. According to McDonald (1962) why do you dislike Dr. Roberts' so intensely?

_____

_____

_____

A Match Made in Heaven? Not in Your Opinion...
(The Associated Effect of Emotions on Attraction, page 229)

7.   Your boyfriend, Greg, has just broken up with you. When you receive the news you are with your new lab partner, Jerry, discussing your chemistry assignment. Considering your new relationship with your lab partner (the semester has just begun), you are likely to respond to him in a negative fashion. Why?

_____

_____

_____

_____

_____

We Can Make Your Teeth Glisten...
(The Affect-Attraction Relationship and Social Influence, pages 229-230)

8.   You are an advertising agent and have just been given an assignment to produce an advertisement campaign for *Star Shine Toothpaste*. Based on the research of Glaser and Salovey, 1998; Harker and Keltner, 2001; and Weisberg, 1990, which investigated the affect-attraction relationship and its influence on our interpersonal evaluations, your task is to design a TV campaign aimed at increasing sales.

You are expected to provide the following:

Music (genre, name(s) of song(s):

_____

We Can Make Your Teeth Glisten…Continued

Predominant colors, scenery:

_____

_____

Actors:

_____

_____

_____

Script:

_____

_____

_____

Advice to the actors:

_____

_____

_____

EXTERNAL DETERMINANTS OF ATTRACTION: PROXIMITY AND OTHERS' OBSERVABLE CHARACTERISTICS

Proximity…Too Close or Too Far?
The Power of Proximity: Unplanned Contacts, page & Why Does Proximity Matter? Repeated Exposure is the Key, page 232)

9.   Define the words, _proximity_ and _mere exposure effect_.

_____

_____

_____

Proximity...Too Close or Too Far?...Continued

How can the ideas of proximity and mere exposure "play" into who we decide to marry?

_____

_____

And To Think They Were Only Merely Exposed...
(Why Does Proximity Matter? Repeated Exposure is the Key, pages 231-232)

10.   Describe the research of Moreland and Beach (1992) investigating the *mere exposure effect*.

_____

_____

_____

_____

_____

_____

The Mere Exposure Effect According to Swap...
(Why Does Proximity Matter? Repeated Exposure is the Key, pages 231-232)

11.   According to Swap (1977), in what instances does the mere exposure effect cease to operate?

_____

_____

_____

Was It Love at First Sight?
(Observable Characteristics of Others: Liking – or Disliking – What We See, pages 233-238)

12.   Okay...there is evidence on how increased exposure can, in most cases, increase our positive evaluation of others. This positive evaluation, then, in turn, can lead to attraction. What, though, about love at first sight? Is it truly possible? Cite evidence provided by Andreoletti, Zebrowitz, and Lachman (2001) and Anderson and Baum (1994).

_____

_____

_____

Everything Has its Beauty, But Not Everyone Sees it. – Confucius

(Physical Attractiveness: Beauty May Be Only Skin Deep, But We Pay a Lot of Attention to Skin, pages 233-235)

13.   One's physical appearance is a powerful determinant in the decision making process of whether or not we like a person. A stereotype based on our concept of what is and what is not attractive plays a key role here. How might that be? Answer this question on the basis of attractiveness being equated with being "more" feminine and "more" masculine (Dion & Dion, 1987; Hatfield & Sprecher, 1986a).

_____

_____

_____

A Stereotypical Problem? Hummmm…

(Physical Attractiveness: Beauty May Be Only Skin Deep, But We Pay a Lot of Attention to Skin, pages 233-235)

14.   Unfortunately, by relying on stereotypes, we do have a problem. According to Feingold (1992) and Kenealy et al. (1991), what is that problem?

_____

_____

Beauty in things exists in the mind which contemplates them. - David Hume

(Physical Attractiveness: Beauty May Be Only Skin Deep, But We Pay a Lot of Attention to Skin, pages 233-235)

15.   What cues help us determine who is attractive and who is not? Answer this by discuss the two procedures designed by Cunningham (1986) and Langlois and Roggman (1990) used to help determine what these cues might be.

_____

_____

_____

_____

_____

_____

A Case of Composite Attractiveness...
(Physical Attractiveness: Beauty May Be Only Skin Deep, But We Pay a Lot of Attention to Skin, pages 233-235)

16.   Why are composite human faces more attractive than "single" faces?

_____

_____

Does this phenomenon hold true with other kinds of images? Cite the findings of Haberstadt and Rhodes (2000).

_____

_____

Attractiveness can be Influenced by The Situation...
(Physical Attractiveness: Beauty May Be Only Skin Deep, But We Pay a Lot of Attention to Skin, pages 233-235)

17.   Explain the *contrast effect*.

_____

_____

Now, read the following scenario: Mary Anne is John's girlfriend. John has just participated in the psychology study conducted by Kenrick and Gutierres (1980) – described in this section. In the study, John viewed a series of photographs depicting very attractive women.

According to the researchers, what might John's perception of his girlfriend be at this time?

_____

_____

Yes, We DO Pay Attention...
(Other Aspects of Appearance and Behavior that Influence Attraction, page 236)

18.   Other factors play a role in attraction. Cheverton and Bynne (1998) and Jarrell (1998), among other researchers, found clothing to be an influence on one's perceived level of attraction. Elaborate on this idea, citing the research of Mack and Rainey (1990) and Meier, Robinson, and Clore (2004).

_____

_____

Still More…
(Other Aspects of Appearance and Behavior that Influence Attraction, page 236)

19.   In addition to clothing, your textbook describes four other factors that influence attraction. Name and describe each.

   1. _____

   _____

   2. _____

   _____

   3. _____

   _____

   4. _____

   _____

I Shall Not Reject You…
(Concern about One's Appearance – and Rejection Because of It, pages 236-238)

20.   Explain *appearance-rejection sensitivity*. Have you ever experienced this before?

   _____

   _____

   _____

FACTORS BASED ON INTERACTING WITH OTHERS: SIMILARITY AND MUTUAL LIKING

I Can at Least Say That I am Quite Similar to Myself…
(Similarity: Birds of a Feather Actually Do Flock Together, pages 238-242)

21.   Webster and Harriet are a couple. Webster likes water sports, enjoys school, and wants to get married and have a large family. Harriet also enjoys water sports, in particular she enjoys skiing. She also likes attending school and participating in the university choir. In addition, Harriet has her sight set on getting married immediately after college and raising a family similar to her own – with at least four children.

I Can at Least Say That I am Quite Similar to Myself...Continued

Elaborate upon the *similarity hypothesis*.

_____

_____

_____

Discuss Newcomb's research.

_____

_____

Are We Attracted to Those Who are Our Opposites?
(Complementarity or Similarity: Which is the Basis for Attraction? Pages 239-240)

22.   Emily is black, from a highly educated family, and has established very high goals for her life. Lonnie is from a relatively uneducated immigrant family and has few, if any, aspirations for his life.

If you were to place odds on these two individuals becoming a pair, would you guess the odds to be 1:10, 1:100, 1:1,000. or 1:10,000?

_____

Why did you choose these odds? Cite research findings in your answer.

_____

_____

_____

_____

Math and Psychology – Why Not?
(Similarity-Dissimilarity: A Consistent Predictor of Attraction, pages 240-241))

23.   Bynne and Welson (1965) broke attraction down to a formula resulting in what is termed, *proportion of similarity*. What is the formula?

_____

_____

Math and Psychology – Why Not?...Continued

A proportion of, let's say, 95% (a relatively high percentage), means what?

_____

_____

Say It's Not True...Could Similarity Actually Have no Effect on Attraction?
(Similarity-Dissimilarity: A Consistent Predictor of Attraction, pages 240-241)

24.   Explain the *repulsion hypothesis* as espoused by Rosenbaum (1986).

_____

_____

_____

_____

It Just Takes a Balance...
(Explaining the Effect of Similarity-Dissimilarity on Attraction, pages 240-241)

25.   Describe the components of the *balance theory*. Make sure you include definitions of balance, imbalance and nonbalance in your answer.

_____

_____

_____

_____

In The Words of a Certain Purple Dinosaur, "I Like You – You Like Me...We're a Happy Family..."
(Reciprocal Liking and Disliking: Liking Those Who Like Us, page 242)

26.   Jonathan "likes" Ginny. Chuck "likes" Tara. Shane "likes" Nicole. According to the *rule of reciprocity*, one thing that should be common in each of these friendships is:

_____

_____

_____

Let's Design the Perfect Partner…
(What do We Desire in Others: Designing Ideal Interaction Partners, pages 242-244)

27. Why do we like others? If you were to give an example of characteristics you would find desirable in a girlfriend, boyfriend or spouse, what would he, she or it be like?

In this study, the researchers had students rate 31 positive characteristics on how important they would be in their "ideal" companion. What were their findings?

_____

_____

_____

Are these findings consistent across all types of relationships? That is, do we tend to desire different characteristics in different people in different roles?

_____

_____

_____

Is it Okay to Say Both?
(The Cultural Foundations of Relationships: Seeing the Social World Through the Lens of Our Culture, page 245)

28. Are close relationships the same cross-culturally? Actually, the answer is both "yes" and "no." Explain…

_____

_____

_____

_____

If We Cannot be Friends, Do We have to be Enemies?
(The Cultural Foundations of Relationships: Seeing the Social World Through the Lens of Our Culture, page 245)

29. What is *enemyship*?

_____

_____

If We Cannot be Friends, Do We have to be Enemies?...Continued

How concerned are we in the United States over this phenomenon?

_____

_____

How concerned are the people of Ghana?

_____

_____

INTERDEPENDENT RELATIONSHIPS: FAMILY AND FRIENDS

Building Bonds...
(Family: Where Relationships and Attachment Styles Begin, pages 246-248)

30.   Describe the interplay between infant and caregiver.

_____

_____

_____

How does this relationship benefit the infant?

_____

_____

_____

First Interactions are VERY Important to Future Interactions...
(The Lasting Importance of Parent – Child Interactions, pages 246-247)

31.   How important are the interactions between the infant and his or her caregiver? Answer this question citing the work of Oberlander (2003) and Foltz et al. (1999).

_____

_____

_____

"Good" Attachment = Security...
(The Lasting Importance of Parent – Child Interactions, pages 246-247)

32.   John Bowlby (1969, 1973) developed a theory of attachment in which he found an infant acquires two basic attitudes. What is "attachment style?"

_____

_____

What are the two basic attitudes that are developed in infancy? Describe each.

_____

_____

_____

Are You Attached to Your Style?
(The Lasting Importance of Parent – Child Interactions, pages 246-247)

33.   There are four attachment styles discussed in this section. Relying upon self-esteem as one dimension and interpersonal trust as the other dimension, match the attachment style with its characteristics.

_____   Secure Attachment Style   _____   Fearful-Avoidant Attachment Style

_____   Preoccupied Attachment Style   _____   Dismissing Attachment Style

A.   Characterized by high self-esteem and low interpersonal trust. People with this form of attachment fear genuine closeness, but believe that they are deserving of good relationships.

B.   Characterized by low self-esteem and high interpersonal trust. These individuals want closeness and readily form relationships. People with this form of attachment tend to be "clingy", but expect to eventually be rejected because they believe they are unworthy of a relationship.

C.   Characterized by high self-esteem and high interpersonal trust. Individuals with this form of attachment are best able to form lasting relationships in life. This type of attachment is associated with a high need for achievement, low fear of failure, and an intense curiosity about their environment.

D.   Characterized by low self-esteem and low interpersonal trust. Individuals with this form of attachment tend to not be able to form close relationships or to have unhappy ones.

Others are Important Too...
(The Role of Other Family Members, page 247)

34. Besides our primary caregiver, as infants and young children we are influenced by other family members including fathers, grandparents, and siblings. What did Kitzmann, Cohen and Lockwood (2002) find regarding children who were raised without siblings?

_____

_____

_____

A True Friendship...
(Friendships: Relationships Beyond the Family, pages 248-249)

35. Amy and Candy have been friends since kindergarten. Today, as they both enter college, they would tell you that they have never been closer. Your textbook describes two distinct characteristics of a true friendship. What are they?

_____

_____

_____

How would someone in Japan characterize a true friendship?

_____

Friendship is Influenced by Gender...
(Gender and Friendships, pages 248-249)

36. What did Fredrickson (1995) and Fehr (2004) determine regarding friendship and gender?

_____

_____

Loneliness Breaks the Spirit – Jewish Proverb
(Loneliness: Life Without Relationships, pages 249-251)

37. Define *loneliness*.

_____

_____

Loneliness Has its Consequences…
(The Consequences of Being Lonely, page 249

38.   What are some of the consequences of loneliness? Match the researcher(s) to the research.

_____ Bell (1993)   _____ Anderson et al. (1994)

_____ Lau and Green (1992)   _____ Cacioppo et al. (2002)

_____ Berg and McQuinn (1989)   _____ Cacioppo, Hawkley and Bernstein (2003)

A.   Loneliness is unpleasant and the negative affect includes feelings of depression, anxiety, unhappiness, dissatisfaction, pessimism, self-blame, and shyness.
B.   Lonely people feel left out and believe they have little in common with those they meet.
C.   Others perceive lonely people as maladjusted.
D.   Loneliness is associated with poor health and life span.
E.   Lonely people have sleep problems.
F.   Lonely people spend leisure time alone, have few dates, and only causal friends

Twin Studies…
(Why Some People are Lonely, pages 249-250)

39.   Identical twins have provided fertile ground for many diverse research opportunities. They have been studied in an effort to give supporting evidence to an "either" "or" side of the nature versus nurture controversy. They have been studied to determine the heritability of intelligence and, as your book states, they have been studied in research investigating the construct of loneliness.

McGuire and Clifford (2000) examined the possible role of genetics in loneliness. Describe this research by providing information on the participants of the study and the results.

_____

_____

_____

_____

_____

Is loneliness nature or nurture or, perhaps, both?

_____

Sources of Loneliness…
(Why are People so Lonely, page 250)

40.   There are three factors that play a role in loneliness. Name and describe each.

1. _____

   _____

2. _____

   _____

3. _____

   _____

The Price of Genes…
(Reducing Loneliness, page 251)

41.   We are products of our genetics and cannot escape them. We can, though, acquire new and more appropriate social skills. What are the two main intervention procedures for acquiring these new skills?

        Name and elaborate upon them.

        _____

        _____

        _____

        _____

ROMANTIC RELATIONSHIPS AND FALLING IN LOVE

"One Word Frees us of All the Weight and Pain of Life: That Word is Love" - Sophocles
(Romance: Beyond Friendship – Far Beyond, pages 252-253)

42.   Your textbook notes two differences between *friendship* and *romance*. What are the differences?

        _____

        _____

Your Schemas are Overlapping...
(Similarities and Differences Between Friendship and Romance, pages 252-253)

43.   It is helpful to think of romantic relationships in terms of three schemas. What are they?

    1. _____

    2. _____

    3. _____

What Do Men *Really* Want?
(Males Seek Female Attractiveness: Youth and Beauty Equal Reproductive Fitness, page 253)

44.   Juan is at the point where he wants to settle down. According to your textbook, what type of woman will he seek?

    _____

    _____

    _____

    How is this evolutionary?

    _____

    _____

Likewise, What do Women Want in a Man?
(Females Seek Mates with Resources: Power Equals Ability to Raise and Protect Offspring, page 254)

45.   Irene wants to marry and have a child before she gets too old. According to your textbook, what will Irene look for in a man?

    _____

    _____

    How are these characteristics evolutionarily determined?

    _____

    _____

    _____

"Love is a Many Splendid Thing..."
(Love: Who Can Explain It? Who Can Tell You Why? Just Maybe, Social Psychologists! Pages 254-258)

46.   The theme song from *Dr. Zhivago* seems to say it all. Love IS a many splendid thing! But what, exactly, is this "crazy, little thing" called love?

_____

_____

_____

You Must be Very Passionate about That...
(Passionate Love, pages 255-256)

47.   Define the term *passionate love*.

_____

_____

_____

Your textbook tells of four components to passionate love. What are they?

1. _____

2. _____

3. _____

4. _____

The Case of One-Sided Love...
(Passionate Love, pages 255-256)

48.   Allison and AJ have been friends "forever." Allison, over the years, has fallen in love with AJ. Over dinner one evening, Allison admits her feelings for AJ. AJ appears to become very uncomfortable and tells her that he, simply, considers her that he loves her too, but more as a big brother would love his sister. In other words, AJ's feelings for Allison do not include love in the way a man would love a woman. This is a poignant example of what type of love?

_____

The Passionate Triad...
(Passionate Love, pages 255-256)

49.   Hatfield and Walster (1981) found that passionate love requires the existence of three factors. Name and describe each of them.

1. _____

_____

2. _____

_____

3. _____

_____

Back to Evolution...
(What is the Origin of Love? Page 256)

50.   Explain the statement, "today's humans may be genetically primed to seek sex" by answering the question – what, from an evolutionary perspective is the reason we fall in love?

_____

_____

_____

Are All of The Components There?
(The Components of Love, pages 256-258)

51.   Five styles of love, besides passionate love, have been identified. Name and elaborate upon each.

1. _____

_____

2. _____

_____

3. _____

_____

Are All of The Components There?...Continued

4. _____

_____

5. _____

_____

"There is no Greater Glory than Love, nor any Greater Punishment than Jealousy" - Lope de Vega
(Jealousy: An Internal Threat to Relationships – Romantic and Otherwise, pages 258-259)

52. Define _jealousy_.

_____

_____

According to your textbook, why do we experience _jealousy_?

_____

_____

MARRIAGE: HAPPILY EVER AFTER – OR – NOT?

Marital Bliss??
(Terman's Early Research on Similarity and Marital Happiness, page 261)

53. Describe Terman's research on marital happiness.

_____

_____

_____

_____

_____

The Return of the Correlation...
(Terman's Early Research on Similarity and Marital Happiness, page 261)

54.   Terman's research is noted to be correlational. In light of this, what can we and what can we not determine from the data?

_____

_____

_____

What is a "Good" Marriage?
(Similarity and Assumed Similarity, pages 261-262)

55.   You read earlier that similarity between spouses is important to marital "bliss." This, though, is not the only characteristic common to a good marriage. Another characteristic is *assumed similarity*. Explain this concept.

_____

_____

Do You Ever Feel Superior to Others? Emotionally Unstable?
(Dispositional Factors, page 262)

56.   Some individuals are, simply, better at the maintenance of good relationships with others. *Dispositional factors* (both negative and positive) are important to any relationship. Define the terms, *narcissism* and *neuroticism.*

_____

_____

_____

_____

Now, discuss what roles these two constructs can play in the development and maintenance of a relationship.

_____

_____

_____

_____

Is Love Truly Blind?
(The Role of Positive Illusions in Marital Happiness, page 263)

57.   The old saying states that "love is blind." *What Social Psychology Tells Us About*...expands on this idea. When we are first falling love, and even into the marriage, we often have the illusion that our significant other is as close to perfect as one can be. The question is – do these illusions tend to predict how happy we will be in the marriage? Miller et al. (2003) conducted research investigating this question. Describe this research and the results.

_____

_____

_____

_____

A Cost Benefit Analysis...
(Costs and Benefits of Marital Interactions, page 264)

58.   Discuss the findings of Clark and Grote (1998).

_____

_____

_____

_____

We Obviously Do Not Understand...
(Problems Between Spouses, page 264)

59.   One factor that contributes to the failure of marriages is the failure to understand the reality of the relationship. Explain this idea.

_____

_____

_____

Yet Another Factor That Can Contribute to Marital Failure...
(Perceiving Love – or at Least Approval – As Contingent on Success, page 265)

60.   There is another factor that contributes to the failure of marriages. Delineate on this factor and describe its effect.

_____

Yet Another Factor That Can Contribute to Marital Failure…Continued

_____

_____

Living on the Fringe of Society – Marginalization…
(External Pressures: The Effects of Being in a Marginalized Relationship, pages 265-266)

61.   Tammy and Tina are lesbians and have a long-standing relationship with each other. Their relationship, though, is marginalized in society. Contributing to this idea is that they wish to be married.

What does it mean to be _marginalized_?

_____

_____

_____

Explain two ways that marginalization can affect a relationship.

_____

_____

_____

Do All Good Things HAVE to Come to an End?
(The Consequences of a Failed Relationship, page 266)

62.   Why is it more difficult to end a marriage than to end a friendship?

_____

_____

_____

Yes, You CAN Get Water From a Turnip…
(The Consequences of a Failed Relationship, page 266)

63.   It is possible to revive a less than flourishing relationship. Those most likely to succeed at this are those in which _____.

Yes, You CAN Get Water From a Turnip...Continued

Name the three factors.

1. _____

_____

2. _____

_____

3. _____

_____

After You Read... MyPsychLab Connection

(1)   Go to *EXPLORE: In Your Face*. Here you will find an amazing activity in which you will be able to "morph" a face. After each "morphing", you will rate the face on six dimensions represented as polar opposites along a continuum. The six dimensions include: warm – cold; kind – unkind; honest – dishonest; attractive – unattractive; strong – weak; and feminine – masculine. What are your impressions of these individuals? Do you believe that you can determine something about someone's character simply by looking at them?

(2)   *WATCH Flirting I and Flirting II*. Monica Moore, PhD, discusses differences between men and women in flirting behavior. Did you know that women tend to giggle, laugh, produce animated faces, and primp when flirting?

(3)   Try *SIMULATE – Birds of a Feather* in which you will be asked to rate the attractiveness of six different people based on their responses to an attitude survey. But, first – before rating the responses of others, you will be asked to give your own responses to the identical questions that the individuals you will be rating completed.

After You Read... Practice Test #1

_____1. ALL of the following are characteristics of social interaction **EXCEPT**
   A.   it serves an evolutionary purpose.
   B.   much of our lives are spent involved in it.
   C.   it is necessary for cooperation between individuals.
   D.   infants must be taught to interact.

_____2. Which of the following is/are true of the need for affiliation?
   A.   People tend to differ in the strength of this need.
   B.   Each person has an "optimal" level of this need.
   C.   We rarely enjoy spending time alone.
   D.   Both A and B are correct.

_____3. When we are ignored by others, we tend to
   A.   feel as if we have lost control.
   B.   like it because we sometimes prefer to be ignored – or, more simply, left alone.
   C.   exhibit increased cognitive function during this time.
   D.   None of the above.

_____4. The need to affiliate tends to increase
   A.   with natural disasters.
   B.   when we wish to be alone.
   C.   when we are reminded of our own mortality.
   D.   Both A and C are correct.

_____5. In his 1959 study, Schachter found participants who expected to receive an electric shock
   A.   preferred to be alone.
   B.   preferred spending time with others who were also facing the shock.
   C.   preferred spending with relatives.
   D.   preferred spending time with no one in particular or just preferred being alone.

_____6. Social comparison involves
   A.   two people having the same fate.
   B.   two people with opposing fates.
   C.   two groups of people.
   D.   two people who are strangers regardless of their fate.

_____7. Affiliation is
   A.   a weak, but basic, need.
   B.   a strong, basic need.
   C.   not important to most people.
   D.   not a basic need.

_____8. Dismissing avoidant attachment style is often seen in those
   A.   who state they have little need for affiliation with others.
   B.   who relish close relationships.
   C.   who want to avoid being alone.
   D.   who dismiss the idea that affiliation is not an inborn trait.

_____9.   Carvallo and Gabriel (2006) hypothesized that
   A.   people who score high on a measure of dismissing attachment style had a high need for affiliation.
   B.   people who score high on a measure of dismissing attachment style had a low need for affiliation.
   C.   people who score low on a measure of dismissing attachment style had a low need for affiliation.
   D.   None of the above is correct.

_____10.   Carvallo and Gabriel (2006) found that
   A.   people who state they have little to no need for affiliation <u>really</u> do not have this need.
   B.   people who state they have little to no need for affiliation <u>really</u> do have this need.
   C.   people who state they have little to no need for affiliation only have the need when they have been alone for a long period of time.
   D.   people who state they have little to no need for affiliation are only trying to look like they can make it alone – kind of an emotional strength issue.

11.   Another word for "trait" is _____.

12.   _____ occurs when another person is present when an emotional state (either negative or positive) is aroused and, because of this emotional state, the person present is associated with this negative or positive arousal.

13.   Quinn just met Richard. Immediately, Quinn arrived at the opinion that he does not like Richard because Richard appears to be very arrogant. According to Swap, if Quinn is exposed to Richard on a repeated basis, this will most probably lead to _____.

14.   One of the things we tend to focus on when determining if we like or dislike someone is _____ attractiveness.

15.   According to Feingold (1992), the majority of our stereotypes concerning appearance are _____.

After You Read... Practice Test #2

_____1.	In the study conducted by Langlois, Roggman, and Musselman (1994), composite faces were rated as
	A.	less attractive than most individual faces.
	B.	more attractive than most individual faces.
	C.	neither more or less attractive than most individual faces.
	D.	equally attractive as most individual faces.

_____2.	Attractiveness has been shown to be an important cue to
	A.	one's personality.
	B.	one's character.
	C.	Both A and B are correct.
	D.	Neither A nor B are correct.

_____3.	Research has shown that men tend to rate their own female partners less positively if they
	A.	are unhappy with their partner.
	B.	are depressed.
	C.	have just viewed photographs of very attractive women.
	D.	have just viewed a photograph of very unattractive women.

_____4.	Interpersonal attraction can be influenced by
	A.	the other person's last name.
	B.	the other person's first name.
	C.	the other person's middle initial.
	D.	the other person's middle name.

_____5.	When one worries about his or her appearance and fears that others will ignore them because they do not measure up due to their appearance, they are experiencing
	A.	appearance sensitivity.
	B.	appearance related sensitivity.
	C.	appearance rejection sensitivity.
	D.	appearance relativity sensitivity.

_____6.	Who gathered correlational data consistent with the idea that married people tend to resemble each other in many aspects?
	A.	Sir Francis Galton.
	B.	Sigmund Freud.
	C.	Michael Newcomb.
	D.	Marion Devont.

_____7.	Culture is an important foundation for a relationship because it
	A.	tells us what to expect from the relationship.
	B.	tells us what obligations each partner will have.
	C.	tells us how these social ties should be formed and how they should be developed.
	D.	All of the above are correct.

_____8.   Attachment style is most appropriately defined as
         A.   the degree of security that one feels in an interpersonal relationship.
         B.   how much one has in common with others.
         C.   the feelings one has to any inanimate object.
         D.   how much love one feels for another.

_____9.   Kitzmann, Cohen and Lockwood (2002) found that school children who have no siblings
         are
         A.   more likely to make friends than those who have siblings.
         B.   more aggressive than those who have siblings.
         C.   prone to display more shyness than those who have siblings.
         D.   more passive than those who have siblings.

_____10.   People who are lonely tend to do **ALL** of the following **EXCEPT**
         A.   spend their leisure time involved in solitary activity.
         B.   have very few dates.
         C.   believe they have a lot in common with others.
         D.   believe that they have little in common with others.

11.   The primary goal of _____therapy is to interrupt negative thoughts

      and feelings and replace them with positive thoughts and feelings.

12.   The most prevalent difference between a friendship and a romance is the presence of

      _____ attraction.

13.   Jennifer and Tim have been "going together" for nearly three years. Jennifer is a very attractive

      female and Tim knows it. According to your textbook, the main reason that Tim finds Jennifer

      not only attractive, but <u>sexually</u> attractive is because he is associating being sexually attractive

      with Jennifer's _____.

14.   According to Hughes, Harrison, and Gallup (2002), a (n) _____ face is

      more attractive than a (n) _____ face.

15.   A study conducted in the Netherlands by Buunk et al. (2002) showed that men prefer women who

      are _____ attractive than themselves.

After You Read... Practice Test #3

_____1.   What type of love involves an intense emotional reaction to another?
    A.   Romantic.
    B.   Passionate.
    C.   Unrequited.
    D.   Logical.

_____2.   The main explanation as to why we experience jealousy is
    A.   the possibility of social rejection threatens our self-esteem.
    B.   we are insecure.
    C.   we are concerned that our significant other will dislike us because of the emotions associated with jealousy.
    D.   None of the above is correct.

_____3.   Terman and Buttenwieser (1935a and 1935b) found that highly similar spouses are
    A.   less satisfied with their relationship.
    B.   less satisfied with themselves.
    C.   more satisfied with their relationship.
    D.   more satisfied with themselves.

_____4.   When we say research is correlational, we are giving what information about the research?
    A.   We are stating that one variable causes the other.
    B.   We are stating that one variable is related to the other.
    C.   We are stating that there is no association between the variables.
    D.   We are stating that both variables in question are insignificant.

_____5.   Markus is a classic narcissist. To be categorized in this way, he must have **ALL** of the following characteristics **EXCEPT**
    A.   a feeling of superiority.
    B.   empathy towards others.
    C.   apathy towards others.
    D.   a desire to acquire feelings of admiration from others.

_____6.   The sexual relationship between Jerry and Randy, both males, has met with much disapproval both from their families and their friends. This relationship can be said to be
    A.   socially constructed.
    B.   marginalized by society.
    C.   socially accepted.
    D.   acknowledged by society.

_____7.   According to your textbook, people tend to engage in social comparisons for **ALL** of the following reasons **EXCEPT**
    A.   to communicate about what is going on.
    B.   to compare their perceptions.
    C.   to make decisions about what to do.
    D.   to gain insight into the opinions of others regarding their trustworthiness.

_____ 8.   Glaser and Salovey (1998) found that we tend to believe that _____ people are typically likeable human beings.
     A.   talkative
     B.   tall
     C.   smiling
     D.   laughing

_____ 9.   If you were going to attempt to write an advertisement designed to sell an item to another person, you should use
     A.   positive wording.
     B.   an attractive spokesperson.
     C.   a depiction of a person having a good time using the item...
     D.   All of the above.

_____ 10.   It seems obvious, people who live close to one another are more likely to experience **ALL** of the following **EXCEPT**
     A.   form friendships.
     B.   get married.
     C.   work together.
     D.   form friendships.

11.   _____ love requires that an appropriate love object, defined as a physically attractive person of the opposite sex who is not married, must be present.

12.   The phenomenon that recurring contact with a new stimulus often results in an increasingly positive evaluation of that stimulus is sometimes referred to as the _____ effect.

13.   Clothing has been shown to influence attraction. In particular the color of clothing has been implicated. Meier, Robinson and Clore (2004) found that bright colors equate with _____; while dark colors are connected with _____.

14.   The idea of _____ would support the union between a person who is recluse and a person who is gregarious.

15.   Yancy likes Marcia. According to the rule of _____, Marcia should also like Yancy.

After You Read... Practice Test #4

_____1. Among ideal partners, the **ALL** of the following traits are important **EXCEPT** for
  A.   trustworthiness.
  B.   cooperativeness.
  C.   agreeableness.
  D.   introversion.

_____2. Peter and Alice's friendship involves spending a lot of time together, interaction in varying situations, a great deal of self-disclosure, and mutual emotional support. We can, then, assume that Peter and Alice are _____.
  A.   romantic partners.
  B.   close friends.
  C.   casual friends.
  D.   lovers.

_____3. Loneliness is
  A.   an emotional reaction.
  B.   a cognitive reaction.
  C.   defined as a reaction to having fewer and less satisfying relationships than one desires.
  D.   All of the above are correct.

_____4. The goal of social skills training is to
  A.   rearrange negative thought patterns to make them more positive.
  B.   encourage new perceptions about social interactions.
  C.   provide examples of socially appropriate behavior.
  D.   promote new expectations about social interactions.

_____5. Men tend to pay more attention to a woman's _____; while women tend to pay more attention to a man's _____.
  A.   level of attractiveness; level of attractiveness
  B.   level of attractiveness, resources
  C.   fitness as a reproductive partner; resources
  D.   Both B and C are correct

_____6. In Miller et al's 2003 study, agreeable behaviors included which of the following
  A.   exceptional cooking ability.
  B.   complimenting one's spouse.
  C.   displaying the trait of being easy-going.
  D.   attractiveness.

_____7. The investment of time and effort, engaging in mutually rewarding activities, planning a future, and expressing the desire for a lasting commitment are reasons why
  A.   ' spouses find their relationship difficult to end.
  B.   friendships are so hard to end.
  C.   both spouses and friends find their relationships so hard to end.
  D.   None of the above is correct.

_____8.   Human beings are apparently
         A.   born with the need to be alone.
         B.   born with the need for affiliation.
         C.   born with the need to interact with people in a cooperative way.
         D.   Both B and C are correct.

_____9.   According to research, a married couple is more likely to reconcile if
         A.   the needs of each partner can be satisfied.
         B.   at least one partner is committed to the continuance of the relationship
         C.   a period of separation has preceded the initial breakup.
         D.   the marriage has lasted greater than 2 years.

_____10.   Being ignored by others induces **ALL** of the following **EXCEPT**
         A.   feeling of being left out.
         B.   hurtfulness.
         C.   decreased sensitivity to interpersonal information.
         D.   less effective cognitive functioning.

11.   People have been shown to respond to others by assessing physical physique. If someone is overweight, they tend to be perceived as _____ and _____.

12.   Evidence points to the idea that opposites _____ attract.

13.   Newcomb (1961) and Heider (1958) both proposed the _____ theory which explains why similarity tends to educe positive affect while dissimilarity educes negative affect.

14.   Individuals who do not tend to form close relationships or, if they do form close relationships, the relationships are unhappy, are assumed to have a _____ attachment style.

15.   _____ tend to have more close friendships than do _____.

When you have finished… Crossword Puzzle

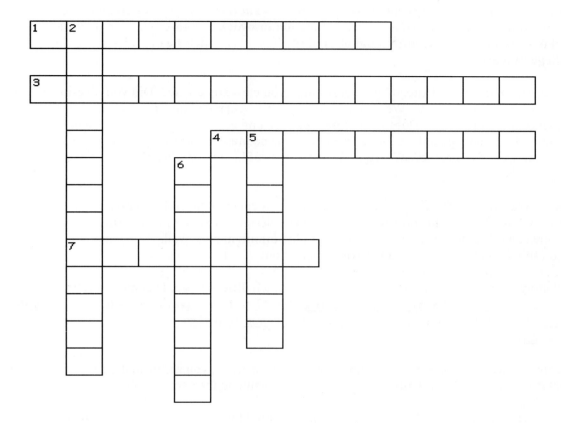

Across

1. Unlike something/someone else
3. How appealing something/someone is
4. How close something/someone is
7. Like something/someone else

Down

2. General expectancies and beliefs about other people regarding trust issues
5. Type of exposure in which the exposure occurs over and over
6. To associate

Created by Puzzlemaker at DiscoverySchool.com

When you have finished... You be the Researcher

Attraction is not only confined to one's feelings towards another person. A person can be said to be attracted to, among a lengthy list, a church, a location in which to build a home and raise a family, a particular store in which the individual often finds items for which he or she is searching, and, yes, a college/university

What is your reasoning behind attending the institution you currently attend? Did you investigate and like the ratio of males to females? Were you lured to this particular college/university by a scholarship that you just could not pass up? Does your present college/university have a program that excels in your chosen major? Is the college/university in a section of the country that appeals to you? Is it close to home? Is it far away from home? We **all** enter institutions of higher learning after a careful thought – often weighing the various pros and cons.

Your task is to determine why some of your fellow students came to the college/university that you are currently attending. You are to construct a questionnaire designed to elicit this information. This questionnaire should be designed to obtain demographic information as well. The demographic information should include age, sex, and sexual orientation.

After designing the questionnaire, you are to have at least ten different people complete your questionnaire. **Make sure that your participants DO NOT put any identifying information on the questionnaire. Identifying information includes, but is not limited to, name, address, phone number, and email address.**

Once you have at least ten participants complete your questionnaire, you are to analyze your data. You are to do this by noting any similarities and any differences among the data you obtained.

Then, assess the demographics of your participants. You might wan to assess the following or provide some ideas of your own: Did you find that the majority of your participants come from the southern United States? Did you find the opposite? Are your participants all over 21? How many of your participants were male? How many were female? Did you have participants who noted that they were homosexual?

Compare your demographic information to the data you obtained regarding why students chose this particular school of higher learning.

As an example, you might want to investigate the question, "Did the majority of my female participants come to this school because it was far away from their home – or close to their home - as the case may be?

You are, then, to prepare a final report on the study following APA format for a research report. If you are not aware of the APA format for a research report, you may find information regarding this on the internet or your professor may be willing to provide you with the information.

Answers - As You Read...Practice Activities

1. To affiliate with others means to associate with them.

    From an evolutionary perspective, our desire to affiliate with others was required of our earliest ancestors in order to survive. We relied upon others to help us obtain food and for protection from any danger.

2. According to research findings, Ethel may be feeling that she has lost any control of the situation. She may also feel sad and angry at the same time because she is being ignored and no longer feels like she is part of the group. She may also be experiencing reduced cognitive functioning due to her increased sensitivity to interpersonal information.

3. Schachter's study (1959) gave a basic explanation for why people tend to respond to stressful situations with friendliness and affiliation. Schachter found that participants in his experiment who were anticipating an electric shock preferred to spend time with other individuals who were also anticipating an electric shock. The control group showed the opposite. The participants in the control group (those who did not expect a shock) preferred to be alone or didn't care either way – either with others or alone.

4. According to Koole, Greenberg and Pyszczynski (2006), the need to affiliate with other is **one of our most basic needs and concerns.**

5. The participants of the study were students.

    The hypothesis was:
    People high in dismissing attachment style (little to no need for affiliation, mood and self-esteem), would not be affected by learning that they were preferred as a future partner.

    The procedure involved:

    (1) Participants exchanged information about themselves with three other participants.

    (2) Participants rated each other and ranked their preference for working with the others.

    (3) ALL participants received the same information about others.

    The two groups were as follows:

    Group I (Experimental group):
    Received information stating that they had received the highest ranking and could choose any other participant as a partner.

    Group II (control group):
    Not given information about being accepted, just assigned to work with a partner.

    Procedure continued:
    (4) Participants were asked to complete a questionnaire measuring mood, self esteem and attachment style (how much need there is to be in a close reationship)

    If one really had a need for affiliation, mood and self-esteem would show an increase after receiving the information on acceptance than if one did not receive the information. This was found. This supports the claim that even people who say they have little to no need for affiliation, still have the need. ALL human beings have affiliation needs even if they tend to deny them.

6. The reason you may harbor such an intense disliking for Dr. Roberts, according to McDonald (1962), is that

Dr. Roberts has provided a punishment in the rating of your class performance. That is, you are being punished with the "F".

7. The association effect is at work here. Jerry is with you when you get the news from Greg. You, therefore, might have the propensity towards snapping at Jerry. What you are doing is associating the bad news with Jerry since he was present at the time the information was delivered resulting in the ending of your relationship with Greg.

8. You can have fun with this one!!

Music:
Should be lively and possibly draw attention. Provide examples of your own.

Colors/Scenery:
Bright colors, eye-catching scenery.

Actors:
Well-liked actors, attractive, possibly actors who have not espoused negative attitudes towards things that people feel strongly about (i.e. negative views towards the president – assuming YOU like the president!)

Script:
Provide your own answer here! Will want include positive wording…

Advice to actors:
Facial expressions – SMILE!!! Provide examples of your own.

The idea is to present *Star Shine Toothpaste* in the best possible light.

9. Proximity can be defined as how close someone or something is to you. The mere exposure effect states that the more repeated exposure we have to a new stimulus, the more positive the evaluation of this stimulus will be.

Studies have recently shown that when people live, work, and recreate in close proximity, they are likely to interact, form friendships, and even marry. Also, the more one sees another, according to the mere exposure effect, the more they will like each other. The like can turn to love and can then lead to marriage.

10.
Assistant I:	Attended class 15 times
Assistant II:	Attended class 10 times
Assistant III:	Attended class 5 times
Assistant IV:	Did not attend class at all

None of the assistants interacted with students.

At the end of the class, students were shown slides of all four assistants and indicated how much they liked each one

Results: More time in class led to greater liking = repeated exposure led to an increase in level of attraction.

11. The mere exposure effect ceases to operate when an individual's original reaction to a stimulus is excessively negative. Repeated exposure in this case can only lead to more negativity.

12. Andreoletti, Zebrowitz, and Lachman (2001) found that if love at first sight is an option, then the way this happens is that there is something about the person that produces positive affect in us and that this reaction is based on past experiences, stereotypes, and attributions that are often inaccurate and irrelevant.

Anderson and Baum (1994) found that if the object of this phenomenon reminds you of someone you know and are fond of, your reaction to them will be positive. Also, if this person belongs to a group for which you have a positive opinion, you will also like this person.

13.   Dion and Dion (1987) and Hatfield and Sprecher (1986a) found that individuals tend to find men and women to be attractive if they are more poised, interesting, sociable, independent, dominant, exciting, sexy, well-adjusted, socially skilled, successful and, also, more masculine or feminine than unattractive persons.

14.   This issue, according to Feingold (1992) and Kenealy et al. (1991), is that most appearance stereotypes are false. Therefore, if we rely on stereotypes to tell us what is attractive versus what is unattractive, we are relying on fictitious information.

15.   Cunningham's approach involved identifying a group who have been rated as attractive and then determining what they have in common. Male undergraduate students were asked to rate photographs of women. The women rated as most attractive were divided into two categories: those with "childlike features" which included women with large, widely spaced eyes, a small nose and a small chin. The other category consisted of women with mature features including prominent cheekbones, high eyebrows, large pupils, and a big smile.

        Langlios and Roggman's approach was designed to determine what is meant by attractiveness. The study began with a few facial photographs and then a computer was used to combine multiple faces into one. The composite faces were divided into tiny squares and each square was then translated into a number representing a particular shade. The numbers were averaged across two or more pictures and the result was translated back into a composite image.

        Langlios and Roggman found that composite faces were rated as more attractive than the single faces used to make the composite. They also found the more faces that were averaged and put into a composite, the more attractive the face was noted to be.

16.   We find composite faces more attractive because what we tend to find attractive comes from our schemas of what is attractive. Schemas are formed on the basis of our experiences with many different faces. Therefore, a composite is much closer to a true schema than would be a single face.

        Haberstadt and Rhodes (2000) found that the idea of composites does not hold up for other kinds of images. The researchers used composite dogs and birds in their study.

17.   The contrast effect is defined as the difference between the attractiveness of individuals in a photograph and strangers. If one is shown attractive persons in a photograph prior to rating a stranger on the construct of attractiveness, he or she will tend to rate the stranger as less attractive.

        According to the research, John would exhibit the tendency to rate Mary Anne as less attractive than if he had not seen the photographs.

18.   Individuals tend to perceive bright colors as "good" and dark colors as "bad."

19.   Culture is an influential factor. This includes the presence of disabilities, behavioral cues that suggest mental illness, perceived age, eyeglasses, and the presence of a beard.

        A person's physique also plays a role. We tend to believe that a round, fat body is indicative of a sloppy person. We also believe that a hard, muscular body is indicative of good health and lack of intelligence. Likewise, a thin and angular body indicates intelligence and fearfulness.

Overt behavior also influences who we find attractive. A youthful walking style produces a more positive response than does the walk of an elderly person. A firm handshake is indicative of a person whose behavior is animated, who actively participates in class, and who acts in a modest fashion.

The last influence is a person's first name. There are many names which tend to elicit both positive and negative stereotypes. Also, a name that is associated with a famous person becomes associated with some of the characteristics of that person. Someone who has a name associated with a famous person, has the stereotypical characteristics then transferred to themselves.

20. Appearance-Rejection Sensitivity occurs when we worry about our appearance and fear that others may give us the cold-shoulder if our appearance does not quite measure up

21. The similarity hypothesis emphasizes the role similarity plays in attraction.

   Newcomb (1956) found that similar attitudes predicted subsequent liking between students. He also found that similarity produces attraction rather than the other way around as had been thought at one time.

22. Seeing as how pairings such as this are relatively rare, you might choose 1:1,000 or 1:10,000 for the probability.

   There are instances where opposites do attract. Markey, Funder, and Ozer (2003) and Sadler and Woody (2003) found that when one party is dominant and the other is submissive, complementarity may exist and there may be an attraction. Swann, Rentfrow and Gosling (2003) found that a relatively shy and quiet person would most probably not be attracted to a person who is verbally strong and expressive.

23. The formula is as follows:

   <u>Number of topics on which two people express similar views</u>
   Total number of topics on which they have communicated

   With a high proportion (95%), there would be greater similarity and, thus, greater liking.

24. Rosenbaum (1986) suggested that similarity does not lead to attraction. Rather, states Rosenbaum, people are repulsed over dissimilarities.

25. The balance theory was used to explain why similarity elicits positive affect; while dissimilarity tends to elicit negative affect. The components of the theory include:

   (1) Balance = state in which two people are attracted and discover they are similar in many areas.

   (2) Imbalance = is emotionally unpleasant. Causes the individuals to move towards a restoration of balance. This is accomplished by one of the partners changing in some way to make the two more in balance.

   (3) Nonbalance = occurs when both parties do not like one another. Here each person is indifferent to any similarities and/or dissimilarities.

26. Each person in each relationship, according to the rule of reciprocity, shows liking towards the other.

27. Trustworthiness and cooperativeness were determined to be the most important traits. These were followed by agreeableness – defined as being kind and showing interpersonal warmth

– and extraversion – defined as being outgoing and sociable.

Yes, we do desire different characteristics of different people in different roles. Cottrell, Neuberg and Li (2007) had participants in their study create ideal members of work project team members, final exam study group members, golf team members, sorority members, fraternity members, close friends, and employees. They found that, across all types of relationships, trustworthiness and cooperativeness were, once again, rated as most important. Agreeableness and extraversion closely followed. Other characteristics were rated as more or less important depending on the type of relationship.

28. Close relationships and the feelings involved tend to be universal to a certain extent. Different cultures, though, do define what is expected in various relationships, the obligations involved, and how close bonds should be constructed and develop.

29. Enemyship refers to a relationship based on hate and abhorrence. In enemyship one person wants to be instrumental in the other person's downfall and attempts to sabotage progress in that person's life.

Femlee and Sprecher (2000) found that in the United States 17% of American students stated they were the target of interpersonal enemies.

In Ghana, a country in African, the researchers found that 79% of the participants believed themselves to be targets of interpersonal enemies.

30. At birth, human infants are very sensitive to the facial expressions, body movements and sounds of those around them. The primary caregiver, usually the mother, is also very sensitive to the infant's facial expressions, body movements and sounds of the infant. The caregiver engages the baby in baby talk; while the infant shows interest in the caregiver by making sounds.

The interplay sets up grounds for the infant's future relationships.

31. Oberland (2003) found that the quality of the interaction between the infant and his or her primary caregiver is a determinant in the child's future interpersonal attitudes and behaviors. Foltz et al. (1999) found that individuals tend to be rather consistent in their interaction patterns in varying relationships.

32. Attachment style is defined as the degree of security one feels in any interpersonal relationship.

The first basic attitude is self-esteem. The caregiver's response to the child gives the child the information that he or she is valued (or not), important (or not) and loved (or not). The second basic attitude is interpersonal trust. This is based on whether or not the caregiver is seen as trustworthy, reliable and dependable.

33. C   Secure Attachment Style

    D   Fearful-Avoidant Attachment Style

    B   Preoccupied Attachment Style

    A   Dismissing Attachment Style

34. Children without siblings tend to be less liked than other children. They also tend to be more aggressive or more victimized by aggressors than do children with siblings.

35. People in true friendships tend to engage in bragging behavior when interacting with others, but act modestly when with

their friends. Also, people in true friendships are less likely to lie to one another. There is an exception to lying, though. When the lie is designed to make the friend feel better, it is acceptable.

In Japan, a true friendship is a give and take relationship. A true friend is someone with whom it is easy to get along with, who does not brag and is considerate and not short tempered.

36. Women report having more friends than do men. Women also exhibit the tendency to place more importance on intimacy in a relationship.

37. Loneliness is defined as an individual's emotional and cognitive reaction to having fewer and less satisfying relationships than he or she desires.

38. B, A, C, E, F, D

39. The participants were pairs of biological siblings, pairs of unrelated siblings (adopted), pairs of identical twins, and pairs of fraternal twins.

The results consistently indicated that loneliness is, in part, genetic. In addition, loneliness was found to be influenced by environment.

Therefore, in the nature versus nurture controversy, loneliness appears to be influenced by both.

40. (1)   Genetic factors
     (2)   Attachment style = insecure attachment is associated with loneliness.
     (3)   Failure to develop social skills = if a child does not learn adequate social skills he or she may engage in self-defeating behaviors such as avoiding others and engaging in verbal aggression. This leads to rejection and subsequent loneliness.

41. Cognitive therapy = disrupts the pattern of negative thought and encourages new, more positive thinking.

Social skills training = the lonely individual is given examples of socially appropriate behavior on videotape and then is asked to copy the observed behavior. The individual is then instructed to practice the appropriate behavior in public.

42. Romance and friendship are different in that romance involves sexual attraction and some level of physical intimacy.

43. Self-schema, a schema of one's perception of their partner, and a schema that encompasses the relationship between the self and the partner.

44. Men are attracted to beauty, long hair (indicative of youth and health), bilateral symmetry in the face and body symmetry. All of these are indicative of youth and health which, in turn, are indicative of genetic fitness and fertility.

45. Women are attracted to a man's resources as well as to an attractive important from an evolutionary perspective because resources are necessary for the man to take care of the woman and any offspring.

46. Actually, the definition of love is relative to the person defining it. What is love to me, to the president, to the lady who serves food in the cafeteria and to you is pretty much up for interpretation.

Your textbook does provide a few thoughts on the definition of love. It states love is something more than a close friendship and something differently from being romantically or sexually interested in another person.

47. Passionate love is a very intense and sometimes idealistic emotional reaction to another individual.

The four components are:
(1) Sex
(2) Strong emotional arousal
(3) Desire to be physically close
(4) An intense need to be loved by the other person as much as you love them

48. This is an example of unrequited love or love that is felt by one in the relationship and not the other.

49. (1) You have to learn what love is. This, in turn, motivates us to seek love.

(2) An appropriate love object must be present. According to your text, appropriate means a physically attractive person of the opposite sex who is not currently married. This, though, differs in some relationships involving passionate love.

(3) The individual must be in a state of physiological arousal that can be interpreted as love.

50. As humans, we fall in love in an effort to reproduce offspring. This, from an evolutionary perspective, serves as a means for continuance of the species.

51. (1) Companionate Love = Based on a very close friendship in which both participants are sexually attracted, have a lot in common, care about each other's well being, and convey mutual liking and respect.

(2) Game Playing Love = In this type of love, behavior such as having two love interests at the same time may be seen.

(3) Possessive Love = Concentrates on the fear of losing the other individual in the relationship.

(4) Logical Love = Based on decisions as to whether or not a partner is suitable.

(5) Selfless Love = One individual in the relationship would rather suffer than see the other suffer.

52. Jealousy is defined as feelings that occur when a romantic person or someone else about whom we care deeply transfer their feelings to another.

We experience jealousy because we fear the rejection which tends to threaten our self-esteem.

53. Terman (1935) hypothesized that if it is mutual attraction, then spouses who are satisfaction with their marriages than of couples completed a measure of happy and the 100 most happy couples study. The couples were matched on occupation. They were, then, asked to determine which contained more than 500 items on which each individual indicated if they felt positive or negative.

The results showed that all individuals tended to marry someone similar to themselves. Also, the degree to which the individuals making up the couples were similar or dissimilar was reflected in the couple's happiness.

54. We can determine a relationship between similarity and marital happiness. What we cannot determine is if similarity actually causes marital happiness. With a correlation, there is no evidence of a cause/effect relationship.

55. Assumed similarity is defined as high when the partners believe that they are even more similar than they actually are.

56. Narcissism is a construct in which one feels superior to most others, someone who seeks admiration of others and lacks empathy. Neuroticism refers to the lack of emotional stability.

People who are narcissistic tend to feel less commitment in relationship. If there are two people in a relationship that are narcissists, it is highly unlikely that they will have a happy relationship.

Likewise, neuroticism can be damaging to a relationship.

57. Newly married couples were studied, longitudinally, for thirteen years. There were four phases: married 2 months, married one year, married two years, and married approximately thirteen years. At each phase, face to face interviews were conducted with participants. Measures of agreeableness (expressed approval) and disagreeableness (expressed disapproval) of the spouse's behavior, ratings of the spouse's overall agreeableness, and love for one's spouse were taken.

Results showed that the stronger the tendency to hold positive illusions about each other, the greater love they reported and the smaller declines in love they experienced during the thirteen years.

58. In attempting to maintain a relationship, parties might engage in potentially positive acts and avoid negative acts. In order to do this, though, both parties must be cognizant of what they do and say so as not to put negativity into the picture. Basically, in a marriage it is important to maximize the benefits and minimize the costs.

59. We have the tendency to begin a relationship with the idea that the other person can do no wrong. The reality is, though, that no one is perfect.

Over time, though, we begin to see the true person and begin to realize that this person may not be as perfect as we first believed. Because of this dissatisfaction will, most likely, set in.

60. The other factor is the perception that one's partner's love is closely linked with success. This is especially a problem for those who have low self esteem. For these people, personal failure spills over into the relationship. This causes the spouse low in self esteem to feel less accepted and more rejected. This can be destructive to a marriage.

61. If something is marginalized, it is not heard of in the public sphere. Marginalization can affect a relationship by reducing their partners' willingness to invest time and themselves in the relationship. This can either hurt the relationship by reducing commitment or it can help a relationship by deepening the commitment through the "I will show them" attitude.

62. People who have been married tend to invest a lot of themselves into the relationship. They share the good and the bad, plan a future together, and express a lifelong commitment (just read the marriage vows). People who are in friendships do not invest as much in them and find it easier to end the friendship than those who are married.

63. A relationship can be revived if the needs of each partner can be satisfied and each of the partners is committed to the relationship. In addition, alternative lovers must not be available.

Answers – Cross Word Puzzle

Across

1. dissimilar
3. similar
4. attractiveness
7. proximity

Down

2. interpersonal
5. repeated
6. affiliate

Answers – Practice Test #1

1. D
2. D
3. A
4. D
5. B
6. A
7. B
8. A
9. B
10. B
11. disposition
12. associated Effect
13. greater dislike
14. physical
15. incorrect

Answers – Practice Test #2

1. A
2. C
3. C
4. B
5. C
6. A
7. D
8. A
9. B

10. C
11. cognitive
12. sexual
13. fertility
14. symmetrical; unsymmetrical
15. more

Answers – Practice Test #3

1. B
2. A
3. C
4. B
5. B
6. B
7. D
8. c
9. D
10. C
11. passionate
12. mere exposure
13. good; bad
14. complementaries
15. reciprocity

Answers – Practice Test #4

1. D
2. B
3. D
4. C
5. D
6. B
7. A
8. C
9. A
10. C
11. sad; sloppy
12. do not
13. balance
14. fearful-avoidant
15. women; men

CHAPTER 8

SOCIAL INFLUENCE:
CHANGING OTHERS' BEHAVIOR

Before You Read...Chapter Summary

The first section of Chapter Eight begins with an explanation of the phenomenon of social influence. In particular, it begins with a discussion of the phenomenon of conformity or doing what we are "supposed" to do in a given situation. As with any psychologically- initiated discussion of conformity, the famous study conducted by Solomon Asch (1951) is discussed. If you have taken another psychology course, in particular, introductory psychology, you have already become familiar with this study. As the chapter progresses, factors that affect one's level of conformity are discussed. You will also discover why we chose to conform. This section comes to an end with an in-depth discussion of another famous study – the Stanford prison study conducted by Dr. Phillip Zimbardo (1973), a highly esteemed social psychologist, and his colleagues.

The next section of Chapter Eight discusses the construct of compliance. Within this section, you will discover the six basic principles upon which compliance is gained. Four of these principles receive further discussion. Within the discussion you will acquire knowledge of some of the most well-known (at least within the world of social psychology) techniques for gaining compliance. They include ingratiation, the foot-in-the-door technique, the lowball procedure, the door-in-the-face technique, and the that's not all technique. This section ends with a brief insert on eating disorders and a discussion of the role the media plays in this disorder.

Finally, you will find discussion of the construct of obedience. Like the topic of conformity, no discussion of obedience would be complete without mentioning the work of Stanley Milgram, which investigated obedience to authority. You will learn why we obey, even when this obedience may lead to destructive consequences. This section, and the chapter, ends with a discussion of strategies that may be employed to resist the strong tendency to obey sources of authority.

Before You Read... Learning Objectives

After reading this chapter, you should be able to:

- Provide a definition for the construct *conformity*.
- Discuss the work of Solomon Asch.
- Discuss the work of Muzafer Sherif.
- Delineate factors that affect one's level of conformity.
- Define *cohesiveness* and indicate the term's relevance to conformity.
- Distinguish between *illicit* and *explicit social norms*.
- Distinguish between *descriptive* and *injunctive norms*.
- Explain the *normative focus theory*.
- Provide reasoning as to why we often choose to conform, including the normative social influence and the informational social influence.
- Explain the downside of conformity.
- Discuss Phillip Zimbardo's infamous Stanford prison study.
- Understand why some people choose not to conform.
- Answer the question – who is more likely to conform – men or women and why?
- Define *compliance*.
- Discuss the six principles that are used to gain compliance.
- Explain the difference between *anorexia nervosa* and *bulimia nervosa*.
- Give details regarding the effect of the media on the eating disorder epidemic.
- Define *obedience*.
- Discuss the research of Stanley Milgram.
- Explain the idea of *destructive obedience*.
- Provide information on the four factors that lead one to obey.
- Describe strategies that individuals use to resist authority.

As You Read...Term Identification

Important Terms to Know
Below are a list of some of the key terms and concepts from this chapter. Make flashcards in order to enhance your recall ability of these terms. Refer to the definitions that are either in boldface or in the margins of this chapter for help. You may also want to include additional terms from this chapter as you deem necessary.

social influence, (p. 273)	normative focus theory, (p. 278)	that's not all technique, (p. 292)
conformity, (p. 274)	normative social influence, (p. 280)	playing hard to get technique, (p. 293)
social norms, (p. 274)	informational social influence, (p. 280)	deadline technique, (p. 293)
compliance, (p. 274)	individuation, (p. 285)	eating disorders, (p. 296)
cohesiveness, (p. 278)	foot in the door technique, (p. 290)	body mass index, (p.
descriptive norms, (p. 278)	lowball procedure, (p. 291)	obedience, (p. 274)
injunctive norms, (p. 278)	door in the face technique, (p. 292)	

As You Read...Practice Activities

CONFORMITY: GROUP INFLUENCE IN ACTION

Has Your Behavior Changed?
(Introduction, page 273)

1. In society, contrary to what some people tend to believe, we simply cannot do as we please. We are confined by certain rules and regulations. These rules and regulations serve one specific purpose – the maintenance and continuance of the society. As citizens of this society, we are expected and encouraged to follow the policies of society. In this, we are performing an act of conformity.

    Define the term *conformity*.

    _____

    _____

    Now, discuss what is meant by *social norms* and describe how social norms contribute to conformity.

    _____

    _____

    As a student, how do your behaviors conform within the boundaries of the school? That is, what are some of the social norms on campus?

    _____

    _____

    _____

    _____

Dos Tipos...
(Introduction, page 274)

2. In question one, you defined what is meant by *social norms*. Now, discuss the two different types of social norms and give examples of each.

    _____

    _____

    _____

Not "ASH" – "ASCH"...

(Asch's Research on Conformity: Social Pressure – The Irresistible Force? Pages 275-277)

3.   Solomon E. Asch (1907 – 1996), due to his famous studies investigating conformity, is probably one of the most cited social psychologists in the history of psychology.

Describe the research conducted by Asch in 1951 and 1955. You are to do this by filling in the missing information in the following schematic.

TASK

Participants were shown a standard line. They were, then, asked to assess

_____

_____

_____.

PROCEDURE

Several people, usually _____ were present during the session. The additional people, though, unknown to the participants, were

_____.

In the _____ trials, the additional people,

offered answers that were clearly _____. In addition, the additional people chose their answer

_____ the "real" participants.

Dilemma Faced by Participants

_____

_____

_____

Not "ASH" – "ASCH"…Continued

```
┌─────────────────────────────────────────────┐
│                 Results                       │
│                                               │
│   _____   │
│                                               │
│   _____   │
│                                               │
│   _____   │
│                                               │
│   _____   │
│                                               │
└─────────────────────────────────────────────┘
```

More Asch…
(Asch's Research on Conformity: Social Pressure – The Irresistible Force? Pages 275-277)

4.   Describe the findings of Asch's research conducted in 1956 and 1959.

_____

_____

_____

_____

No One Knows What Goes on Behind Closed Doors: Public Conformity versus Private Acceptance…
(Asch's Research on Conformity: Social Pressure – The Irresistible Force? Pages 275-277)

5.   Distinguish between *public conformity* and *private acceptance*.

Public Conformity:_____

_____

Private Acceptance:_____

_____

Not "Sheriff" – "Sherif"...
(Sherif's Research on the Autokinetic Phenomenon: How Norms Emerge, page 277)

6.   Muzafer Sherif, another prominent social psychologist, conducted a study in 1973 investigating private acceptance of social influence. In this study, Sherif focused on two questions. What were they?

1.. _____

_____

2. _____

_____

Sherif used a fascinating phenomenon in his study. Name and describe this phenomenon.

_____

_____

_____

Does the Extent of Group Cohesiveness Influence Conformity? Yes, Strongly...
(Cohesiveness and Conformity: Being Influenced by Those We Like, page 278)

7.   Cohesiveness is one factor that has been determined to influence conformity. What is *cohesiveness*?

_____

_____

Susan and Marsha are both members of the Alpha Beta Delta Sorority. In fact, not only are they members, they are, respectively, the president and the vice-president of their school chapter. Tiffany is a new-comer to the campus and has decided to pledge to Alpha Beta Delta. Since her older sister is an Alpha Delt, as they are called, she wants very much to become one of them.

According to Crandall, 1998; Latane and L'Herrou, 1996; Noel, Wann and Branscombe, 1995, what should Tiffany's degree of conformity be? Why?

_____

_____

_____

_____

Group Size as an Influential Factor...
(Conformity and Group Size: Why More is Better with Respect to Social Pressure, page 278)

8. Both Asch and Sherif found that conformity tends to increase as group size increases. First of all, the fact that one variable increases as the other increases represents what type of correlation?

    _____

    What are some of the findings of other researchers regarding group size and conformity?

    _____

    _____

    _____

    _____

What is the Difference?
(Descriptive and Injunctive Social Norms: How Norms Affect Behavior, pages 278-279)

9. Explain the difference between *descriptive social norms* and *injunctive social norms*.

    Descriptive social norms _____

    _____

    Injunctive social norms _____

    _____

    Give an example of a descriptive norm for driving. Also, give an example of an injunctive norm for driving.

    (1) _____

    _____

    (2) _____

    _____

A New Theory...
(Descriptive and Injunctive Social Norms: How Norms Affect Behavior, page 278-279)

10. Cialdini et al, (1990) proposed the normative focus theory. What question does this theory address?

    _____

A New Theory…Continued

What answer did Cialdini (1990) provide?

_____

_____

_____

_____

There is a Norm for Every Situation and a Situation for Every Norm…
(Situational Norms: Automaticity in Normative Behavior, page 279)

11.   You are going to a party on Friday night. You will be with friends at the party. You will interact with others and will listen to music. On Sunday, you are going to attend church. You will probably site with your friends during the church service. You will interact with others and will, also, listen to music. What is the difference though? Surely, the answer is that you will act quite differently at the party than you will at the church service. In other words, you will adhere to different situational norms.

What is a situational norm and how is the situational norm at a party different than a situational norm at a church service?

_____

_____

_____

_____

Describe the work of Aarts and Dijksterhuis (2003) regarding situational norms.

_____

_____

_____

_____

_____

_____

Why Do We Follow the Norms?
(Normative Social Influences: The Desire to Be Liked, page 280)

12.   Janet has gone out to buy clothing for her upcoming freshman year away at college. Prior to doing this, though, Janet, who wants to fit in with others, made sure that she was aware of the latest fashion trends for the fall by searching the advertisements in various fashion magazines.

Janet's need to be suited in the latest fashion trends is representative of her desire to conform to the current fashion standards, as she is sure her classmates will. This is need is illustrative of what type of social influence? How do you know?

_____

_____

We ALL Want to Be Right!
(The Desire to Be Right: Informational Social Influence, page 280)

13.   What is *informational social influence*? Give an example.

_____

_____

_____

_____

The Good, The Bad, and The Ugly…
(The Downside of Conformity: When Pressures to Go Along Produce Harmful Effects, page 280)

14.   Within your textbook, the topic of conformity to gender norms is discussed. It is noted that adherence to the societal beliefs regarding gender can be limiting (particularly to women) and can influence our personal happiness. One way that gender norms have been shown to influence our personal happiness is that the gender norms can impede sexual enjoyment.

Sanchez, Crocker, and Boike (2005) conducted an intriguing study investigating the suggestion that conformity to gender norms can hinder sexual enjoyment. State their hypothesis and their results.

_____

_____

_____

_____

_____

Effects of Conformity – A Study by social psychologist, Phillip Zimbardo, PhD
(Why Good People Sometimes Do Evil Things: The Powerful – But Not Invincible – Effects of Situations, Norms and Conformity Pressure, pages 282-284)

15.   Dr. Phillip Zimbardo is well-known within the psychological world by his famous prison study. This study, conducted in 1973 by Zimbardo and his colleagues, Haney, Banks and Jaffe, provided a poignant example of the construct of conformity. Participants in the study were divided into two groups: prisoners and prison guards. What was the purpose of the study?

_____

_____

What did Dr. Zimbardo find?

_____

_____

_____

_____

A More Optimistic Suggestion…
(Why Good People Sometimes Do Evil Things: The Powerful – But Not Invincible – Effects of Situations, Norms and Conformity Pressure, page 282-284)

16.   Thirty-two years later, Reicher and Haslam, jointly with the BBC, conducted a similar prison experiment. Though the research was similar to Zimbardo's research, some differences existed. What are two of these differences?

1.   _____

_____

2.   _____

_____

One of the Longest Words in the Dictionary – Antiestablishmentarianism: Going Against the Grain…
(Resisting Pressures to Conform: Why, Sometimes, We choose Not to Go Along, pages 284-285)

17.   Someone who refuses to accept and adhere to social norms is sometimes called "anti-establishment." According to your textbook, there are three factors involved in an individual's ability to resist social norms. Name and describe each of them.

1.   _____

_____

One of the Longest Words in the Dictionary – Antiestablishmentarianism: Going Against the Grain…Continued

2. _____

_____

_____

3. _____

_____

_____

A Return to the Age-Old Issue of Women Versus Men…
(Making Common Sense: Do Women and Men Differ in the Tendency to Conform? Page 287)

18. What did Eagly and Carli (1981) find concerning any differences in men and women as far as their differences in conformist behavior?

_____

_____

_____

Later research tended to refute Eagly and Carli's claim. Explain.

_____

_____

_____

Still later, Eagly (1987) suggested a reason for his original data. What did Eagly suggest?

_____

_____

_____

Even if You are a Minority of one, the Truth is the Truth - Mohandas Gandhi
(Minority Influence: Does the Majority Always Rule? Page 286)

19.	You and eleven of your fellow citizens have been selected to sit on a jury for a murder trial. The defense rested two days ago and the case has been handed over to the jury by the judge in charge. For those two days, you and the other jurors have been deliberating and today is the day that the jury foreman is going to take a vote to see if there is a consensus either for acquittal or a guilty verdict.

When the vote is taken, three of the jurors vote for acquittal and the rest (the majority) vote for a guilty verdict. You happen to be one of the jurors who votes for acquittal. As the psychology genius that you are, you are aware that it is possible for the minority to sway the majority.

Your textbook describes three conditions under which the minority can influence the majority. Identify the three conditions and describe each one.

1. _____

_____

2. _____

_____

3. _____

_____

COMPLIANCE: TO ASK – SOMETIMES – IS TO RECEIVE

Acquiescence...
(Introduction, page 288)

20.	Define *compliance*.

_____

_____

Acquiescence – Part Two...
(Compliance: The Underlying Principles, pages 288-290)

21.	Define the term *compliance professional*.

_____

_____

Acquiescence – Part Two...Continued

Now, give two examples of individuals who would be considered compliance professionals.

_____

_____

Principles of Compliance...
(Compliance: The Underlying Principles, page 288-290)

22.   Robert Cialdini (1994, 2006) conducted research on compliance. Through this research, Cialdini theorized that there are six basic principles for gaining acceptance of a request.

Match the following principles to their description.

_Y___   Authority

_B___   Friendship/liking

_____   Social Validation

_____   Scarcity

_D___   Commitment/Consistency

_____   Reciprocity

A.   We are generally more willing to comply with a request from an individual who has provided a favor to us in the past than an individual who has not.

B.   We are more willing to comply with requests from friends and people we are fond of than people who we dislike or are strangers to us.

C.   We place importance on and try to acquire outcomes or objects that are in scarce supply.

D.   We are more willing to comply once we have committed ourselves to a position or action and the requests are consistent with this position or action.

E.   We are more willing to comply with requests from an individual who is considered an authority.

F.   We are more willing to comply with requests for action if this action is consistent with what we think other individuals are doing or thinking.

Are You Trying to Manage My Impression?
(Tactics Based on Friendship or Liking: Ingratiation, page 290)

23.   Define the term _impression management._

_____

Are You Trying to Manage My Impression?...Continued

What are the three techniques of ingratiation as delineated in your textbook?

1. _____

2. _____

3. _____

Excuse Me, but Your Foot is in the Door...
(Tactics Based on Commitment or Consistency: The Foot-In-The-Door and the Lowball, page 290-291)

24.   Explain the *foot-in-the-door* and the *lowball* techniques of gaining compliance from others. In your explanation, provide examples of situations in which each technique might be used.

_____

_____

_____

_____

_____

_____

_____

_____

And That's Not All - Don't Let the Door Slam in Your Face...
(Tactics Based on Reciprocity: The Door-in-the-Face and the "That's Not All" Approach, page 292-293)

25.   A gentleman calls you with a request to help the students of XYZ Academy get to band camp this summer. He initially asks that you contribute $100.00. You tell the caller that you recently had to get your car fixed after the air conditioner broke and you, simply, do not have the money right now. The caller then states, "Well, I understand what that is like. Unfortunately, things often happen when we least expect them. If $100.00 is too much for you, do you think you could contribute $10.00?"

The caller is using the _____ technique for gaining your compliance with his request.

Your sister is aware of your sewing abilities and has asked you to make a Halloween costume for her to wear to her boyfriend's upcoming party. She tells you that she will pay you $25.00 for making the costume. You tell your sister that you are studying for finals right now and do not see

And That's Not All - Don't Let the Door Slam in Your Face...Continued

that you will have the time to help her. Your sister states, "Please!!! I will not only pay you for your time, I will also do your chores for the next week."

Your sister is using the _____ technique for gaining your compliance with her request.

You are Playing Hard to Get...
(Tactics Based on Scarcity: Playing Hard to Get and the Fast-Approaching-Deadline Technique, page 293)

26.   Explain the *hard to get technique* for obtaining compliance.

_____

_____

Discuss what Williams et al. (1993) found regarding the hard to get technique.

_____

_____

We are Reaching the Deadline...
(Tactics Based on Scarcity: Playing Hard to Get and the Fast-Approaching-Deadline Technique, page 293)

27.   Explain the *deadline* technique for gaining compliance.

_____

_____

SYMBOLIC SOCIAL INFLUENCE: HOW WE ARE INFLUENCED BY OTHERS EVEN WHEN THEY ARE NOT THERE

Mental Representations...
(Introduction, pages 294-295)

28.   Psychological presence can best be described as mental representations. For example, you are going to a party this weekend. Since you are far away from home at school right now, you feel that you can make your own decisions as to when you will get back to the dorm after the party. While at the party, though, you are constantly looking at your watch and have even pictured your mother yelling at you for being out past your curfew. Kind of scary, huh?

Anyway, your picture of your mother in your mind is what could be termed a psychological presence. How can the mental picture of your mother influence your behavior?

Mental Representations...Continued

Your textbook speaks to two mechanisms through which this can occur. Describe each.

1. _____

_____

2. _____

_____

Fitzsimmons, Bargh and Mental Representations...
(Introduction, page 295)

29.   Discuss the research of Fitzsimmons and Bargh (2003). NOTE: There are TWO studies.

_____

_____

_____

_____

_____

_____

_____

_____

_____

Eating Disorders: They are NOT Just About the Numbers...
(The Epidemic of Eating Disorders, pages 296-297)

30.   Individuals with eating disorders hear a reverberating refrain – You will NEVER be thin enough!
In reality, the only person they will never be thin enough for themselves. Unfortunately, some of
these individuals will die before they reach the point where they can say they are thin enough.

Your textbook provides a wonderful explanation of eating disorders. If, though you want more
information, I encourage you to go to the internet or to the library and Learn! Learn! Lean!

Name, compare and contrast the two eating disorders delineated in your textbook.

1. _____

2. _____

What are the Causes of Eating Disorders?
(The Epidemic of Eating Disorders, page 296-297)

31.   An eating disorder can be attributed to a multitude of things. Research has shown a biological component, there are psychological components and there are societal components. Perhaps one of the most germane causes, as stated in your textbook, is the media.

How do the media contribute to this dangerous behavior?

_____

_____

_____

_____

How is this issue being addressed?

_____

_____

_____

_____

A Commanding Force...The Media...
(The Epidemic of Eating Disorders, page 296-297)

32.   Why is the media such a powerful force - so powerful that it can contribute to the deaths of our children - in our society?

_____

_____

_____

_____

Obedience – Blind or Opened Eyes?

(Obedience to Authority: Would You Harm an Innocent Stranger if Ordered to Do So? Pages 298-300)

33.   Define the term *obedience*.

_____

_____

_____

Now, describe Stanley Milgram's work (1963, 1965a, 1974) work investigating the topic.

_____

_____

_____

_____

_____

_____

_____

_____

Destructive Obedience...

(Obedience to Authority: Would You Harm an Innocent Stranger if Ordered to Do So? Page 298-300)

34.   *Destructive obedience* is obedience that results in potential harm to others. Four factors have
        been identified as contributing to this phenomenon. Describe each of the factors.

1. _____

    _____

2. _____

    _____

3. _____

    _____

4. _____

    _____

Just Say "No?"
(Destructive Obedience: Resisting the Effects, pages 300-301)

35.   It may not be that easy. Several researchers have identified four ways that may be helpful in resisting destructive obedience. What are they?

1. _____

_____

2. _____

_____

3. _____

_____

4. _____

_____

After You Read... MyPsychLab Connection

(1)   What are some of the techniques used to gain compliance? You probably are more familiar with these than you would think. Salespersons, telemarketers and the like are very well aware of these techniques and use them often. So the likelihood that you have been exposed to any or all of these techniques is very good. Go to *LISTEN: Door-in-the-face Technique, Foot-in-the-Door Technique, and Lowballing Technique.* All of these are worth your time!

(2)   Visit *EXPLORE: Why We Obey* for a wonderful activity exploring the experiment conducted by Stanley Milgram investigating obedience. Great discussion!

(3)   *WATCH: Public Service Ad Mistakes.* Here is your chance to hear Robert Cialdini, a researcher often cited in this chapter. In this short video clip, Cialdini discusses the principle of social validation and his most recent research into this construct.

(4)   This is a must! *WATCH: Milgram Obedience Study* for some video footage of the original experiment. Excellent!

After You Read... Practice Test #1

_____1.   Social influence is best defined as
    A.   way in which people produce changes in others.
    B.   way in which people produce changes in themselves.
    C.   way in which people produce changes in others and in themselves.
    D.   way in which people maintain social contact with others.

_____2.   Change in attitudes is to change in overt behavior as
    A.   compliance is to conformity.
    B.   conformity is to persuasion.
    C.   persuasion is to conformity.
    D.   persuasion is to compliance.

_____3.   Change induced by the issuance of a specific request is
    A.   conformity.
    B.   compliance.
    C.   obedience.
    D.   persuasion.

_____4.   Conformity is change induced by
    A.   direct orders.
    B.   rules.
    C.   commands.
    D.   compliance.

_____5.   A social norm is
    A.   a rule indicating how we should behave.
    B.   a suggestion.
    C.   a direct order.
    D.   norm that is present in ALL societies.

_____6.   Bobby is teaching his brother to play soccer. Prior to going to the field to practice, he has his brother read a short manual on the rules and regulations involved in soccer. These rules are, therefore
    A.   implicit.
    B.   explicit.
    C.   not specifically stated.
    D.   substantial.

_____7.   Regarding social norms
    A.   most people follow them 25% of the time.
    B.   most people follow them most of the time.
    C.   most people follow them about 60% of the time.
    D.   most people follow them about 78% of the time.

_____8.   In Solomon Asch's study (1951), the materials used included
    A.   three concentric circles.
    B.   a standard line and four additional lines of varying lengths.
    C.   two circles and one standard line.
    D.   a standard line and three additional lines of varying lengths.

_____9.   Participants in Solomon Asch's study were
    A.   one "true" participant and six through eight participants who were actually assistants to the experimenter.
    B.   five "true" participants.
    C.   Both A and B.
    D.   Neither A nor B.

_____10.   Participants voiced agreement with the incorrect answers
    A.   twenty-five percent of the time.
    B.   ninety-five percent of the time.
    C.   one hundred percent of the time.
    D.   thirty-seven percent of the time.

11.   Officer Marx has stopped Mrs. Walls for speeding. Mrs. Walls states that there was no speed limit sign for the past 30 miles and she was not sure what the speed limit was – so how could she be speeding? Officer Marx points to a sign just a few feet from the spot where he has stopped Mrs. Walls. The sign states that the speed limit is 45 – 15 MPH less than Mrs. Walls was traveling. The speed limit sign represents a _____ social norm.

12.   _____ refers to doing or saying what others around us say or do.

13.   Marilyn is going to visit her boyfriend's home this weekend. Barry, Marilyn's boyfriend, is Jewish and Marilyn is a Christian. This weekend, Barry's family will be celebrating his brother's Bar Mitzvah. Marilyn is a bit nervous and asks Barry if there are any behaviors in which she should or should not engage. Norms concerning behavior that is approved or disapproved in a particular situation are known as _____ norms.

14.   The infamous prison study was conducted by _____ and his colleagues.

15.   _____ is defined as being distinguishable from others in certain aspects.

After You Read... Practice Test #2

_____1.   Asch's study investigated
      A.   compliance.
      B.   obedience.
      C.   conformity.
      D.   persuasion.

_____2.   Public conformity is to private conformity as
      A.   think/feel is to do/say.
      B.   emotions is to behavior.
      C.   do/say is to think/feel.
      D.   None of the above.

_____3.   In his research, Sherif (1937) used the phenomenon known as
      A.   autokinesthetic.
      B.   autoimmune.
      C.   autokinetic.
      D.   autoprocessing.

_____4.   Another word for public acceptance would be
      A.   commitment.
      B.   conformity.
      C.   compliance.
      D.   cohesiveness.

_____5.   One factor that affects conformity is defined as "the extent to which we are attracted to a group and want to belong to it. This factor is
      A.   commitment.
      B.   cohesiveness.
      C.   compliance.
      D.   obedience.

_____6.   The relationship between group size and conformity is
      A.   as one increases, the other decreases.
      B.   as one increases, the other also increases.
      C.   a negative correlation.
      D.   Both B and C are correct.

_____7.   It is to ought as
      A.   injunctive is to descriptive.
      B.   descriptive is to non-descriptive.
      C.   descriptive is to injunctive.
      D.   non-descriptive is to descriptive.

_____

8.   Normative focus theory (Cialdini et al., 1990) states that norms influence behavior only
         to the extent that they are
         A.   salient.
         B.   descriptive.
         C.   correct.
         D.   explanatory.

_____9.   Norms that guide our behavior in certain environments are
         A.   environmental norms.
         B.   confounding norms.
         C.   standard norms.
         D.   situational norms.

_____10. One reason we conform to social norms is
         A.   we are pressured to do so.
         B.   normative social influence.
         C.   we have learned that doing so will win approval.
         D.   Both B and C.

11.   The tendency to conform is _____ in individualist countries than it is in

       _____ countries.

12.   Eagly and Carli (1981) found that _____ are slightly more accepting of social

       norms than _____.

13.   The _____ technique of gaining compliance involving, first,

       making a small request, getting the individual to accept the request and, then, making a larger

       request.

14.   The definition "getting others to like us so that they will be more willing to agree to our requests"

       is best suited for the term _____.

15.   Ron is desperately attempting to get Yvonne to notice him. The other day he spoke with Yvonne

       and told her how busy he was going to be this weekend trying to decide which one of his

       "potential" girlfriends he will be taking to the winter carnival. Ron is engaging in the technique

       of _____ which is designed to induce compliance.

After You Read... Practice Test #3

_____1. A compliance professional
- A. is a person whose success depends on his or her ability to convince others to say "yes"
- B. by example, a priest.
- C. by example, a salesperson.
- D. Both A and C.

_____2. Basic principles basic principles for gaining compliance include all, EXCEPT
- A. authority.
- B. reciprocity.
- C. degree of conformity.
- D. scarcity.

_____3. Flattery is to self-promotion as
- A. praising others is to praising self.
- B. praising self is to praising others.
- C. getting others to like us is to getting us to like others.
- D. ingratiation is to conformity.

_____4. Phillip Zimbardo's participants in his prison study were divided into
- A. those who conformed and those who did not conform.
- B. prisoners and guards.
- C. males and females.
- D. deviants and nondeviants.

_____5. Zimbardo's study (1973), primarily, showed
- A. it was the situation that largely determined his participants' behavior.
- B. it was personality traits that largely determined his participants' behavior.
- C. it was the number of people present that largely determined the participants' behavior.
- D. it was the actual ability to conform that largely determined the participants' behavior.

_____6. According to Dr. Zimbardo
- A. under the right situational factors, most humans might commit evil acts.
- B. under the right situational factors, about 10% of all humans might commit evil acts.
- C. under the right situational factors, ALL humans might commit evil acts.
- D. under the right situational factors, about 50% of humans might commit evil acts.

_____7. The factors that affect our ability to resist pressure to conform include ALL of the following, EXCEPT
- A. the need to maintain our individuality.
- B. the need to maintain control over our own lives.
- C. the need to control others.
- D. certain social norms which urge us to be individuals.

_____8.   Individuation refers to
            A.   the desire to be indistinguishable from others.
            B.   the desire to be like others.
            C.   the desire to be different from others.
            D.   the desire to be superior to others.

_____9.   Low conformity is to high conformity as
            A.   collectivist is to individualist.
            B.   individualist is to collectivist.
            C.   high compliance is to low compliance.
            D.   low compliance is to high compliance.

_____10.   Eagly and Carli (1981) conducted
            A.   a meta analysis of 145 different studies.
            B.   a study of obedience among college students.
            C.   a study of differences in conformity between people 65 and over and 65 and under.
            D.   an observational study on conformity.

11.   _____ involves altering our behavior to meet the expectations of others.

12.   According to the six basic principles of gaining compliance, the principle of _____ states that we are more willing to comply with requests from someone who holds legitimate power.

13.   Renee was approached the other day and was asked to fill out a questionnaire regarding her opinions regarding her college campus. The individual who asked her to complete the questionnaire told her that if she fills it out, she will get a free gift. This is an example of the _____ technique for gaining compliance.

14.   _____ is defined as a type of social influence in which one individual directly gives another individual orders.

15.   A _____ professional is one who makes his or her living attempting to get people to acquiesce to his or her requests.

After You Read... Practice Test #4

_____1. Sanchez, Crocker and Bolke (2005) found that
    A.   conforming to gender roles can interfere with sexual enjoyment in both sexes.
    B.   conforming to gender roles can interfere with sexual enjoyment only in men.
    C.   conforming to gender roles can interfere with sexual enjoyment only in women.
    D.   conforming to gender roles does not interfere with sexual enjoyment in either sex.

_____2. Conforming to gender roles has been shown to
    A.   reduce sexual enjoyment.
    B.   influence personal happiness.
    C.   influence acceptance of the "rape myth" that women provoke rapists.
    D.   ALL of the above.

_____3. Phillip Zimbardo is famous for his
    A.   study on the effect of norms concerning various social roles.
    B.   shock study on obedience.
    C.   line study assessing conformity.
    D.   A and B are correct.

_____4. This method for gaining compliance involves inducing the target person to, first, agree to a small request.
    A.   Door-in-the-face.
    B.   Lowball.
    C.   Ingratiating.
    D.   Foot-in-the-door.

_____5. Automobile salesmen often use
    A.   the lowball procedure for gaining compliance.
    B.   the foot-in-the-door for gaining compliance.
    C.   ingratiating.
    D.   highball technique for gaining compliance.

_____6. The that's not all technique involve es ALL of the following, EXCEPT
    A.   an initial request.
    B.   the principle of reciprocity.
    C.   something extra being thrown in to sweeten the deal.
    D.   ALL of the above are correct.

_____7. A tactic for gaining compliance that is often used in the area of romance is
    A.   foot-in-the-door.
    B.   deadline.
    C.   playing it hard to get.
    D.   lowball.

_____8.   Eating disorders are
        A.   seen only in females.
        B.   seen in males and females.
        C.   seen only in teenagers over 14.
        D.   not a pervasive issue in our society.

_____9.   Refusal to eat is to purging as
        A.   bulimia is to anorexia.
        B.   eating disorder is to mental disorder.
        C.   anorexia is to obesity.
        D.   anorexia is to bulimia.

_____10.   Stanley Milgram's research was originated because of
        A.   the atrocities of WWII.
        B.   social deviance in present society.
        C.   Asch's studies concerning conformity.
        D.   Zimbardo's prison study.

11.   If one begins to actually feel or think as others do, he or she is engaging in _____

       acceptance.

12.   In his 1937 study, Muzafer Sherif used the phenomenon known as the

       _____ phenomenon.

13.   _____ is defined as the extent to which we are attracted to a particular

       social group and want to belong to it.

14.   Social norms that are unspoken or implied are referred to as _____ norms.

15.   _____ influence is based on our tendency to rely on

       others as sources of information about aspects of the world.

When you have finished... Crossword Puzzle

Across

1.   Pressure to behave in ways that are viewed an appropriate
4.   Specifically stated
6.   Social influence in which someone orders another to do what they want them to do

Down

1.   Efforts to get others to change their behavior
2.   Involves the ways in which we produce changes in others
3.   Unspoken
5.   Being distinguishable from others in certain respects

Created by Puzzlemaker at DiscoverySchool.com

When you have finished... You be the Researcher

In this chapter, your author delineated several of the techniques used to gain compliance. If you need to, go back to your textbook and re-read that section now.

Now, you are the primary researcher in a study in which you will investigate one of the compliance gaining techniques discussed in your book. You may use any of the research methods previously discussed in your textbook. Determine which research method you will employ and design your research study. **NOTE: You will NOT have to conduct this study. One reason for this is that certain types of studies (as you already know) require IRB approval and, due to time constraints, this is probably not possible.**

Once you have designed your study, compose your hypothesis (es), determine what your participants will be like (demographics, etc), and establish "fantasy" data. Have fun with this! This data may or may not support your hypothesis.

Finally, after "collecting" your data, analyze it and formulate conclusions. You should provide a final research report in APA format. This report should include all the elements of a standard research report. Yes, this means you will have to provide a reference page as you will be required to write an introduction. And, yes, this means you will have to visit the library (again). Just remember…the more you write research reports, the better you get! And, this is a beneficial skill to have!

The standard research report should include the following divisions:

(1)   **Title page**

(2)   **Abstract**

(3)   **Introduction**

(4)   **Methods**

      A.   Participants
      B.   Apparatus
      C.   Design
      D.   Procedure

(5)   **Results**

(6)   **Discussion**

(7)   **References**

Answers - As You Read...Practice Activities

1. Conformity is defined as pressure that is exerted upon us to behave in ways that are consistent with rules that specify how we should or ought to behave.

    Social norms are defined a rules and regulations that tell us how to behave in given situations.

    The social norms of your campus environment should be very similar to other campuses. What do you do when in class? Do you sit quietly and listen to the professor? Do you speak loudly and disregard what the professor is saying? When writing down the social norms, you might want to assess how the norms in a philosophy class (for example) are quite different from the norms in a theatre class (once again, an example).

2. The two types of social norms discussed in the textbook are explicit and implicit. An explicit social norm is one that is specifically stated and is often very detailed. An example of an explicit norm would be a sign noting the speed limit. You are to provide examples of your own.

    An implicit social norm is one that is unspoken or implied. An example of an implicit norm would be that you should cover your nose and mouth when you sneeze. You are to provide additional examples.

3. Task = Participants were shown a standard line. They were, then, asked to assess *three additional lines to determine which of the three lines matched the length of the original line.*

    Procedure = Several people, usually *six to eight* were present during the session. The additional people, though, unknown

to the participants, were *assistants of the experimenter.*
In the *critical* trials, the additional people, offered answers that were clearly *wrong.* In addition, the additional people chose their answer *before* the "real" participants.

Dilemma Faced by Participants: *Should they acquiesce and go along with the other participants or should they stick to their own judgments?*

Results   *A large majority of the participants in the study chose to conform. Seventy-six percent of participants went along with the group's incorrect answers at least once. They voiced agreement with these errors thirty-seven percent of the time. Only five percent of the control group voiced agreement. Almost twenty-five percent of the participants never gave way to the group pressure. Some participants went along with the others nearly all of the time. Asch found that those who went along with the group tended to think that they were wrong and the others were right.*

4. Conformity was reduced in all conditions involved in the study. The reduction was greatest when the opposing assistant expressed views more extreme or more wrong than the majority. This suggests that unanimity of the group is important to eliminate resistance.

5. Public conformity refers to doing or saying what others what us to do or say.

    Private acceptance refers to actually arriving at the point where one tends to think or feel as others do.

6. The two questions addressed by Sherif are: (1) How do norms develop in a social group? (2) How strong is the influence of the norms on behavior once they emerge?

The autokinetic phenomenon refers to the idea that, when placed in a completely dark room and exposed to a single point of light, people have the tendency to perceive the light as moving.

7. Cohesiveness is defined as the extent to which one is attracted to a particular social group and wants to belong to the group.

    Tiffany should exhibit a high level of conformity because she very much wants to be part of the sorority.

8. If one variable increases along with another variable, we have a positive correlation. What this tells us is that the two variables, in this case group size and conformity, are, simply, related.

    Gerard, Wilhelmy and Conolley, 1968, found that conformity only tends to increase with groups of three to four members. If the group is larger than this, the level of conformity tends to level or even decrease. A later study, Bond and Smith (1996), found that conformity tends to increase with size up to eight or more group members.

9. Descriptive social norms are norms that describe what most people do in certain situations.

    Injunctive social norms are norms that describe what one should do in certain situations.

10. When do injunctive norms influence our behavior?

    People will adhere to injunctive norms when they think about them and see their as relevant to their actions. That is, when the injunctive norms are germane.

11. A situational norm is defined as a norm that guides behavior in a certain situation. The norm for a party is quite

different from that of a church service. One issue you might address is the type of music as a situational norm. You may listen to rap at a party; while you listen to hymns at church. Provide some of your own examples.

Aarts and Dijksterhuis (2003) had their participants look at photographs of a library or of a railway station. Some of the participants who saw the photo of the library were told that they would later visit the library. Other participants were not given that information. Participants were then asked to read, aloud, a list of ten words. The volume of their voices upon reading the list of words was the dependent variable in the study.

The researchers found that participants who were told they would later visit a library demonstrated a lower volume than did the participants who were not provided with that information.

12. This is consistent with the normative social influence which suggests that we depend on others as sources of information about aspect of the social world.

13. Informational social influence is based on our propensity to depend on others as a source of information.

    Provide your own example.

14. The hypothesis was that those who felt it necessary to adhere to gender norms would be more concerned with conforming than they would be with their own sexual fulfillment.

    Results showed strong evidence in support of the hypothesis. The more one felt it necessary to adhere to gender norms, the less personal sexual fulfillment they experienced.

15. The purpose of the Zimbardo study was to determine if participants in his study would conform to the social norms associated with their roles of either prisoners or prison guards.

Dr. Zimbardo found that the participants did very willingly conform to their roles. The "guards" gained the idea that they were superior to the "prisoners." They began treating the prisoners in demeaning ways and treated them in ways that showed that they (the guards) were in charge. The "prisoners" began feeling that they were, truly, inferior to the "guards." They began to feel humiliated and degraded. In fact, the results were so powerful that the study had to be stopped after six days.

Evidence supported the idea that it is very much the situation, as opposed to personality traits, that contributes to conformity.

16. Guards were told they could promote prisoners to guard status.

Early in the study, both guards and prisoners were told that no differences existed between the two groups.

17. 1.   The need to maintain our individuality, culture and resistance to conformity. We want to be individuals in society. We do not want to be like everyone else. In other words, we have a need for individuation.

2.   We also have the need to control our own lives. We do not want to feel controlled in any way. We want to be masters of our own destinies.

3.   There are certain norms in society that are specific to certain groups. These norms actually make it the norm to go against the social norms. An example of a group that tends to make to acceptable to go against social norms is a gang.

18. Eagly and Carli (1981) found that only a slight difference in conformist behavior exists between men and women. The difference was found to be that women conform slightly more than do men.

Later research showed that these differences, though very small, actually may not exist. It was suggested that many of the studies that had investigated difference in conformity between men and women used situations and materials that were more familiar to men than women. This supposed flaw appeared to have influenced the data.

Even later, Eagly (1987), adhering to their original data found that the differences they had found were due to the difference in status between men and women. Since women tend to have lower status in society than do men, the researcher suggested that because of this, women tended to conform more than men.

19. (1)   Members of the minority must be consistent in their disagreement with majority opinion.
(2)   Members of the minority must avoid appearing inflexible and unbending.
(3)   The opinion of the minority must be within the current social context.

20. Compliance is defined as getting a person or persons to say "yes" to your request(s).

21. A compliance professional is someone whose achievements depend on their skill of getting others to say "yes" to their requests.

You are to provide your own examples. The textbook also contains examples.

22. E, B, F, C, D, A

23. Impression management is defined as using a variety of techniques to make a good impression on others.

    1.   Flattery
    2.   Self-promotion
    3.   Incidental Similarity

24. The foot-in-the-door technique involves first persuading an individual to accept a minor initial request and then making a larger request of the individual. The larger request is the one that was desired all along.

The lowball technique involves first offering a good deal to an individual. After that individual accepts the deal, something happens to require adjustments be made to the initial deal. The deal involving the adjustments is actually what was desired by the individual attempting to gain compliance.

25. Door-in-the-face technique; that's not all technique.

26. The playing hard to get technique involves making believe that you are uninterested in your actual goal state.

Williams et al. (1993) found that the playing hard to get technique tends to work very well.

27. The deadline technique has to do with time. One might tell someone that time to comply is running out and that they need to make a decision. In other words, the person trying to gain compliance is rushing the other person to make a decision.

28. There may be a triggering of "relational schemas." These are defined as mental representations of people with whom we have relationships and also the relationships themselves. When the relational schemas are activated goals that are relevant to these mental representations are also activated.

Secondly, the mental representations may trigger goals that the person in the mental representation wishes for us to achieve.

29. In their 2003 study, Fitzsimmons and Bargh approached individuals at an airport and asked them to think of either a good friend or a coworker. They were asked to write down the initials of the individual about whom they were thinking. Then, participants were asked to answer questions about the person whose initials they wrote down. Participants were finally asked if they would be willing to answer a longer set of questions. Results showed that those who thought about a friend were more willing to assist the researcher.

In another study, Fitzsimmons and Bargh asked participants to think about and describe their mother or to think about neutral events. These neutral events were not to include other people. Participants were then given a seven letters and were asked to make up as many words as possible from these. Results showed that individuals who thought about their mother and wanted to make her proud did much better than those who simply thought about their mother but did not have the goal of making her proud. Those in the control condition, neutral events, showed no effect regardless of whether or not they wanted to make their mother proud.

30. Anorexia nervosa is characterized by an extreme fear of being overweight and a refusal to eat an adequate daily diet.

Bulimia nervosa is characterized by the binge-purge cycle. That is, the individual will eat huge amounts of food and then vomit or use large doses of laxatives to rid their body of the food.

31.   The media portrays the "normal" female as being thin, in fact, painfully thin. Our children are seeing this and are trying to emulate this image. Also, in our society, models that are viewed by our children in so many faucets of the media are pencil thin and very unhealthy.

One thing that is being done concerning models is that legislation is being sought to require them to have a certain body mass index.

32.   The media is such a powerful force because it, simply put, has the power to influence us. Also, media is everywhere and it is exceptionally difficult to insulate our children from it.

33.   Obedience is defined as a type of social influence in which one individual directly instructs one or more others to behave in a specific way.

In Milgram's experiment the all male participants were advised they were participating in a study designed to investigate the effect of punishment on learning. Participants were divided into pairs and one was designated the teacher. The other was the learner. The learner, who was actually a member of the research team and was "in" on the study, was to perform a task of memory and the teacher was to punish (by electric shock) errors made by the learner. The machine that delivered the shocks had 30 switches that were numbered according to the volts each switch, when activated, would deliver. The learner made many errors during the experiment and was, therefore, shocked with a progressive increase in the "voltage."

After a while, the learner began to scream and carry on as if he were really being shocked. This tended to produce concern on the part of the teacher in that he assumed the learner was really in pain. Each time the teacher was reluctant of continuing, he was encouraged by a researcher that he must continue.

The results of this study showed that 65% of the teachers showed total obedience to the researcher.

34.   (1)   The individual(s) in charge relieve those individuals who obey of the responsibility for their own actions.

(2)   The individual(s) in charge often display badges or signs of their authority.

(3)   The individual(s) in charge displays a gradual escalation of their orders.

(4)   Often the events involving destructive obedience move very quickly.

35.   (1)   Individuals need to be reminded that they are responsible for their own actions.

(2)   Individuals need to be reminded that at a certain point obedience may be inappropriate.

(3)   Individuals should question the expertise of the so-called authority figures.

(4)   Knowing how strong the power of authority figures to command destructive obedience may be helpful.

Answers – Cross Word Puzzle

Across

1. conformity
4. explicit
6. obedience

Down

1. compliance
2. socialinfluence
3. implicit
5. individuation

Answers – Practice Test #1

1. A
2. D
3. C
4. B
5. A
6. B
7. B
8. D
9. A
10. D
11. explicit
12. public conformity
13. injunctive
14. Phillip Zimbardo
15. individuation

Answers – Practice Test #3

1. D
2. C
3. A
4. B
5. A
6. C
7. C
8. C
9. B
10. A
11. normative social influence
12. authority
13. that's not all
14. obedience
15. compliance

Answers – Practice Test #2

1. C
2. C
3. C
4. A
5. B
6. B
7. C
8. A
9. D
10. D
11. conform, collectivist
12. women, men
13. foot-in-the-door
14. ingratiation
15. playing hard to get

Answers – Practice Test #4

1. A
2. D
3. A
4. D
5. A
6. D
7. C
8. B
9. D
10. A
11. private
12. autokinetic
13. cohesiveness
14. implicit
15. informational social influence

CHAPTER 9

PROSOCIAL BEHAVIOR:
HELPING OTHERS

> ### *Before You Read...Chapter Summary*

Prosocial behavior, as discussed in Chapter Nine, is defined as actions that help others even when there is no immediate benefit to the person performing the actions. But what are some of the motives for people helping others? The first section of this chapter addresses this question by discussing five basic reasons why people help others. One of the reasons involves the construct of empathy. Individuals who experience empathy have the ability to put themselves into someone else's place and understand how the other feels. When one feels empathy towards someone who needs help, the empathetic individual has the desire to alleviate the state that is being experienced by the individual in need of help. In order to relieve this state, the empathetic individual performs an act of prosocial behavior – he or she "helps" the person in need. This being the motive, one could most definitely see this as a selfless action. Another reason for helping others resides in the negative –state relief perspective. This perspective states that individuals tend help others because it alleviates any negative, unpleasant emotions experienced by the helper. In this case, the act is more of a selfish than selfless. The other three reasons for helping are empathetic joy, competitive altruism, and kin selection.

The chapter then covers a five step model of prosocial behavior. The first step is noticing that something unusual has happened. This is pretty much common sense in that, of course, one must know something is happening in order to do something about it. The next step is making the correct determination that an event is actually an emergency. The concept of pluralistic ignorance is relevant at this stage. This occurs when a group of strangers is present as an emergency situation arises, but not one acts because no one knows what is happening. The main reason for this is that we often look to others for cues and if no one is sending us relevant cues that an emergency is happening, we may interpret the situation as normal. It is kind of like the game Follow the Leader. The final three steps are determining that is it your responsibility to act, deciding that you have the knowledge or skills to act, and, finally, making the ultimate decision to act.

Section three of Chapter Nine identifies some of the external and internal factors that can influence helping behavior. Some of the external factors are addressed by the following questions, (1) Do we like the individual who is in need of help? (2) Does the victim have values that are similar to ours? And (3) Is the person in need responsible for the conditions that contribute to the need for help? Internal factors include emotions. If you are in a negative mood do you think you would be more or less likely to help someone in need? You will find the (not-so-simple) answers in this section. Likewise, would you be more or less likely to help someone in need if you were in a positive mood? The remainder of the chapter presents a look at personal factors that influence our desire to help others. The authors revisit the construct of empathy and how empathy is developed. The role of personality in helping is also discussed. Chapter Nine ends with an interesting discussion of volunteering as a form of helping.

Before You Read... Learning Objectives

After reading this chapter, you should be able to:

- Discuss the concept of prosocial behavior.
- Provide an answer to the question, "Why do people help?"
- Define *empathy*.
- Explain the *empathy-altruism hypothesis*.
- Discuss *selective altruism*.
- Explain the *negative-state relief model* and the *empathic joy hy*pothesis.
- Explain the *competitive altruism approach.*
- Discuss the meaning of the term *diffusion of responsibility*.
- Outline the five steps used to determine whether one will help or not.
- Delineate some of the external and internal factors that tend to either augment or restrain our desire to help.
- Discuss the potential downside to helping.
- Outline the five dimensions that are characteristic of those who engage in prosocial behavior in an emergency situation.
- Discuss *volunteering*.
- Provide an answer to the question, "Are helping and hurting really opposites?"

As You Read...Term Identification

Important Terms to Know
Below are a list of some of the key terms and concepts from this chapter. Make flashcards in order to enhance your recall ability of these terms. Refer to the definitions that are either in boldface or in the margins of this chapter for help. You may also want to include additional terms from this chapter as you deem necessary.

prosocial behavior, (p. 306)	competitive altruism approach, (p. 308)	altruistic personality, (p. 326)
empathy, (p. 306)	kin selection theory, (p. 310)	locus of control, (p. 122)
empathy-altruism hypothesis, (p. 306)	diffusion of responsibility, (p. 313)	generativity, (p. 330)
negative-state relief model, (p. 308)	pluralistic ignorance, (p. 315)	self-interest/egoism, (p. 331)
empathetic joy hypothesis, (p. 308)	social exclusion, (p. 328)	moral integrity, (p. 337)

As You Read...Practice Activities

"We make a living by what we get, but make a life by what we give." – Winston Churchill
(Introduction, page 306)

1. William is a senior in college. For the past 10 years he has devoted himself to doing volunteer work at the local children's hospital. For his work with the children, William accepts no monetary compensation. He does, though, believe that he gets an extrinsic reward – the chance to be with children – and, to Will, this is reward in itself.

    Will is engaging in prosocial behavior. Explain this concept.

    _____

    _____

    _____

WHY PEOPLE HELP: MOTIVES FOR PROSOCIAL BEHAVIOR

"When a good man is hurt all who would be called good must suffer with him." - Euripides
(Introduction, page 306)

2. Kristie works as a volunteer at her local crisis center. Because of her volunteering activities, she has developed a sense of empathy for those contemplating suicide.

    Define empathy.

    _____

    _____

    _____

    Your book states that empathy can be both an unselfish and a selfish state. Why is this true?

    _____

    _____

    _____

    _____

Altruism and Prosocial Behavior...
(Introduction, pages 306-307)

3.   Explain Batson and Oleson's (1991) empathy altruism hypothesis.

_____

_____

_____

_____

Non-positive Condition Reprieve...
(Negative State Relief: Sometimes, Helping Behavior Reduces Unpleasant Feelings, page 308)

4.   What is the negative state relief model proposed by Cialdini, Baumann and Kenrick in 1981?

_____

_____

_____

Empathy and Joy Seem to Go Hand-in-Hand...
(Empathic Joy: Helping as an Accomplishment, page 308)

5.   Smith, Keating and Stotland (1989) proposed the empathic joy hypothesis. What does this
        hypothesis state?

_____

_____

_____

Describe the research of Smith, Keating and Stotland (1989).

_____

_____

_____

_____

Isn't the Saying "Nice People Always Finish Last"? Maybe Not...
(Why Nice People Sometimes Finish First: Competitive Altruism, pages 308-310)

6.   What does the competitive altruism approach suggest?

_____

_____

_____

Discuss the research of Hardy and Van Vugt (2006).

_____

_____

_____

_____

Who Are We More Likely to Help – Our Sister or a Stranger?
(Kin Selection Theory: Helping Ourselves by Helping People Who Share Our Genes, pages 310-311)

7.   Hypothetical scenario: You are on a bus with your sister and approximately fifty strangers. The bus blows a tire and runs off the road. The bus rolls down a hill and comes to a sudden, abrupt stop. Several of the passengers are thrown from their seats and all you hear are screams. You are astonished to find that you apparently have no injuries and you immediately turn to the other passengers in an effort to help the injured. You find your sister's seat and notice that both she and the lady sitting beside her appear to be bleeding heavily and are unconscious. The lady in the seat next to your sister, though, appears in much worse condition than does your sister. Her legs both appear to be broken and are bent under her. Someone up in the front of the bus notes that there are flames coming from under the hood and everyone needs to get out of the bus IMMEDIATELY. You are left with a dilemma – do you get your sister out first or do you tend to the more injured person sitting next to her?

Answer the question posed above according to Cialdini, Brown, Lewis, Luce, and Neuberg's (1997) kin selection theory.

_____

_____

_____

Why, Then, Do We Help Strangers...
(Kin Selection Theory: Helping Ourselves by Helping People Who Share Our Genes, page 310-311)

8.   Explain the reciprocal altruism theory.

_____

_____

_____

RESPONDING TO AN EMERGENCY: WILL BYSTANDERS HELP?

The More People Around – The More Likely Someone Will Help? Not!
(Helping in Emergencies: Apathy – Or Action? page 312)

9.   One would assume that the more people there are around an emergency situation, the more likely one would be to receive help. However, this assumption, though, is untrue! Discuss the Kitty Genovese assault which refutes the above assumption.

_____

_____

_____

_____

_____

Dispersion of Accountability...
(Is There Safety in Numbers? Not Always! page 313)

10.   What impact did the Genovese assault have on John Darley and Bibb Latane? That is, discuss how they explained what happened in the Genovese case.

_____

_____

_____

_____

How Do We Decide?
(Five Crucial Steps Determine Helping versus Not Helping, pages 314-317)

11.   There are two things that we need to know prior to acting in a helping situation. What are they?

1. _____

2. _____

Do You Notice?
(Noticing, or Failing to Notice, that Something Unusual is Happening, page 314)

12.   Will we or won't we help? One factor upon which the answer depends is noticing or failing to notice the need for help.

Describe the research of Darley and Batson (1973) regarding this factor in the decision making process.

_____

_____

_____

_____

Interpreting the Event as an Emergency...
(Correctly Interpreting an Event as an Emergency, page 314-316)

13.   We must interpret the event as an emergency in order to help. What did Wilson and Petruska (1984) find regarding the presence of ambiguous information?

_____

_____

Going Against the Grain:
(Correctly Interpreting an Event as an Emergency, page 314-316)

14.   The other evening at the Psi Rho Fraternity house one of the new pledges, Mario, was celebrating by drinking heavily. A few of the "brothers" had noted that Mario was becoming highly inebriated and thought it was funny at the time. Around 11:00 PM, three of the partygoers noticed that Mario was lying face down in the backyard. He was not moving. Joey, one of the brothers, later stated that he wanted to check on Mario to see if he was okay, but he feared that the other brothers would make fun of him and state that he was only drunk. What phenomenon was Joey exhibiting?

_____

Inhibiting Helping…
(Correctly Interpreting an Event as an Emergency, page 314-316)

15.   What did Rutkowski, Gruder and Romer (1983), Levin et al. (1994), and Steele, Critchlow and Liu (1988) find regarding the inhibiting effect of the presence of others?

Rutkowski, Gruder and Romber (1983): _____

_____

Levin et al. (1994): _____

_____

Critchlow and Liu (1988): _____

_____

You are the Leader – Do Something!
(Deciding That it is Your Responsibility to Provide Help, page 316)

16.   When it is not clear who is responsible, we have the tendency to assume what?

_____

_____

To Act, You Must First be Able to Act…
(Deciding that You have the Knowledge and/or Skills to Act, page 316)

17.   Mr. O'Day, a 400 lb gentleman who resides in a local nursing home, has just fallen and calls for help. The nurse in charge, Marcie, is very tiny and weighs less than 100 lbs. It is certainly clear that Marcie will not be able to pick up Mr. O'Day by herself. She calls for help.

The scenario above is illustrative of one of the steps in making the decision to help. To most people this step would very much be common sense. What is this step?

_____

_____

_____

And…Finally…
(Making the Final Decision to Provide Help, page 317)

18.   What is the final step in the decision making process of whether or not to provide help when it is needed?

_____

_____

EXTERNAL AND INTERNAL INFLUENCES ON HELPING BEHAVIOR

Who are We Most Likely to Help?
(Situational (External) Factors that Enhance or Inhibit Helping, page 318)

19.   According to your textbook, we are most likely to help people depending on the presence of one, two or three characteristics. What are these characteristics? Explain each.

      1. _____

Who are We Most Likely to Help?...Continued

      2. _____

      3. _____

You Did This to Yourself…
(Helping Those who are Not Responsible for Their Problem, page 318)

20.   Discuss the results of the research of Higgins and Shaw (1999).

_____

_____

Feed the Kitty…
(Exposure to Prosocial Models Increases Prosocial Behavior, pages 319-320)

21.   You are going to a local craft fair. You read in the paper this morning that they are asking for a $10.00 donation at the door. You are also informed that all money collected will go to a local charity. As a long-suffering college student, you really do not have the money to spare, but feel that since it is stated as a "donation" you will not be "required" to pay.

When you arrive at the craft fair, you first note that a large glass container is on the table at the entrance to the fair. This container is half filled with dollars, fives, tens, and coins. According to Macauley (1970) what are you most likely to do?

_____

_____

The Power of TV…
(Exposure to Prosocial Models Increases Prosocial Behavior, pages 319-320)

22.   Sprafkin, Liebert and Poulous (1975) conducted a study investigating the power of the TV as a contributor to the creation of a social norm that encourages prosocial behavior. Describe this study.

_____

_____

_____

_____

Ask Me the Next Time I Am in a Good Mood…
(Positive Emotions and Prosocial Behavior, pages 320-321)

23.   What does research indicate about the link between the experience of positive emotions and acts of prosocial behavior? Cite findings from the research of Wilson (1981), Isen and Levin (1972), Cunningham (1979), and Baron (1990b).

_____

_____

_____

_____

_____

On the Other Hand, You Might Not Want to Ask Me to Help if it is Going to Interfere with My Good Mood...
(Positive Emotions and Prosocial Behavior, pages 320-321)

24.   There is evidence that being in a positive mood can actually decrease the probability that we will help others. Explain why this might be true.

_____

_____

_____

The Negative Mood and Helping Connection...
(Negative Emotions and Prosocial Behavior, page 321)

25.   Zack is in a very bad mood. His alma mater lost the football game today that would have made them a "shoe-in" for the playoffs. Zack was sure that they would win. According to Cialdini, Kenrick and Bauman (1982), if Zack were to come upon a stranger in need of help just shortly after the loss, how would he respond?

_____

_____

Empathy – a Good Quality to Have...
(Empathy: An Important Foundation for Helping, pages 321-322)

26.   Define the term "empathy." Name three occupations in which empathy is a necessity.

_____

_____

_____

_____

A Cognitive Component + An Affective Component = Empathy...
(Empathy: An Important Foundation for Helping, pages 321-322)

27.   The two components of empathy are (1) a cognitive component, and (2) an affective component. Explain these two components.

_____

_____

_____

Tres Perspectivos...
(Empathy: An Important Foundation for Helping, pages 321-322)

28.   What is perspective taking? Name and describe the three types.

_____

_____

_____

Helping Someone in Another Group is Sometimes Difficult
(Empathy and Helping Across Group Boundaries, page 322)

29.   Stan is a member of the football team at the local university. Quin is a member of the football team that Stan's team refers to as their arch rivals. Quin's team is having a car wash to earn money for a summer trip to Mexico in which the football team will act as teaching coaches to a local Mexican elementary school football team. Stan has a filthy car. What are the odds that Stan will drop by the car wash to have his car washed? According to your textbook the odds do not appear to be very good because it is a rival football team.

Is helping those in our out-group a more arduous task than helping those in our in-group? Actually, according to the research of Stuermer, Snyder, Kropp and Siem (2006), the answer is yes. Why? Describe their research and findings.

_____

_____

_____

_____

_____

_____

_____

_____

_____

_____

_____

The Development of Empathy…
(How Does Empathy Develop? pages 322-323)

30.   What is the role of genetics in the development of empathy? Discuss the findings of Janet Strayer (1997a).

_____

_____

_____

_____

Factors of Enhancement…
(How Does Empathy Develop? Pages 322-323)

31.   What kinds of experiences either enhance or inhibit our development of empathy? Describe the findings of Milulincer et al. (2001), Azar (1997) and Coles (1997).

_____

_____

_____

_____

Exclusion and Helping Behavior…
(Social Exclusion: When Being Left Out Reduces Helping, pages 323-325)

32.   Define social exclusion and how does it influence helping?

_____

_____

_____

Everything Has a Downside – Sometimes it Just Takes Us a Long Time to Find Out What it is...
(The Downside of Being Helped: Why, Often, It May Actually Be Better to Give Than to Receive, pages 326-327)

33.   Sometimes when help is given, those we help may experience negative reactions as opposed to the positive reactions we would tend to think they would be experiencing. Why might this be the case?

_____

_____

Describe the research of Nadler and Halabi (2006).

_____

_____

_____

_____

Is Helping Related to Personality Characteristics?
(Personality and Helping, page 326

34.   Your textbook delineates two aspects of personality that are related to prosocial behavior. Name and discuss these.

1. _____

_____

2 _____

_____

Explain what an altruistic personality is. Then name and describe the five dimensions that are characteristic of persons high in the measurement of altruism.

1. _____

_____

2. _____

_____

3. _____

4. _____

_____

5. _____

_____

LONG-TERM COMMITMENT TO PROSOCIAL ACTS

Cultural Diversity in Helping...
(Volunteering: Helping as an Ongoing Commitment, pages 328-329)

35. Timothy is an African American, Jacob is a Caucasian, Li is an Asian American, and Juan is a Hispanic American. According to your textbook, how might each person be influenced by their culture in their helping behavior?

_____

_____

_____

_____

_____

_____

Connection Between AIDS and empathy...
(Motives for Volunteering, pages 328-329)

36. According to Pullium (1993), under what circumstances do people tend to have less empathy for AIDS patients?

_____

_____

_____

Mandated Volunteering – Directing Someone to Volunteer...
(Volunteering Because of Mandates, Altruism, or Generativity, pages 330-331)

37.   Define generativity.

_____

_____

_____

People who are high in generativity have certain characteristics – what are they?

_____

_____

_____

_____

A Severe Overestimation...
(Self-Interest, Moral Integrity, and Moral Hypocrisy, pages 331-332)

38.   Explain the description, "Holier Than Thou" as it applies to helping.

_____

_____

_____

Do You Help – or – Do You Not?
(Motivation and Morality, page 332)

39.   There are three relevant motives in one's deciding whether to help someone or not. Name and elaborate upon each.

1. _____

_____

2. _____

_____

3. _____

_____

Polar Opposites?? Helping and Aggression?
(Are Helping (Prosocial Behavior) and Hurting (Aggression) Really Opposites? pages 333-334)

40.   Define the term aggression.

_____

_____

Now, answer the question posed above, "Are helping and hurting really opposites?"

_____

_____

_____

_____

After You Read... MyPsychLab Connection

(1)   Go to MyPsychLab. The two *EXPLORE* modules are well worth your time. In *Decision Model of Helping* you will take an interesting look at Latane and Darley's model of the decision making process involved in the determination of if one will help or not.

(2)   Why do people help? You have been given a thorough look into the answer. *EXPLORE: Why do People Help*, provides further explanation of four of the reasons regarding why people help. These four reasons include social norms, social learning, instinct, and empathy.

After You Read... Practice Test #1

_____1. Actions performed by individuals that help others with no immediate benefit to the helper are
  A.   social preferences.
  B.   prosocial behaviors.
  C.   antisocial actions.
  D.   social benefactors.

_____2. The saying, "It is better to give than to receive," can be used to explain the
  A.   prosocial competition model.
  B.   negative-state relief model.
  C.   competitive altruism model.
  D.   empathic joy hypothesis.

_____3. Kenneth is in a bad mood. He got his calculus test back today and found that he had made an F. On his way back to his dorm, he sees a stranger chasing after a dog who has apparently gotten off of his leash. Though in a bad mood, Kenneth begins to help the man chase down his dog and helps get him safely back on the leash. Kenneth is engaging in helping in an effort to ease his negative mood. This is best known as the
  A.   empathic joy hypothesis.
  B.   prosocial competition model.
  C.   negative-state relief model.
  D.   selective altruism hypothesis.

_____4. Pete and his girlfriend Ginny attended a rock concert last night. They were really enjoying themselves when they noticed a woman who had passed out. It was apparent to Pete and Ginny that others also noticed the woman. No one helped the woman. A social psychologist would explain this as
  A.   diffusion of responsibility.
  B.   diffusion of empathy.
  C.   empathic relief.
  D.   diffusion of trust.

_____5. It may seem like common sense, but in order to help someone
  A.   one has to notice that there is a need for help.
  B.   one has to be able to help the person.
  C.   one has to correctly interpret the situation as an emergency.
  D.   All of the above are correct.

_____6. An individual is part of a group and looks at the behavior of the other group members to determine if he or she should act. This is an example of
  A.   empathetic comparison.
  B.   pluralistic ignorance.
  C.   social diffusion.
  D.   Both A and B are correct.

_____7.   Larry likes Pam very much. On the other hand, Larry is not fond of Janet. According to your textbook, who is Larry most likely to help should they need it?
A.   Janet.
B.   Pam.
C.   He is equally likely to help Pam and Janet.
D.   Neither Pam nor Janet.

_____8.   If someone is in a negative mood he or she is
A.   less likely to help others if the action will generate negative feelings.
B.   more likely to help strangers.
C.   more likely to help others if the action will generate positive feelings.
D.   Both A and C are correct.

_____9.   Research indicates that people are more willing to help others if
A.   they are not tired.
B.   they have been spending time out of doors on a bright sunny day.
C.   they have just taken a bath.
D.   they have just finished eating a meal.

_____10.   What appears to be the greatest contributor to our degree of empathy?
A.   Our friends.
B.   Our relationship with those of the opposite sex.
C.   Our parents.
D.   Our entire social support network.

11.   An aspect of personality that involves distrust, cynicism, egocentricity, and the desire to manipulate and control others is _____.

12.   Generativity is defined as an adult's interest in and commitment to the wellbeing of

_____.

13.   Gregory has decided to spend his summer in New Orleans helping Habitat for Humanity build houses for the people who lost their homes in Hurricane Katrina. He wants to do something helpful for those who really need his help. Gregory's actions support the

_____ hypothesis.

14.   Terry is going to go with Gregory. Her motivation, though, is quite different. She wants to get into a popular sorority on campus and she feels that this will aid her in being asked to become a member in the fall. Terry is supporting the _____ approach.

15.   _____ is defined as a view that suggests that individuals may be willing to help because those who help often are themselves helped on a later occasion.

After You Read... Practice Test #2

_____1.   Research has investigated possible gender difference in the expression of empathy. Which of the following statements is correct?
   A.   Men express more empathy than women.
   B.   Women express more empathy than men.
   C.   Research has shown that there is actually no difference between men and women in the expression of empathy.
   D.   Which gender expresses the most empathy is dependent on the situation.

_____2.   Lillie had a rough childhood. Her parents were not the caring, warm parents that would have been optimal. Instead her parents tended to use anger to control her and her brother. According to Azar (1997a) and Carpenter (2001)
   A.   Lillie should have a high degree of empathy.
   B.   the parenting style should have no effect on her degree of empathy.
   C.   Lillie should have inhibited development of empathy.
   D.   None of the above.

_____3.   People who are considered to be the most altruistic describe themselves as
   A.   responsible and conforming.
   B.   intelligent and socially adept.
   C.   powerful and competitive.
   D.   trustworthy and reliable.

_____4.   Alicia and Rob are members of the school newspaper staff. Alicia is a person who can be relied upon to help in anyway she can. She is very reliable. Rob, on the other hand, is unreliable and is someone who never seems to be around when help is needed. According to Bierhoff, Klein and Kramp (1991)
   A.   Alicia is more likely than Rob to have an internal locus of control.
   B.   Alicia is more likely than Rob to have an external locus of control.
   C.   Alicia is probably very self-absorbed.
   D.   Rob is probably low in the construct of egocentrism.

_____5.   According to Pullium (1993)
   A.   people show less willingness to help people with AIDS if the patients acquired AIDS by engaging in homosexual acts.
   B.   people show more willingness to help people with AIDS if the patients acquired AIDS through a blood transfusion.
   C.   people show less willingness to help people with AIDS if the patients acquired AIDS by to sharing needles.
   D.   Both A and C are correct.

_____6.   Much of an individual's behavior is aimed at seeking that which provides the greatest satisfaction. This is the definition of
   A.   self-interest.
   B.   moral integrity.
   C.   social impact.
   D.   generativity.

_____7.   Lauren is a social work major. She is currently taking a course in gerontology. As a requirement of the course, Lauren is mandated to volunteer at a nursing home facility for 30 hours during the semester. According to your textbook, mandated volunteering
A.   tends to result in a large attrition rate in class numbers.
B.   tends to cause students to view volunteering as unfavorable.
C.   tends to result in a strong intention to volunteer their time even after the course is over.
D.   tends to result in a negative attitude towards volunteering.

_____8.   The capacity to experience others' emotional state, feeling sympathetic toward them, and taking their perspective is
A.   the definition of empathy.
B.   the definition of apathy.
C.   the definition of prosocial behavior.
D.   the definition of diffusion of responsibility.

_____9.   Ginny works at a local homeless shelter. She has contributed so much to the shelter in the form of volunteering that the city is going to give her an award as volunteer of the year. Ginny is very excited, but is most humble when told how admirable it is for her to give so much to the community. She feels that volunteering at the shelter is a reward in itself. Ginny's helping can be explained on the basis of
A.   the negative state relief model.
B.   the competitive altruism approach.
C.   selective altruism.
D.   the empathetic joy hypothesis.

_____10.   Which of the following statements is consistent with kin selection theory?
A.   We are more likely to help people we consider different from us than those we consider similar to us.
B.   We are more likely to help a cousin of ours than a complete stranger.
C.   We are less likely to help a relative with whom we are angry.
D.   None of the above is correct.

11.   _____ is a view that suggests that we may be willing to help people unrelated to us if the helping is reciprocated.

12.   If a person is similar to you with respect to age and nationality, we are _____ likely to help them.

13.   When a bystander who is in a good mood encounters an ambiguous emergency situation, they tend to interpret the situation as a _____.

14.   When someone is in a bad mood, they may be _____ likely to help if the helping act if the act might generate positive feelings.

15.   Perspective taking can involve a feeling of empathy for a fictional person. This type of perspective taking involves _____.

After You Read... Practice Test #3

_____1.   When someone states that she believes that we are all responsible for doing our best to help anyone who needs it, she is espousing the _____ characteristic of someone with a altruistic personality.
   A.   empathy
   B.   low egocentrism
   C.   belief in a just world
   D.   social responsibility

_____2.   Your textbook states that there are several aspects of personality that are related to prosocial behavior. The two that are delineated in your book are interpersonal trust and
   A.   altruism.
   B.   personal trust.
   C.   egocentrism.
   D.   machiavellianism.

_____3.   In the United States, Blacks are more likely than Whites to help
   A.   animals.
   B.   emergency personnel.
   C.   cultural enterprises.
   D.   the environment.

_____4.   Recruitment of volunteers is more successful if
   A.   there is an emphasis on multiple reasons to become involved.
   B.   there is an emphasis on a single, concentrate reason to become involved.
   C.   there is an emphasis on the amount of time the person will have to commit to the effort.
   D.   there is an emphasis on turnover rate.

_____5.   People who are high in generativity
   A.   perceive bad events as opportunities to create good outcomes.
   B.   engage in acts that will continue to have beneficial effects even beyond their own lifetime.
   C.   make efforts to contribute to the betterment of society.
   D.   All of the above are correct.

_____6.   Self-interest can be substituted with the word
   A.   moral integrity.
   B.   egoism.
   C.   moral honesty.
   D.   self-esteem.

_____7.   _____ is helping one particular individual even though it means neglecting others that may need your help.
   A.   Empathic joy
   B.   Selective altruism
   C.   Competitive altruism
   D.   Empathic understanding

_____8.   Not helping because you believe that someone else will help is called
    A.   social responsibility.
    B.   altruism.
    C.   competitive altruism.
    D.   diffusion of responsibility.

_____9.   In order to act on an event that calls for helping, we must <u>first</u>
    A.   interpret the event to be an emergency.
    B.   notice the event happening.
    C.   determine if it your responsibility to help.
    D.   decide to help.

_____10.   Bryan and Test (1967) found that motorists were much more likely to stop and help someone with car trouble if
    A.   they had previously seen someone with car trouble being helped.
    B.   they were in a good mood.
    C.   they were in a bad mood and wished to elevate their mood.
    D.   they knew they were going to be paid in some way for their help.

11.   _____ can be defined as the tendency of an individual surrounded by others to hesitate and do nothing in an emergency situation based on the assumption that someone else in the group will do something.

12.   In making the final decision about whether or not to help, we weigh both the _____ and the _____ aspects of helping.

13.   The _____theory suggests that we are more likely to help others to whom we are related than to others to whom we are not related.

14.   When there are multiple people in need of help, our helping response to the situation tends to _____.

15.   Helping is a positive form of social behavior. Aggression is a more _____ form of social behavior.

After You Read... Practice Test #4

_____1.   According to Anderson (1993), _____ outnumbered _____ two to one among those who helped the Jews during WWII.
A.   men, women
B.   boys, girls
C.   Christians, Jews
D.   Japanese, Chinese

_____2.   Receiving help may not always be a positive experience. One problem with being helped is that our _____ can suffer as a result.
A.   self-control.
B.   self-esteem.
C.   self-interest.
D.   self-conscious.

_____3.   By definition, _____ produces harm and _____produces benefits.
A.   punishment, rewards
B.   punishment, altruism
C.   altruism, empathy
D.   aggression, prosocial behavior

_____4.   Assess the following statement: The more witnesses present, the more likely it is that the victim will receive help.
A.   This statement is true in every situation.
B.   This statement is completely false.
C.   This statement is true, but only in certain situations.
D.   This statement is false. It should read: the less witnesses present, the less likely it is that someone will help.

_____5.   The second step in deciding whether or not we will help is
A.   correctly interpreting the situation as an emergency.
B.   noticing the situation.
C.   deciding if you have the skills to act appropriately.
D.   None of the above.

_____6.   The impact of negative emotions on helping can be
A.   both negative and positive.
B.   solely negative.
C.   solely positive.
D.   None of the above because negative emotions have no impact on helping behavior.

_____7.   Volunteering is a type of _____.
A.   apathy.
B.   prosocial behavior.
C.   egocentrism.
D,   None of the above is correct.

_____8.   The decision to volunteer is based on ALL of the following EXCEPT
            A.   the desire to enhance one's own development.
            B.   the change to gain related experience.
            C.   the desire to maintain close contact with those in need.
            D.   the need to improve one's own personal relationships.

_____9.   A _____ is defined as a group or society in which people will
            engage in mutual help, support and kindness.
            A.   social location
            B.   community
            C.   social standard
            D.   communal guide

_____10.   When one performs some type of helping behavior as a means of boosting his/her own
            status and reputation this is known as _____.
            A.   competitive altruism.
            B.   competitive empathy.
            C.   empathic joy.
            D.   status seeking behavior.

11.   The idea that someone responds to the needs of a victim because he or she wants to accomplish

       something and that helping, to this person, is a reward in itself is encompassed within the

       _____ hypothesis.

12.   When an individual helps one person even though there are others that need help, the person is

       engaging in _____.

13.   The two researchers who researched the diffusion of responsibility principle are Darley and

       _____.

14.   Research has shown that _____ of a social context by inducing people to

       think about the presence of others tends to reduce helping behavior in subsequent, unrelated

       situations.

15.   The more _____ a victim is to you, the more likely you will be to help.

When you have finished... Crossword Puzzle

Across

5.	An altruistic person tends to have an _____ locus of control

Down

1.	_____ trust is an aspect of personality related to helping behavior
2.	There are two components to empathy. They are a cognitive component and a
	_____ component
3.	An adult's interest in and commitment to the wellbeing of future generations
4.	_____ integrity refers to a form of motivation in which there is concern about the
	goodness and fairness of an act.

Created by Puzzlemaker at DiscoverySchool.com

When You have finished... You be the Researcher

This chapter deals with prosocial behavior. In particular, Chapter Nine involves a look at the prosocial behavior of helping others. Through your reading, you have become aware of why we tend to help, the external and internal influences on helping behavior, and the effects of being helped – to name just a few of the topics. In addition, you have been given information on the research of some of the premiere researchers on the topic of prosocial behavior.

Now, it is your turn. You will be the researcher. In this activity, you are to conduct a special type of observational research – the participant observation. A researcher conducts participant observation by actually interacting on some level with the participants. Even though you will be participating, conducting this study in an unobtrusive fashion is still necessary. As is common with all types of observational research in which you desire to view natural behavior, your participants are not to know that they are actually participating in a research study.

The procedure for this study is as follows:

(1)   You are to choose from the two topics listed below:

> A.   You are carrying a huge stack of books, they become quite cumbersome, and you drop them.
>
> B.   You are carrying a huge stack of books and you need to open a door.

(2)   Once you have chosen a topic, you are to create a hypothesis concerning the behavior that you are expecting to see. You may want to focus on the race of the helpers, the sex of the participants, or the approximate age of the participants. The last is approximate because you will not ask the participants their ages, you will simply guess as to their age or age group.

(3)   You will set up your scenario and will decide where you will collect your data. A good choice would be the student common. Here you should find ample opportunity for participants.

(4)   You will obtain your data. During the data collection period, you will have to rely on your memory for data storage. Therefore, you might want to take a break every now and then and write down the information before you forget it. The data you will be obtaining will involve sex, race, and age.

> You will want to have a brief period between trials. A trial is to be counted as each time a person helps. The reasoning behind taking a brief period between trials is that you do not want to have the same person help again.

(5)   Analyze your data and draw conclusions. Did you support or did you not gain support for your hypothesis? Why do you think this might be so?

(6)   Finally, you will provide a report in APA format to your professor. You also might want to include graphs to add emphasis.

Above all, have fun!!! At least this will get you out of the classroom for a while!!!

Answers - As You Read...Practice Activities

1. Prosocial behavior is defined as the actions of an individual that help others. There is no immediate benefit to the individual who is helping.

2. Empathy is defined as the capacity to be able to experience the emotional states of others, feel sympathy towards them and take their perspective.

   Empathy is unselfish in that we offer help with no extrinsic motivation. Empathy, though, can also be considered to be selfish in that we often gain intrinsic rewards – like feeling good about ourselves.

3. The empathy-altruism hypothesis suggests that some acts of prosocial behavior are motivated solely by the desire to help others and this desire outweighs all other considerations, including engaging in unpleasant, dangerous and life-threatening activity.

4. Basically, the negative state relief model states that we may engage in prosocial behavior in an effort to alleviate a negative mood or state.

5. The empathetic joy hypothesis states that the helper responds to the needs of the victim because he or she wants to accomplish something and, through the response of helping, the individual is getting rewarded.

   The researchers had participants watch a videotape in which a female college student stated that she was contemplating dropping out of college because she felt isolated and distressed. The student was described as being similar to the participant (high empathy) or dissimilar to the participant (low

empathy). After watching the tape, participants were asked to provide advice to the woman. Some of the participants were told that they would receive feedback concerning the effectiveness of their advice. Other participants were told they would not learn of the effectiveness of their advice.

Results showed that empathy by itself was not enough to produce a prosocial response. That is, individuals would only be helpful in the condition where there is high empathy and feedback about the impact of the advice on the victim.

6. The competitive altruism approach suggests that one reason individuals help others is because doing so enhances their status and reputation and, because of this, ultimately brings them great benefits.

   In 2006, Hardy and Van Vught had a group of high school students take part in a "public good dilemma." This was a game in which the participants could win money for themselves or for their group. At the beginning, participants were each given 100 pence and were told they could contribute a part of their money or the entire sum of their money to a private fund. The private fund would be kept by the individual. They could also contribute to a group fund, which was divided among the entire group. In condition one, the participants received information on the other players' contributions to both funds. They were also told that information regarding their own contributions would be made known to the others. This was known as the "reputation" condition. In condition two, the "no reputation" condition, participants received no information on the other players' choices. Therefore, in this condition acting in a prosocial way would not boost the donor's reputation and status.

In the reputation condition, the more each participant donated, the higher his or her status. In the no reputation condition prosocial behavior had no impact on status.

8. The reciprocal altruism theory suggested that we may be willing to help people who are not our relatives because helping is often reciprocated.

9. Kitty Genovese was assaulted by a man in an area where there were many people around to see and hear what was happening. The man assaulted Kitty for awhile, left, and then returned to continue the assault. No one reported the incident to the authorities. After learning of this incident, two social psychologists, John Darley and Bibb Latane, wanted to find out why no one intervened or even called the police.

10. Darley and Latane considered many possibilities, but settled with the idea that everyone assumed that someone else would do the helping so that is why they failed to help. This is referred to as diffusion of responsibility.

11. First, we must determine what is happening. Second, we must think about what we should do, if anything, about what is happening.

12. Darley and Batson (1973) conducted their study using students who were training to become clergy as participants. Participants were instructed to walk to a specific building on campus in order to give a presentation. The researchers created three conditions. (1) Told that they had extra time to get to the building where the presentation was to be delivered. (2) Told that they were on schedule with just enough time to get to the other building. (3) Told that they were late for the presentation and needed to rush. The idea was that group one would be the least occupied and the third would

be the most occupied. As they walked to the building, they came upon a staged emergency. A research assistant acting as a stranger appeared to be injured.

Results showed that the stranger was noticed by all of the students. Sixty-three percent of group I helped. Forty-five percent helped in group II. In group III, 9% helped the stranger.

13. Wilson and Petruska (1984) suggested that the presence of multiple witnesses may inhibit helping because it is embarrassing to misinterpret the situation and to act in an inappropriate fashion.

14. Joey was exhibiting the phenomenon of pluralistic ignorance in which the person does not help for fear of being ridiculed.

15. Rutkowski, Gruder and Romer found that the inhibiting effect is less if the group consists of friends as opposed to strangers.

Levin et al. found that people in small towns are more likely to help one another than those living in large cities.

Steele, Critchlow and Liu found that drinking alcohol tends to increase the tendency that one will help another.

16. When responsibility is not clear, we tend to assume that the person in charge or the leader will or must take responsibility.

17. The person who is contemplating helping another must have the capabilities to help. In the scenario, the nurse cannot lift Mr. O'Day by herself. She realizes that she does not have the capabilities to pick up Mr. O'Day.

18. The final step is that we must do a cost benefit analysis and weigh the pros and cons of helping.

19. 1. We are most likely to help those who are similar to us in age, nationality or some other factor.

     2. We are most likely to help those who are physically attractive.

     3. We are most likely to help those who hold values similar to our own.

20. We are more likely to help someone that we believe is NOT responsible for their situation.

21. You will, most likely, pay the money to get into the fair due to the fact that the physical presence of the money means that others have paid to get in.

22. Participants were six year olds. The children were divided into three groups. Group I was shown a *Lassie* episode in which there was a rescue scene. This was the model for the prosocial behavior. Group II watched a *Lassie* episode that did not contain a prosocial act. The third group watched an episode of *The Brady Bunch* which did not contain a prosocial act. After watching the shows, the children played a game in which the winner would receive a prize. During the game a group of whining, hungry puppies was brought into the room. The children were now faced with a dilemma, should they help the puppies and lose their chance to win the game or should they ignore the puppies and continue playing. The children who had watched the episode of helping stopped and helped the puppies more than did the other two groups.

23. Wilson (1981) found that people are more willing to help a stranger when their mood is elevated by listening to a comedian. Cunningham (1979) found that people are more willing to help a stranger when the weather outside is pleasant. Isen and Levin (1972) found that after finding money left in the coin slot in a pay telephone individuals were more likely to help a stranger. Finally, Baron (1990b) found that being exposed to a pleasant fragrance leads to be more inclined to help a stranger.

24. If one is in a good mood he or she will exhibit the tendency to resist helping if the actions are difficult or unpleasant (Rosenhan, Salovey, & Hargis, 1981). Simply put, if we are in a good mood, we do not want to do anything that will impinge upon that mood.

25. If the act of helping is likely to put Zack who is in a bad mood into a good mood, he may actually be more willing to help than if he were in a good or neutral mood. The theory behind this is the act of helping another may put Zack into a good mood.

26. Empathy is defined as emotional reactions that are focused towards others and include feelings of compassion, sympathy, and concern. It is, basically, putting yourself in someone else's shoes and feeling their pain.

27. The affective component is the feeling component. As humans who possess the quality of empathy, we have the tendency to feel the pain of others and can, therefore, understand and put ourselves in their place.

     The cognitive component includes the ability to consider another's viewpoint.

28. Perspective taking is defined as the ability to "put yourself into someone else's shoes." The three types of perspective taking include taking the "imagined other" perspective. In this perspective, one can imagine how another person perceives an event and how he or she might feel as a result.

     The second type is taking the "imagined self" perspective. Here one would imagine how they, themselves, would feel if they were in the situation.

The third type involves fantasy. This involves feeling empathy for a fictional character such as one in a book, a movie, etc.

29.   The research was conducted using two groups of male students in Germany. One of the groups had a German cultural background and the other group had a Muslim cultural background. The participants learned of a serious issue that was facing another person. Basically, the issue was that this person was out of money and had no place to live. This hypothetical person was represented either as a member of their own group or a member of another group. Participants then completed a measure of empathy toward the hypothetical person and were also asked to indicate the likelihood that they would help him.

The hypothesis was that empathy would encourage helping and that this would be stronger within groups that across groups. The hypothesis was supported by the data. Empathy and, therefore, helping increased when the person was in their in-group and diminished when the person was in their out-group.

30.   Janet Strayer theorized that we are born with the biological capacity for empathy and it is through experience that the determination is made as to whether or not this potential becomes part of our lives.

31.   Milulincer et al. found that having a secure attachment style facilitates empathy.

Azar found that empathy tends to develop if one's mother is a warm person, if both parents emphasize how others are affected by hurtful behavior and if there is open discussion in the

household where emotions can be discusses in a supportive atmosphere.

Coles, like Azar, emphasizes the role parents play in the development of empathetic behavior.

32.   Social exclusion is defined as being left out of social activities. Oftentimes when one is experiencing social exclusion, they do not, simply, have the resources to help others. Basically, they are busy helping themselves because being excluded is a very painful experience.

33.   When people receive help, there are times that the helping can cause their self-esteem to suffer. This appears to be especially true when the person who is being helped is of a lower status than the person who is helping.

Nadler and Halabi (2006) had Jewish Israelis and Arab Israelis as participants in their study. The participants were exposed to situations in which they received or did not receive help from members of their own group or the other group. The hypothesis was that people in the lower status group would be reluctant to receive help from the higher status group. In other words, the researchers expected the Arab Israelis who have lower status in Israel than do the Jewish Israelis would react negatively to help from the Jewish Israelis. The hypothesis in this study was supported by the data obtained.

34.   Two aspects of personality related to prosocial behavior include interpersonal trust and Machiavellianism. Interpersonal trust refers to how much one trusts others. Interpersonal trust is positively related to helping. Machiavellianism refers to an aspect of personality involving distrust, cynicism, egocentricity, and the desire to manipulate and control others.

Machiavellianism is negatively related to helping.

Someone with an altruistic personality would be someone who holds a high degree of empathy for others and also engages in a high amount of prosocial behavior.

1. empathy
2. belief in a just world.
3. social responsibility.
4. internal locus of control.
5. low egocentrism.

35. African Americans are more likely to aid someone who is homeless or hungry, groups fighting for minority rights and religious institutions. Caucasians are more likely to help animals, the environment, and emergency personnel such as police officers and fire fighters. Asian Americans are more likely to help museums and other artistic and cultural projects. Hispanic Americans are more likely to help immigrants and people from other countries.

36. People are less likely to experience empathy for an AIDS patient and less willingness to help when the patient has engaged in homosexual acts or shared needles than when the patient received the disease from a blood transfusion.

37. Generativity is defined as an adult's interest in and commitment to the wellbeing of future generations.

People who are high in generativity show their interest in the wellbeing of future generations by becoming parents, by teaching young students and by engaging in acts that will have positive effects beyond their own lifetimes. They also have a high need to help others, possess moral values that give purpose to their lives, perceive bad events as opportunities to create good outcomes, and make an effort to

contribute to the progressive development of a better society.

38. As human beings we tend to overestimate our own moral actions and we also tend to believe that we are more likely to engage in selfless and kind behavior than are most people.

39. The three motives are self-interest, moral integrity, and moral hypocrisy. Self-interest means that a lot of our behavior is directed towards seeking whatever gives us the most pleasure. Moral integrity means that we tend to care about goodness and fairness when we act and often accept some self-sacrifice in order to do that which is right. Self-hypocrisy is when we just appear to be doing the right or moral thing. In reality, we are actually driven by self-interest and self-motivation. That is, with self-hypocrisy, we are more concerned with appearance than the actual helping process.

40. Aggression is defined as intentional efforts to harm others in some way.

Most people would be very quick to say that prosocial behavior and aggression are, indeed, polar opposites. Social psychologists suggest, though, that they are not polar opposites. In fact, they tend to overlap. First, one must consider the motives behind the actions. The apparent motivation for helping is to do something good for the recipient.

Aggression is to do something bad or harmful to the recipient. Sometimes, though, the motivation of helping is more selfish than selfless. Helping sometimes becomes a means by which to gain a positive reputation.

Acts of aggression which are above noted to do harm to the victim can actually serve a positive purpose – such as the example in the textbook of the coach who makes the player run laps.

These actions are actually taken to help the athlete be a better athlete.

As far as the effects of aggression and prosocial behavior, the short term effects of aggression may seem harmful, but in the long term picture, they may actually be helpful. Likewise, prosocial acts may at first seem beneficial, but may later prove to be harmful.

There is also evidence that aggression and prosocial behavior are sometimes used by the same individuals to gain popularity and status.

Answers – Practice Test #1

1.   B
2.   D
3.   C
4.   A
5.   D
6.   B
7.   B
8.   D
9.   B
10.   C
11.   Machiavellianism
12.   future generations
13.   empathic altruism
14.   competitive altruism
15.   reciprocal altruism

Answers – Practice Test #2

1.   B
2.   C
3.   A
4.   A
5.   D
6.   A
7.   C
8.   A
9.   D
10.   B

In other words, the answer to the question posed is "no."

Answers – Cross Word Puzzle

Across

5.   internal

Down

1.   interpersonal
2.   affective
3.   generativity
4.   moral
11.   reciprocal altruism theory
12.   more
13.   nonemergency
14.   more
15.   fantasy

Answers – Practice Test #3

1.   D
2.   D
3.   C
4.   A
5.   D
6.   B
7.   B
8.   D
9.   B
10.   A
11.   diffusion of responsibility
12.   positive; negative
13.   kin selection
14.   decrease
15.   negative

Answers – Practice Test #4

1.	A
2.	B
3.	D
4.	B
5.	A
6.	A
7.	B
8.	C
9.	B
10.	A
11.	empathic joy
12.	selective altruism
13.	Latane
14.	priming
15.	similar

CHAPTER 10

AGGRESSION:
ITS NATURE, CAUSES, AND CONTROL

Before You Read...Chapter Summary

Chapter Ten begins with a discussion of some of the theoretical perspectives through which psychologists tend to view aggression. These perspectives include biological theories, drive theories and other, more modern, theories of aggression. In this section, you will learn that the oldest theory of aggression is that of the biological perspective which states that we are preprogrammed, by the transmission of genes from parent to child, to act aggressively. You will also learn about a particular drive theory known as the frustration – aggression hypothesis. Finally, as this section closes, you will gain knowledge of the social learning perspective.

The next section of this chapter begins with an explanation of some of the causes of aggression. These causes include social, cultural, personal, and situational factors. Within this section, you will be provided with a discussion of the frustration aggression hypothesis and will discover that there are two kinds of provocation that may lead to aggression condescension and teasing. In an extensive portion of this section, there is a lengthy discussion of the connection between exposure to media violence and the performance of aggressive acts. This discussion involves an explanation of the research of Dr. Bandura, a psychologist famous for his work investigating the role media violence plays in the acquisition of aggression. Later in this chapter, you will find an explanation of two behavior patterns A and B and their relationship to aggression. This section ends with a discussion of heat and alcohol as determinants of aggression.

Have you ever wondered why people engage in bullying and if there are gender differences in bullying behavior? Well, within this section, you will find your answer. In addition, you will learn about workplace aggression: What it is? What forms of aggression actually take place in the workplace? And, what are the causes of workplace aggression? In the final section of Chapter Ten, you will find a discussion of catharsis as a possible way to reduce aggression. Finally, there is a brief discussion of the topic of forgiveness.

Before You Read... Learning Objectives

After reading this chapter, you should be able to:

- Discuss the role biology plays in aggression.
- Elucidate drive theories as explanations for aggressive behavior.
- Explain the social learning perspective.
- Discuss the GAM model as an account of the foundations of human aggression.
- Expound upon some of the causes of human aggression, including social, cultural, persona, and situational factors.
- Explain the frustration – aggression hypothesis.
- Discuss provocation as a cause of aggression.
- Explain how and why repeated exposure to media violence can lead to aggression.
- Give details of Bandura's work involving observational learning.
- Explain the term desensitization and the conditions under which it occurs.
- Discuss the role violent pornography can play in the induction of aggressive behavior.
- Answer the question, "What is a culture of honor?"
- Discuss how heat and alcohol can affect our tendency to aggress.
- Give details on the topics of bullying and workplace aggression.
- Understand what is meant by "abusive supervision."
- Discuss why we punish aggression.
- Explain the circumstances under which punishment works best.
- Define and explain catharsis.
- Explain forgiveness as a means of reducing aggression.

As You Read...Term Identification

Important Terms to Know
Below are a list of some of the key terms and concepts from this chapter. Make flashcards in order to enhance your recall ability of these terms. Refer to the definitions that are either in boldface or in the margins of this chapter for help. You may also want to include additional terms from this chapter as you deem necessary.

aggression, (p. 338)	cultures of honor, (p. 352)	bullying, (p. 364)
thanatos, (p. 338)	sexual jealousy, (p. 354)	workplace violence, (p. 365)
drive theories, (p. 339)	TASS model (p. 356)	workplace aggression, (p. 366)
frustration aggression hypothesis, (p. 340)	type A behavior pattern, (p. 357)	effect danger ratio, (p. 366)
social learning perspective, (p. 340)	type B behavior pattern, (p. 357)	punishment. (p. 368)
general aggression model, (p. 340)	hostile aggression, (p. 357)	self regulation, (p. 370)
frustration, (p. 343)	instrumental aggression, (p. 357)	forgiveness, (p. 371)
provocation, (p. 344)	narcissism, (p. 358)	catharsis hypothesis, (p. 372)
teasing, (p. 345)	sensation seeking, (p. 358)	
excitation transfer theory, (p. 346)	bistrategic controllers, (p. 360)	

As You Read…Practice Activities

PERSPECTIVES ON AGGRESSION: IN SEARCH OF THE ROOTS OF VIOLENCE

Aggression…Do We "Learn" it – or is it Occur "Naturally?"
(Introduction, pages 338-339)

1.   Wayne is what his teachers call "highly aggressive." He has difficulty sitting still in class, frequently gets involved in (or initiates) fights on the playground, picks on other students, and is often belligerent in class.

One of the oldest theories that would suggest an explanation for Wayne's behavior was espoused by Sigmund Freud. What, exactly, would Freud consider to be a reason for Wayne's behavior?

_____

_____

_____

A similar view on aggression was promoted by Konrad Lorenz. How would Lorenz explain Wayne's behavior?

_____

_____

_____

Same Subject – Different Perspective…
(Introduction, page 339)

2.   For years, social psychologists have challenged Freud and Lorenz's views on aggression. Recently, the evolutionary perspective of psychology supplied its own interpretation of human aggression. What is the view on aggression from an evolutionary standpoint? That is, compare and contrast the evolutionary perspective to the perspective held by Freud and Lorenz that aggression is innate.

_____

_____

_____

_____

_____

And Another...
(Drive Theories: The Motive to Harm Others, page 339-340)

3.　　A third type of theory as to why human have the propensity towards aggression is known as the *drive theory*. Basically, these theories suggest that human aggression comes from an externally educed drive to do harm to another individual. One of the external factors that can, according to the drive theories, bring out the human tendency to behavior in an aggressive fashion is frustration.

　　　　One of the most well-known drive theories was provided by Dollar et al. (1939). Name and discuss this theory.

_____

_____

_____

_____

_____

Albert Bandura – A Psychology "Classic"...
(Modern Theories of Aggression, page 340)

4.　　In 1997, Albert Bandura, recipient of the 2004 Outstanding Lifetime Contribution to Psychology award as given by the American Psychological Association, proposed a theory known as The Social Learning Perspective.

　　　　Describe this perspective and what individuals tend to learn through the process.

_____

_____

_____

_____

_____

_____

GAM – The General Aggression Model...
(Modern Theories of Aggression, pages 340-341)

5.　　Discuss Anderson's (1999) general aggression model (GAM). In your discussion, make sure that you offer definitions for situational variables and personal variables.

_____

GAM – The General Aggression Model...Continued

_____

_____

_____

CAUSES OF HUMAN AGGRESSION: SOCIAL, CULTURAL, PERSONAL, AND SITUATIONAL

Frustration is a Precursor to Aggression...
(Frustration: Why Not Getting What you Want (or What you Expect) can Sometimes Lead to Aggression, pages 343-344)

6.   One reason we behave aggressively is frustration. Your textbook defines frustration as a feeling that one tends to experience when he or she is prevented from getting what he or she wants or is expecting.

Now that you know the definition of frustration and are aware of the definition of aggression, describe the frustration aggression hypothesis.

_____

_____

_____

What was the later assessment of this hypothesis?

_____

_____

_____

I am Very Frustrated. If you Provoke Me, You Might Be Sorry...
(Direct Provocation: When Aggression (or Even Teasing) Breeds Aggression, page 344)

7.   What is direct provocation?

_____

How does direct provocation apply to aggression?

_____

_____

Two Types of Provocation…
(Direct Provocation: When Aggression (or Even Teasing) Breeds Aggression, page 344)

8.   There are two types of provocation discussed within your textbook - condescension and teasing. Define both terms.

_____

_____

_____

_____

Yes, I am Mad at You; But…I am Going to Kick the Fence That Just Stepped out in Front of My Car Instead…
(Heightened Arousal: Emotion, Cognition, and Aggression, page 346)

9.   Explain the concept of transferal of aggression from one target or situation to another.

_____

_____

Why does this appear to happen?

_____

_____

The Media's Contribution…
(Exposure to Media Violence, page 347)

10.   Does exposure to violence increase aggression in children and/or adults? Research into this question has determined that there are three basic conclusions regarding this issue.

What are the conclusions? Describe each.

1. _____

_____

2. _____

_____

3. _____

_____

The Long and Short of It...
(Exposure to Media Violence, page 347)

11. Dr. Morrison's psychology class is going to help him collect some data on his study investigating the effect of "gangsta" rap on violence in adolescent boys. Dr. Morrison is giving them a short introduction into two types of research that are often used in collection of data on media violence. What are the two types of research he is describing? Name and discuss each type.

1. _____

_____

_____

2: _____

_____

_____

A Classic...
(Bandura's Famous "Bobo Doll" Studies: Televised Violence Visits the Laboratory, pages 348-349)

12. Dr. Bandura conducted one of the "classic" studies in psychology, the "Bobo Doll" Study. Discuss this research and the results. Also provide a discussion of the work of Liebert and Baron (1972).

_____

_____

_____

_____

_____

_____

Making a Connection...
(Bandura's Famous "Bobo Doll" Studies: Televised Violence Visits the Laboratory, pages 113-114)

13.   Within the past few years, numerous children have been injured and even killed at the hands of other children. One reason for this, according to some of the children, is that they were "practicing" wrestling "moves" that they saw on television.

Your task is to discuss the connection between the research of Dr. Bandura and the statistics concerning the possibility that these children did, indeed, learn these "moves" from television viewing.

_____

_____

_____

_____

_____

_____

Okay...But, Why?
(The Effects of Media Violence: Why do They Occur? pages 348-349)

14.   Let's answer that question. According to the research of Bushman and Anderson (2002), just WHY do they occur?

_____

_____

And...Yes, There is Another...
(The Effects of Media Violence: Neuroscience Evidence for the Impact of Desensitization, pages 350-351)

15.   Another factor has been used to explain the connection between the media and aggression. What is this factor and how might it explain this obvious connection?

_____

_____

_____

_____

Event-Related Brain Potential, in Particular P300 Waves, and Desensitization...
(The Effects of Media Violence: Neuroscience Evidence for the Impact of Desensitization, pages 350-351)

16.   Tina was a participant in the study conducted by Bartholow, Bushman, and Sestir in 2006. One thing that she distinctly remembers from the study is that she had to be, in her words, "hooked up to a machine." It turns out the "machine" was an EEG machine and she was "hooked up" to it to record her brain wave activity. In particular, the researchers were assessing P300 brain waves.

    What appears to be the connection between P300 brain waves and aggression?

    _____

    _____

    _____

Watching Violence May be Hazardous to Your Health...
(The Effects of Media Violence: Neuroscience Evidence for the Impact of Desensitization, pages 350-351)

17.   How does exposure to violence in movies, on television, or in video games increase the tendency to act aggressively towards others? Discuss the two reasons delineated within this chapter.

    _____

    _____

    _____

Pornography and Aggression – A Potent Mix (No Pun Intended)...
(Violent Pornography: When Sex and Aggression Mix – and Perhaps Explode! Page 351)

18.   I am sure you know someone who would have absolutely LOVED to be a participant in this study. I know I do! Discuss the research of Linz, Donnersiem, and Penrod (1998) regarding the strong connection between pornography and aggression.

    _____

    _____

    _____

    _____

"Half the ho's hate me, half them love me. The ones that hate me only hate me 'cause they ain't f... me. And they say I'm lucky. Do you think I've got time to f... all these ho's?"
- Ja Rule, "Livin' It Up"
(The Effects of Sexually Aggressive Song Lyrics, page 352)

19. The lyrics above are from Ja Rule's *Living It Up*. It does not take a rocket scientist to see that this "song" is not only sexually explicit, it is also sexually degrading/aggressive. Research has shown that it is not only watching violence that can lead to aggression, but that it is also listening to violence/aggression in songs.

    Describe the research of Fischer and Greitmeyer (2006) investigating the effect of violent song lyrics and aggression.

    _____

    _____

    _____

    _____

Culture is an Important Factor...We are Truly Victims of our Environment...
(Cultural Factors in Aggression: "Cultures of Honor" and Sexual Jealousy, pages 352-353)

20. First define the meaning of the term cultural factors.

    _____

    _____

    What is a culture of honor?

    _____

    _____

    Now, answer the question. Why did the norms associated with the culture of honor develop?

    _____

    _____

    _____

    _____

I'm Jealous...
(Sexual Jealousy: One Key Effect of Concern with One's Honor, page 354)

21.   In cultures of honor (as discussed above), is jealousy truly as powerful a determinant of aggression as researchers have found it to be? Answer this with a discussion of the findings of the research of Vandello and Cohen (1997, 2003).

_____

_____

_____

Are You Showing Your TASS??
(Personality and Aggression: Why Some People are More Aggressive Than Others, pages 356-357)

22.   Describe the TASS model and explain how the TASS model relates to aggression. Make sure you discuss the work of Marshall and Brown (2006) in your answer.

_____

_____

_____

_____

_____

_____

Are You an "A" or a "B?"
(Personality and Aggression: Why Some People are More Aggressive Than Others, page 357)

23.   Two distinct behavior patterns are seen in humans. One is termed the type ":A" behavior pattern and the other is termed the type "B" behavior pattern. What are some of the characteristics of a type "A" person? A type "B" person?

Type A:_____

_____

Type B:_____

_____

Are You an "A" or a "B?"...Continued

Which type of behavior pattern do you have? How do you know?

_____

_____

Hostile versus Instrumental...Do You Know the Difference?
(The Type A Behavior Pattern: Why the A in Type A Could Stand for Aggression, page 357)

24.   What is the difference between hostile aggression and instrumental aggression?

_____

_____

_____

How do these two types of aggression related to type A and type B behavior patterns?

_____

_____

_____

"It is Not Love that Should be Depicted as Blind, But Self-Love." - Voltaire
(Narcissism, Ego-Threat and Aggression: On the Dangers of Wanting to be Superior, page 358)

25.   I love myself! I am the best! I am better than anyone and that includes you! Narcissism is truly an interesting (and, perhaps, annoying) thing. In simple terms, one could say that a narcissist is "full of his or herself." Give a more formal definition for the term _narcissism_. Also, explain why people who are narcissists tend to respond with high levels of aggression to insults or snubs from others.

_____

_____

_____

_____

For it is Sensation we seek...
(Sensation Seeking and Aggression, pages 358-359)

26.   In your own words, describe a sensation seeking personality.

_____

For it is Sensation we seek...Continued

Sensation seeking is very closely related to aggression. Discuss the two theories on why this might be true.

_____

_____

_____

_____

_____

As is Typically Thought – Are Men Really More Aggressive Than Women?
(Gender Differences in Aggression, pages 359-360)

27.   Research has shown that there are truly differences between males and females in the amount and degree of aggression that they exhibit. The size of theses differences tend to vary across situations. Explain the last sentence of the paragraph above by citing research evidence.

_____

_____

_____

_____

_____

_____

_____

_____

SITUATIONAL DETERMINANTS OF AGGRESSION: THE EFFECTS OF HEAT AND ALCOHOL

Okay, It Is 105 Degrees Outside – Wouldn't You be a Little Aggressive??
(In the Heat of Anger: Temperature and Aggression, pages 360-361)

28. Sam, a semi-professional boxer, lives in the "deep" south. Today the temperature in his hometown is going to approach 110 degrees. In other words, it is going to be "hot."
     Use your critical thinking skills along with research evidence and answer the following question: If Sam is going to fight in a boxing match this afternoon, how will he do?

_____

_____

_____

Alcohol and Aggression – A Positive Correlation; But, Not a Good Mix...
(Alcohol and Aggression: A Potentially Dangerous Mix, pages 361-363)

29. Recent findings have shown that the effects of alcohol on aggression may be the end result of reduced cognitive functioning and its effect on our social perception. Bartholow et al. (2003) conducted a study that supports this idea. Discuss the findings of Bartholow et al.'s study.

_____

_____

Hey...You Don't Even Have To Drink It For It To Produce an Effect!
(Alcohol and Aggression: A Potentially Dangerous Mix, pages 361-363)

30. Research has shown that even in the mere presence of things that are associated with the consumption of alcohol, alcohol's effect on aggressive tendencies is seen. Discuss the research of Bartholow and Heinz (2006) who investigated this phenomenon.

_____

_____

_____

_____

AGGRESSION IN ONGOING RESEARCH: BULLYING AND AGGRESSION AT WORK

Bullying: Hard to Accept at Any Age, But, Especially Hard on Children...
(Bullying: Singling Out Others for Repeated Abuse, page 364)

31.   Emily is a very tiny woman. If you were to ask her about her experiences in school prior to entering college, she would tell you that her experiences were "awful." Emily was constantly being made fun of because she was so tiny and petite.

   Today, as an adult, Emily has learned that the saying, "Sticks and stones can break my bones, but words will never harm me," is true. In other words, she has risen above allowing others to impact her when they make fun of her or, in other words, bully her.

   Define the term *bullying*.

   _____

   _____

   Why do people engage in bullying?

   _____

   _____

   _____

   _____

Bullies as Bullies, Victims as Victims, and Bullies as Victims...
(The Characteristics of Bullies and Victims, pages 364-365)

32.   Individuals who are the bullies in one setting may be the victim in another. There are three patterns that have been shown. What are these three patterns? Name and discuss each of the patterns.

   1. _____

   _____

   2. _____

   _____

   3. _____

   _____

Can Bullying Be Stopped – or – At the Very Least - Reduced?
(Reducing the Occurrence of Bullying, page 365)

33.   Your textbook delineates four things that can be done to reduce bullying. Name each of these.

1. _____

_____

2. _____

_____

3. _____

_____

4. _____

_____

This Brings to Mind The Idiom, "Going Postal"…
(Workplace Aggression: Harming Others at Work, pages 365-366)

34.   In your own words, define workplace violence.

_____

_____

What are two facts that one might want to keep in mind regarding workplace violence?

1. _____

_____

2. _____

_____

Violence vs. Aggression – What a Fight!
(Workplace Aggression: Harming Others at Work, pages 355-356)

35.   What is the difference between workplace violence and workplace aggression?

_____

_____

_____

You Seem to Be Expressing Your Hostility…
(Workplace Aggression: Harming Others at Work, pages 365-366)

36.   Your textbook discusses the term expression of hostility. How does the textbook define this
        term?

_____

_____

_____

What are the three types of expression of hostility to which your book speaks?

1. _____

_____

2. _____

_____

3. _____

_____

Have You Ever Wondered What Causes Workplace Aggression? Well, Now You Know!
(Workplace Aggression: Harming Others at Work, page 365-366)

37.   There are numerous factors that can play a role in workplace aggression. One of these factors,
        though, has surfaced over and over again in research findings of studies investigating this subject.
        What is this one factor?

_____

_____

_____

What are some other factors that play a role in workplace aggression?

_____

_____

_____

The Abusive Boss...
(Abusive Supervisor: Bosses Who Make Workplaces Unbearable, pages 367-368)

38.   Jamie recently became employed at a company that produces computer software. Even though she is new to the company, she was yelled at yesterday by her boss because she failed to do a check of the output prior to leaving for the day. Jamie feels that since she is new, there should be a little bit of patience for her as she learns the ins and outs of her job. In her mind, everyone makes mistakes and her boss was, in her words, "out of line" for shouting at her.

What is the term that describes how Jamie was treated?

_____

Why do bosses do this to their employees?

_____

_____

_____

THE PREVENTION AND CONTROL OF AGGRESSION: SOME USEFUL TECHNIQUES

"Only a Man Who Has Enough Good in Him to Feel the Justice of the Penalty can be Punished; The Others can Only be Hurt" – William Ernest Hocking
(Punishment: Just Desserts or Deterrence, pages 368-370)

39.   In your own words, what is punishment?

_____

_____

Your textbook describes one form of punishment – capital punishment. What exactly is capital punishment?

_____

_____

Why do some societies punish aggressive acts?

1. _____

_____

2. _____

_____

3. _____

_____

How Effective is it to Punish Aggression?
(Punishment: Just Desserts or Deterrence, page 368-370)

40.   Provide an answer to the following questions: "Does punishment tend to work? And, if so, when?

_____

_____

_____

_____

Can We Control Aggression on Our Own?
(Self-Regulation: Internal Mechanisms for Controlling Aggression, pages 370-371)

41.   Define self-regulation and explain why, even with self-regulation, aggression erupts.

_____

_____

_____

_____

_____

THE SCIENCE OF SOCIAL PSYCHOLOGY: MAKING SENSE OF COMMON SENSE

There are Times in Which We, Simply, Have to "Blow off Steam" Before We Burst!
(Catharsis: Does "Blowing off Steam" Really Help? page 373)

42.   Quinn is majoring in physics and often puts tremendous pressure on himself to do well in his "core" courses. The other day, Quinn was really feeling the pressure. To calm this down a bit, Quinn got into his car, drove to the interstate, turned the radio up as high as it would go, rolled down the windows and just drove. This is a way that Quinn learned to calm himself down so that he can go back to his studies and continue working on his goals.

   In your own words, define the word *catharsis*.

   _____

   _____

   Does catharsis work in reducing aggression?

   _____

To Forgive – Divine...
(Forgiveness: Compassion Instead of Revenge, page 373)

43.   Define forgiveness.

   _____

   _____

   _____

   _____

   How does forgiveness work?

   _____

   _____

   _____

After You Read... MyPsychLab Connection

---

(1)   Are you interested in the "Bobo" doll experiment? Actual footage of the original experiment is seen at *WATCH: Archival Footage of the Bandura Study.* This is well-worth the one minute and one second you will spend!!

(2)   The date is April 20, 1999. In the small town of Littleton, Colorado, two seniors at Columbine High School, Dylan Klebold and Eric Harris, set forth with a plan to kill hundreds of their peers. When the massacre was over, twelve students, one teacher, and the two boys were dead. *WATCH: Students Discuss Columbine.*

(3)   *WATCH: Road Rage* for a frank discussion of the phenomenon. Begins with a very powerful discussion of the death of a woman, Pam, due to road rage. Pam had been shot through the heart.

(4)   John Murray, PhD. discusses three different kinds of effects of viewing TV violence. They are aggression, desensitization and fear. Dr. Murray explains these three constructs in *WATCH: Television Violence.*

After You Read... Practice Test #1

_____1.   Sigmund Freud, one of psychology's "classics", believed that aggression arises, for the most part, from a powerful death wish. Freud referred to this death wish as
    A.   libido.
    B.   thanatos.
    C.   the Id.
    D.   the Super Ego.

_____2.   Konrad Lorenz, an ethologist, believed that aggression comes mainly from an inherited instinct. Lorenz referred to this instinct as a(n) _____ instinct.
    A.   basic
    B.   aggressive
    C.   fighting
    D.   anger

_____3.   The instinct mentioned above, according to Konrad Lorenz, assures that the strongest males will have mates and that they
    A.   will engage in aggressive behavior on a consistent basis.
    B.   will die at an older age than if they did not have mates.
    C.   will raise their children in an aggressive fashion.
    D.   will pass their genes to the next generation.

_____4.   From a(n) _____ perspective, humans reproduce to provide for continuance of the species.
    A.   biological
    B.   social
    C.   behavioral
    D.   evolutionary

_____5.   According to research findings, males tend to be more aggressive towards
    A.   males than females.
    B.   strangers than friends.
    C.   those of low social status versus those of high social status.
    D.   non-attractive females than attractive females.

_____6.   Because aggression appears to stem from an innate drive
    A.   all humans are predisposed to being aggressive and must follow that predisposition.
    B.   only those humans who have this drive will aggress.
    C.   aggression is something that is learned.
    D.   all humans have the potential to be aggressive.

_____7.   Drive theories
    A.   propose that external conditions provoke us to act in an aggressive fashion.
    B.   postulate that frustration, especially, influences our tendency to aggress.
    C.   believe that the activation of the aggressive drive often leads to overt acts of aggression.
    D.   All of the above are correct.

_____8.   Dollard et al. (1939) developed the _____ hypothesis.
      A.   aggression frustration
      B.   frustration aggression
      C.   inborn drive
      D.   aggression non aggression

_____9.   Albert Bandura is well-known for his theory on aggression. This theory is known as the
      A.   social learning perspective.
      B.   aggression through learning perspective.
      C.   observational learning perspective.
      D.   societal aggression perspective.

_____10.   According to Bandura's theory, human beings
      A.   are born with an innate propensity towards aggression.
      B.   are creatures of their biology.
      C.   acquire aggressive responses through direct experience or by observing others.
      D.   engage in aggression more than 1/3 of their lives.

11.   _____ is defined as the delivery of aversive consequences.

12.   _____ is defined as giving up the desire to punish someone who has hurt us, and, instead, seeking to act in a kind, helpful way towards them.

13.   According to Sigmund Freud, we have a powerful instinct, _____, that is initially aimed towards self-destruction, but is soon thereafter directed outward towards others.

14.   The _____ postulates that frustration leads to the arousal of a drive whose primary goal is to harm another individual or an object.

15.   Bandura espoused the _____ perspective of aggression.

After You Read... Practice Test #2

_____1.　The General Aggression Model (Anderson, 1997; Anderson & Bushman, 2000) theorizes that
A.　aggression cannot be divided into different types.
B.　aggression can be divided into 4 different types of aggression.
C.　the chain of events that may lead to the performance of aggressive acts is initiated by two factors – situational and personal.
D.　the chain of events that may lead to the performance of aggressive acts is initiated by one single factor – the situation.

_____2.　According to the General Aggression Model, the factors that lead to overt displays of aggression do so through their impact on all of the following except
A.　cognitions.
B.　affective states.
C.　physiological arousal.
D.　social factors.

_____3.　The frustration aggression hypothesis
A.　postulates that all frustration leads to aggression.
B.　postulates that only a high degree of frustration lead to aggression.
C.　postulates that aggression only stems from frustration if the frustration is due to a personal attack.
D.　postulates that aggression is very rarely due to frustration.

_____4.　Direct provocation
A.　can be either verbal or physical.
B.　according to research, after frustration, is the second strongest cause of aggression.
C.　can be either verbal or physical; but, most often is verbal.
D.　has very little effect on our tendency to aggress.

_____5.　"Expressions of arrogance or disdain on the part of others" is an appropriate definition for
A.　teasing.
B.　condescension.
C.　aggressive egotism.
D.　retaliation.

_____6.　Research investigating teasing behavior has shown that
A.　teasing does not have to hostile; it can be done in a playful fashion.
B.　teasing can range from mild to that which is aimed at purposeful harm.
C.　teasing is a form of provocation.
D.　All of the above are correct.

_____

7.   In individualist cultures, such as the United States
   A.   individuals respond more positively to teasing than individuals in collectivist cultures.
   B.   individuals response more negatively to teasing than individuals in collectivist cultures.
   C.   individuals are more capable of ignoring teasing than individuals in collectivist cultures.
   D.   individuals show no more negative or positive response than individuals in collectivist cultures.

_____8.   The idea that once one is physiologically aroused by anger, the anger may persist as the individual moves from one situation to another is termed
   A.   anger transferal theory.
   B.   arousal theory.
   C.   physiological transfer theory.
   D.   excitation transfer theory.

_____9.   From research findings, it appears that exposure to media violence
   A.   tends to produce short-term effects.
   B.   is relatively small in its effect.
   C.   increases the likelihood of aggressive behavior.
   D.   increases the likelihood of aggressive behavior only if the exposure occurs over a long period of time.

_____10.   Albert Bandura's famous study on the effect of exposure to violence and the tendency to aggress in children involved
   A.   all children viewing TV shows portraying hostile aggression between two individuals.
   B.   two conditions in which some of the children viewed an individual performing aggressive acts towards another individual and others viewed an individual performing no aggressive acts.
   C.   all children viewing TV shows portraying hostile aggression between one individual and a "Bobo" doll.
   D.   two conditions in which some of the children viewed an individual performing aggressive acts towards a "Bobo" doll and others viewed an individual not performing aggressive acts.

11.   The General Aggression Model situational and personal variables lead to overt aggression through their impact on three basic processes: _____, _____, and _____.

12.   Expressions of arrogance or disdain on the part of others is the definition for

_____.

13.   Direct provocation can be either _____ or _____.

14.   Research in which the same participants are studied for an extended period of time is known as

_____.

15.   The _____ expectation bias is defined as a strong expectation that others will behave aggressively.

After You Read... Practice Test #3

_____1.   When an individual is exposed to large amounts of violence on a consistent basis
   A.   they become less sensitive to the violence.
   B.   they become less sensitive to the consequences of the violence.
   C.   they become desensitized to the violence.
   D.   All of the above are correct.

_____2.   It appears that exposure to violent pornography
   A.   can decrease men's willingness to aggress against women because men tend to vicariously participate through their exposure.
   B.   when viewed on a consistent basis, can desensitize those individuals who watch such programming.
   C.   tends to increase one's emotional reactions to the sexual mistreatment of others.
   D.   leads both males and females to doubt the rape myth, which states that women "ask" to be raped.

_____3.   There is a strong connection between exposure to media violence and performance of aggressive acts. According to researchers who have investigated the connection between violence in the lyrics of songs and aggression, this connection
   A.   exists only in individuals under 40 years of age.
   B.   exists only in males over the age of 10.
   C.   exists in both males and females.
   D.   exists in males over 10 years of age and females over 14 years of age.

_____4.   Songs that express negative attitudes and describe sexual aggression towards women
   A.   are called "misogynous" songs.
   B.   increase aggression by males against females.
   C.   increase aggression by females against males.
   D.   Both A and B are correct.

_____5.   The _____ model suggests that there are aspects of our personality that tend to function in a threshold-like manner and that once this threshold is reached these aspects of our personality influence our behavior.
   A.   generalized susceptibility
   B.   trait activation situational system
   C.   traits as situational sensitivities
   D.   trait establishment

_____6.   Wendell is very driven. In addition, he is very competitive and always appears to be in a hurry. Wendell is displaying
   A.   a type B behavior pattern.
   B.   stress.
   C.   a type A behavior pattern.
   D.   an abnormal behavior pattern.

_____7.   Someone with a type _____ behavior pattern is more likely to display hostile aggression.
            A.   A
            B.   B
            C.   Both are equally likely to display hostile aggression.
            D.   Neither behavior pattern has shown a direct link to hostile aggression.

_____8.   Which of the following is false about individuals who are high in sensation seeking?
            A.   They are often attracted to aggression - eliciting situations.
            B.   They are less likely to focus on the immediate consequences of their behavior.
            C.   They are more likely to display anger and aggression.
            D.   All of the above are true.

_____9.   Research studies that have investigated the relationship between temperature and aggression have found that
            A.   temperature and aggression are not related.
            B.   the lower the temperature, the higher the incidence of aggression.
            C.   the higher the temperature, the higher the incidence of aggression (up to a point).
            D.   while temperature is related to aggression, there are differing opinions as to what this relationship is.

_____10.   Punishment is to aggression as:
            A.   Aggression is to media violence.
            B.   Night is to day.
            C.   Mental is to physical.
            D.   None of the above is correct.

11.   Though Martin plays some rather violent video games on a regular basis (sometimes 6 – 8 hours per day), he feels that he is no more violent than those who do not play the games. In other words, according to Martin, he has not experienced _____ to the aggression.

12.   Individuals who watch violent pornography tend to have high _____.

13.   Cultures with strong norms indicating that aggression is an appropriate response to insults to one's honor are called _____.

14.   _____ songs tend to increase aggression by women against a male victim.

15.   For individuals high in _____ even weak provocations will stimulate an aggressive reaction.

After You Read... Practice Test #4

_____1.   Evidence has shown that punishment only works if it meets four requirements. The requirements include all of the following except
A.   it must be prompt.
B.   it must be certain to occur.
C.   it must be strong.
D.   it must be perceived by the person doing the punishing as just.

_____2.   An effective internal mechanism for restraining anger and overt displays of aggression is the definition of
A.   self-restraint.
B.   self-motivation.
C.   self-regulation.
D.   self-repression.

_____3.   According to the catharsis hypothesis, when individuals vent their anger and hostility in nonharmful ways, they will engage in harmful types of aggression
A.   less often.
B.   equally often.
C.   more often.
D.   as a means of compensating for lack of initiative.

_____4.   Forgiveness
A.   is defined as giving up the desire to punish someone who has hurt us.
B.   works by contributing to a feeling of apathy for the other individual.
C.   tends to cause us to think, repeatedly, about things that have been done to us.
D.   Both A and B are correct.

_____5.   Donald is known around his school as a "bully." He is constantly picking on other children and teasing them. The other day he pushed Sarah in the lunchroom line because he felt that she had inappropriately received a larger helping of pie than he had. Research has been conducted investigating the question. "What makes some people bully others?" These studies have found that
A.   bullies tend to have little social support.
B.   bullies tend to believe that others act the way they do intentionally.
C.   bullies tend to have a higher self - esteem than those that do not bully others.
D.   bullies tend to have a lower IQ than those that do not bully others.

_____6.   Research findings have given several suggestions for the reduction of bullying. They include all of the following except
A.   potential victims must be provided with a direct means for handling the bullying.
B.   if bullying occurs, someone in authority must take a stand against it.
C.   bullying must seem like a serious problem to all involved parties.
D.   outside help.

_____7.   The majority of workplace aggression is performed by
           A.   employees of the workplace in which the aggressive acts take place.
           B.   supervisors in the workplace.
           C.   people who do not work at the workplace in which the aggressive acts take place.
           D.   lower level staff in the workplace in which the aggressive acts take place.

_____8.   Workplace aggression appears to be more _____ than _____.
           A.   overt; covert.
           B.   covert; overt
           C.   controlled; hasty
           D.   hostile; aggression outside of the workplace.

_____9.   Behavior that is designed to impede the target's performance in the workplace is known
           as
           A.   incivility.
           B.   obstructionism.
           C.   impediment aggression.
           D.   hostile impediment.

_____10.   If an abusive supervisor is not seeking power over others because he or she already has it,
           what, according to Horstein (2004), is the abuse supervisor seeking?
           A.   A means of venting his or her frustration.
           B.   The sheer pleasure of exercising his or her power over subordinates.
           C.   An increase in self-esteem.
           D.   All of the above are correct.

11.   Allen is sure that he is the most talented person on earth. He plays the guitar "better than

       anyone," gets better grades than all of his friends, always has his "pick of females," and feels

       the world would, most certainly, be "in trouble without him." It does not take a rocket scientist to

       see that Allen suffers from an extremely high degree of _____.

12.   Someone who combines high levels of aggression with prosocial behaviors is a

       _____ controller.

13.   Gender differences are _____ when there is not provocation compared to when

       there is provocation.

14.   Tonya has been spreading the rumor that her ex-boyfriend is seeing a married woman. Ronny,

       Tonya's ex-boyfriend is extremely angry over this false rumor and wants to find out who started

       it. He has asked numerous friends, but no one knows where it came from. Ronny is experiencing

       _____ aggression.

15.   Sigmund Freud believed that aggression came from a death wish, or _____, which

       is possessed by everyone.

When you have finished... Crossword Puzzle

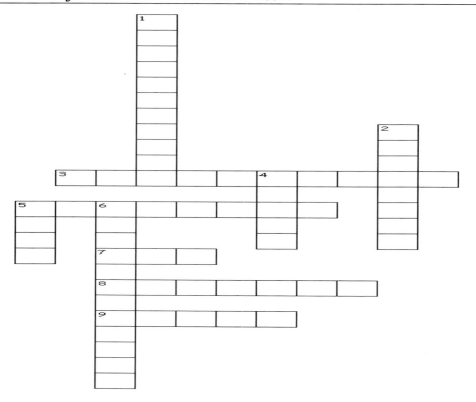

Across

3.   Delivery of aversive consequences
5.   Behavior in which aggression is one-way
7.   General aggression model
8.   Provoking statements designed to call attention to one's flaws and imperfections
9.   Type of theory that states external conditions arouse the desire to harm someone

Down

1.   According to the frustration-aggression hypothesis, this always leads to aggression
2.   Death wish
4.   Type of culture in which there are strong norms indicating that aggression is an appropriate response to an insult to one's reputation
5.   Type of doll used in Bandura experiment on media and aggression
6.   Research that is performed on the same participant over a long period of time

Created by Puzzlemaker at DiscoverySchool.com

When you have finished... You be the Researcher

You are going to conduct a hypothetical experiment. This experiment is going to investigate the relationship between watching football / playing football and aggressive behavior in young boys. Since this study will involve the use of participants, you have submitted your proposal for research to the IRB.

Yesterday, you received a letter from the IRB regarding your study. The IRB has noted that your proposal is not complete. The board informs you that they cannot give you authorization to proceed until you provide them with a copy of the consent form that is to be used in your study.

Having forgotten to provide the consent form and feeling a bit foolish, you remember that you have yet to even create a consent form. You had been so busy making sure everything was in order, that you forgot it. You immediately plan to work on the form and get it to the IRB as soon as possible.

Knowing what you know about an APA approved consent form, your task is to develop a consent form for your study. Make sure that you have all of the required information in the consent form so that the IRB will be able to quickly give you the "go-ahead" to begin your research.

If you are not completely sure about what the requirements are for an informed consent form, you might have to go the APA website or to your school library and do a bit of research.

Good luck and do not forget to make your consent form thorough!

Answers - As You Read...Practice Activities

1. Sigmund Freud believed that aggression stems from a potent death wish or thanatos. He also believed that this death wish is possessed by all human beings.

    Konrad Lorenz suggested that aggression stems from an inherited fighting instinct. This fighting instinct assures that the strongest males obtain mates and that their genes will be passed down to the next generation.

2. The evolutionary perspective suggests that one way of eliminating competition between males is through aggressive actions. Males that were adept at aggressive behavior may have been more successful in obtaining a desirable mate and, thus, passing his genes down to the next generation. Also, through this perspective, males would not have strong tendencies to aggress against females. The reasoning behind this is that if they were to aggress against females it would most likely discourage the females from accepting them as mates. Females, though, might aggress equally against males and females.

3. Dollard et al. (1939) proposed the frustration-aggression hypothesis. According to this hypothesis, frustration leads to the arousal of a drive and the drive has the primary goal of harming a person or object – the perceived cause of the frustration. Basically, the frustration experienced towards another person or an object leads one to aggress against that person or object.

4. Albert Bandura's social learning perspective states that, rather than being born with the innate drive toward aggression, we acquire the drive through direct experience and by observation of the behavior of others.

    Within this perspective, we learn various ways that we can harm someone, which people or groups are appropriate targets of our aggression, what actions by others justify retaliation, and what the situations are in which aggression is permitted or even approved.

5. According to the general aggression model, it is a sequence of events that ultimately leads to aggressive acts and that these aggressive acts can be initiated by two types of variables. One variable is factors that relate to the current situation. These are called situational variables. The second variable is factors that relate to the person(s) involved. These are called person factors.

    Variables that fall into the situational variable category include frustration, provocation from another individual (such as an insult), exposure to other people displaying aggression and pretty much anything that causes an individual to experience discomfort. Variables in the second category include traits that predispose some individuals to act aggressively, certain attitudes and beliefs concerning violence, a tendency to perceive hostile intentions in others' behavior, and specific skills related to aggression.

    The situational and person variables lead to aggression through their impact on three processes. The first process is arousal – they can increase physiological arousal. The second process is affective states – they can arouse hostile feelings and outward signs. The last process is cognitions – they can induce individuals' interpretations of the current situation.

6. The hypothesis makes two assumptions. First, it postulates that frustration always leads to aggression and, second, that aggression always stems from frustration.

   Subsequent research showed that there is too much emphasis on frustration as a determining factor in aggression. The studies also showed that aggression does not act as an automatic response to frustration.

   It was also found that not all aggression stems from frustration.

7. Direct provocation is defined as something that leads to aggression. It can be verbal or physical. The response to provocation often involves reciprocation – sometimes returning as much aggression as we perceived from the provocation. The response can also involve more aggression than the initial provocation, especially when it is thought that the person doing the provocation meant to hurt us.

8. Condescension is defined as expressions of arrogance or disdain on the part of others.

   Teasing is defined as provoking statements that call attention to an individual's flaws or imperfections. Teasing can be serious or playful.

9. Transferal of aggression occurs when we are frustration about one situation and those feelings tend to carry over into other situations.

   Transferal of aggression occurs because physiological arousal tends to dissipate very slowly over time and a portion of this arousal may persist and move from one situation to another.

10. (1)   Research on exposure to violent media indicates that these materials significantly   increase the likelihood of aggressive behavior in persons being exposed to them.
    (2)   These effects are both long-term and short-term.
    (3)   The extent of these effects is large.

11. The two types of research that are commonly employed in the investigation of the effect of different forms of media on aggression are short-term laboratory experiments and longitudinal procedures.

    Short-term laboratory experiments involve children or adults being exposed to violence on film and in television programs. What these studies have shown is that both children and adults who are exposed to this form of media violence have the tendency to display more aggression that those who were not exposed to the media,

    Longitudinal studies are studies in which the same participants are studies for an extended period, normally many years. Results of this type of study have shown that the more violent films of television programs that are watched as children, the higher level of aggression they will tend to display as adolescents and adults. This finding has been replicated in many countries, including Australia, Finland, Israel, Poland, and South Africa (Botha, 1990).

12. Dr. Bandura's study involved TV shows that were made by the researchers. In one TV show, an adult was shown being aggressive towards a "Bobo doll." There was one condition in this study in which the TV show featured an adult showing no aggression towards the doll. This was the control condition.

    The children were exposed to one of the two programs and were then placed in a room with toys that included toys those used in the TV program to strike the doll in an aggressive manner. The children played freely for 20 minutes with the toys during which time their behavior was being observed. The observers were to indicate the number of aggressive acts displayed by each child.

Results showed that children who were exposed to the program in which the adults showed aggression toward the doll showed strong tendencies to imitate these behaviors. Those who were not exposed to the aggressive acts did not show similar results.

Bandura and his colleagues summarized that the children had "learned" creative ways to act in an aggressive fashion.

Liebert and Baron (1972) had children watch parts of a violent TV show, *The Untouchables* or parts of a film about a horse race. The children in each group were then provided with a task in which they were to either hurt or help another child by either pressing a green or red button. The children who viewed the violent TV show displayed more willingness to hurt the child, while those who saw the film about the horse race tended to displayed less willingness to hurt the child.

13.   You are to make the connection. You might include something about how the children learn the "moves" by watching wrestling, which is an aggressive sport, similarly to the way Bandura's participants learned to act in certain aggressive ways by viewing videos of aggressive behavior on the Bobo doll.

14   Bushman and Anderson (2002) found that recurring exposure to violence in the media can affect cognitions relating to aggression. This exposure causes individuals to act aggressively. Thus, it does appear that GAM does play a role in the effects of media violence.

15.   The other factor that may play a significant role is desensitization.

Desensitization means that one becomes less sensitive to the violence and its consequences. Research (Funk et al., 2004) has shown that this may, indeed, be the case.

16.   The hypothesis in this study was if individuals had been desensitized to violence through their past experiencing in playing violent video games, P300 activity would be smaller when they viewed the violent images in the study. This was exactly what the researchers found.

17.   (1).   Viewing violence reduces an individual's emotional reactions to the violence, so they perceive the violence as being nothing outside of the norm.

      (2).   Viewing violence strengthens beliefs, expectations, and other cognitive processes related to aggression. What this means is that we develop strong knowledge structures relating to aggression.

18.   Linz, Donnerstein, and Penrod (1988) found that exposure to pornography - in particular violent pornography - can increase a man's willingness to act aggressively towards women. In addition, repeated exposure to this type of pornography can lead to desensitization. Due to this desensitization, those with repeated exposure no longer see the violent pornography as disturbing. Another thing this exposure to violent pornography appears to do is encourage the acceptance of unfeeling attitudes towards sexual violence which may lead to the acceptance of the rape myth that women deserve to be raped. This acceptance is not only in men, though, as it would also be seen in women.

19.   Fischer and Greitmeyer (2006) had their participants listen to songs with either

neutral lyrics, misogynous lyrics, or men-hating lyrics. After they had listened to the songs, they were asked to perform a word completion task which was designed to measure the degree to which the songs encouraged aggressive thoughts and ideas. The participants were then told that the study was completed, but were asked to participate in another experiment designed to assess the relationship between temperature and intellectual performance. As participants in this study, they were told that another individual would have to put his or her arm into cold water for a predetermined amount of time and they would have to determine how long the other person would have to continue this treatment. The longer the participants suggested that the other person keep his or her arm in the water, the greater the aggression.

Results showed that songs that expressed a negative attitude towards women tended to increase aggression by men against females. In addition, songs with the men hating lyrics increased aggression by women against men.

20. Cultural factors are beliefs, norms and expectations of a given culture.

A culture of honor is a culture in which there are strong social norms that indicate that aggression is a suitable response to insults to one's honor.

According to Cohen and Nisbett (1994, 1997), these norms can be traced to the fact that in some areas, affluence was once concentrated primarily in assets that could be readily stolen. Because of this, it became necessary for individuals to show no tolerance for such thefts or any other threat to their honor. Because of this, norms that pardon violence in response to an insult to one's honor emerged and became accepted.

21. Vandello and Cohen (1997, 2003) rationalized that the code of what they called "male honor" is particularly strong in Latin America and the southern United States. Because of this, those living in these areas or originally from these areas would be more likely to react to situations that induce jealousy with strong aggressive responses.

22. TASS stands for the traits as situational sensitivities model. TASS suggests that there are many facets of our personality that function in a threshold manner. What this means is only when the strength of situational factors is strong enough to trigger certain aspects of personality do these aspects affect behavior.

TASS postulates the prediction that the tendency to act in an aggressive fashion (trait aggression) will only influence overt behavior when situational factors are strong enough to activate the aggression. People who are high in trait aggressiveness require weak provocation to stimulate the aggressive response. The opposite is seen in those who are low in trait aggression.

23. A type A behavior pattern is characterized by extreme competitiveness, always being in a hurry, irritability, and aggression.

A type B behavior pattern is characterized by a low degree of competitiveness, relatively persistent state of relaxation, patience, and the ability to remain calm even in the face of strong aggravation.

24. Hostile aggression is defined as aggression in which the primary objective is to hurt someone. Instrumental aggression is defined as aggression in which the primary objective is to obtain goals other than hurting another person.

The connection between the two types of aggression and type A and B behavior patterns is that type B's tend to engage in hostile aggression, while type A's tend to engage in instrumental aggression.

25. Narcissism is defined as the tendency to over-estimate one's own abilities and importance.

Narcissists tend to react with a very high level of aggression to "slights" involving their self image because it calls into attention the possibility that their egos which are fully inflated may not be as accurate as they may think.

26. A sensation seeking personality describes someone who seeks new opportunities and experiences, primarily those that are dangerous and involve some type of risk.

The GAM offers some reasons as to why people who have sensation seeking personalities tend to also have high levels of aggression. (1) People who high in sensation seeking may experience feelings of aggression and hostility more other than those who are low in sensation seeking. (2) The emotions of those high in sensation seeking may have lower thresholds for becoming angry. (3) Their apparent tendencies to get bored and seek new experiences may lead them to have more hostile thinking patterns.

In addition, there have been three tendencies that sensation seeking personalities tend to have that are related to aggression. These are: (1) They are attracted to aggression eliciting activities and situations. (2) They are more likely to experience anger and hostility. (3) They are more likely to focus on the immediate rather than delayed consequences of their behavior.

27. Gender differences tend to be larger when there is provocation than when there is none. Bettencourt and Miller (1996) found that males are more likely to aggress against others when they have not been provoked.

The size and direction of gender differences tend to vary greatly with the type of aggression in question. Bjorkqvist et al. (1994) found that males are more likely to engage in various forms of direct aggression, which consists of actions that are aimed directly at a target and are clearly due to the aggressor. The researcher also found that females are more likely to engage in indirect aggression. Indirect aggression involves actions that allow the aggressor to conceal his or her identity from the victim.

For both men and women, aggression can be seen as a social "plus." This seems to be especially true if one combines aggression with high levels of relationship enhancing actions such as high social skills and high levels of extraversion. Individuals who combine aggression with relationship enhancing actions are known as bistrategic controllers.

28. According to research, Sam should do relatively well. Research has shown that when there is a rise in temperature, the tendency for individuals to react in an aggressive fashion tends to increase. But, it is of note that the temperature cannot be too hot as that will tend to result in an actual decrease in aggression because people become so hot that all they are only interested in cooling off.

29. Bartholow et al. found that alcohol tends to impair higher order cognitive functions such as the ability to evaluate stimuli and memory. In itself, this impairment makes it harder for individuals to evaluate the intentions of others. The impairment also makes it

harder to assess the effects of various forms of behavior on the part of the evaluator. This includes aggression.

30. Research evidence has shown that cues associated with alcohol (such as the picture of a fifth of vodka, a martini shaker, empty beer bottles) can trigger aggression even if the alcohol is not consumed. The idea is that the person has associated the items with aggressive behavior in the past and this association produces aggressive behavior even without the alcohol itself.

   Bartholow and Heinz (2006) exposed their participants to either alcohol advertisements or to neutral ads for paper towels and cheese. Both groups read descriptions of another individual and rated the individual on various dimensions. The hypothesis was that participants who read the alcohol advertisements would perceive more hostility in the actions of a stranger than the other group. The hypothesis was supported by the data. These findings indicate that even presence of advertisements for alcohol, the relationship between alcohol and aggression is noted.

31. Bullying is defined as a form of behavior in which aggression is which one individual displays the aggressive behavior and another individual is on the receiving end of the aggression.

   Two particular motives seem to play a major role in bullying. One is the motive to have power over others. The other motive is to be part of a group that is seen as tough and high in status.

32. (1) Pure bullies = people who are always bullies, never the victim.

   (2) Pure victims = people who are always victims; never the bully.

33. (3) Bully victims = people who switch from being the bully to being the victim and back again.

33. (1) The act of bullying must be seen as a serious problem by all those involved.

   (2) If and when bullying occurs, individuals in authority must draw attention to it and take a stand against it.

   (3) Potential victims must be provided with direct means for dealing with the bullying

   (4) Outside help is useful in the identification of the cause of bullying and in devising programs to reduce it.

34. Workplace aggression is defined as dramatic events in which employees show aggression towards other employees or their bosses. Workplace aggression can have fatal consequences.

   Two facts the one should keep in mind include:

   (1) The greatest majority of workplace aggression incidents are performed by people who do not work at the place where the violence is seen.

   (2) Recent survey research has shown that threats to do harm in the workplace are very rare.

35. Workplace aggression is much more common than workplace violence. Workplace aggression is defined as any form of overt behavior through which individuals seek to harm others in the workplace.

36. Expressions of hostility are behaviors that are primarily verbal or symbolic in nature.

The types of expressions of hostility include:

(1) Obstruction = behaviors designed to obstruct or impede the target's performance

(2) Incivility = low intensity deviant behavior with ambiguous intent to harm the target, in violation of workplace norms for mutual respect

(3) Overt aggression = behaviors that typically have been included under the heading "workplace violence"

37. The factor appears over and over again in research studies investigating workplace violence is perceived unfairness. Perceived unfairness is defined as the feelings of an individual that he or she has been treated unjustly by others in the organization.

Some other factors include reductions in staff, unexpected layoffs, and increased part time employees. The latter produces feelings of insecurity among full time employees who begin to fear for their own jobs.

38. Jamie has been exposed to abusive supervision.

The reason that bosses tend to act in this manner is because it is an outlet through which the bosses can vent their own frustrations. It is also thought that abusive supervision is used by supervisors for the sheer pleasure of exerting their power over their subordinates and serves as a means by which to gain self-esteem.

39. Punishment is defined as the delivery of aversive consequences and is designed to reduce aggression.

Capital punishment is the legal execution of a convicted criminal.

The three reasons societies punish aggressive acts are:

(1) There is a belief that people deserve to be punished if they have inflicted harm on others.

(2) Punishment is used as a mechanism to deter people from in the future engaging, in the behavior that is punished.

(3) Also, some types of punishment simply remove the person committing the aggressive act(s) from society.

40. Punishment can work in reducing aggression. The punishment, though, must meet four basic requirements:

(1) It must be prompt.

(2) It must be certain to occur. In other words, the person being punished must learn that punishment will follow the particular act of aggression that it was designed to reduce.

(3) It must be strong enough to leave an impression.

(4) It must be justified.

41. Self regulation is defined as our capacity to regulate many aspects of our own behavior. This includes aggression.

Even when one is very good at self-regulation, the system can fail and aggression can erupt. The reason for this is that we have invested so much effort in other tasks that we simply do not have the reserve to perform this function.

42.   Catharsis is defined as a way for individuals to vent their anger and hostility (or stress) in nonharmful ways.

Research has shown that this technique does not work.

43.   Forgiveness is defined as giving up the desire to punish someone who has hurt you and seeking to act kindly towards them. Forgiveness is possibly a way towards the reduction of subsequent aggression.

Forgiveness works by encouraging feelings of empathy. It also aids the individual by allowing them to avoid ruminating on what has caused them to forget in the first place.

Answers – Cross Word Puzzle

Across

3. punishment
5. bullying
7. GAM
8. teasing
9. drive

Down

1. frustration
2. thanatos
4. honor
5. Bobo
6. longitudinal

Answers – Practice Test #1

1. B
2. C
3. D
4. D
5. A
6. D
7. D
8. B
9. A
10. C
11. punishment
12. forgiveness
13. thanatos
14. frustration aggression hypothesis
15. social learning

Answers – Practice Test #2

1. C
2. D
3. A
4. A
5. B
6. D
7. B

8. D
9. C
10. D
11. arousal, cognitions, affective states
12. condescension
13. verbal, physical
14. longitudinal
15. hostile

Answers – Practice Test #3

1. D
2. B
3. C
4. D
5. B
6. C
7. B
8. D
9. C
10. A
11. desensitization
12. levels of arousal
13. cultures of honor
14. misogynous
15. trait aggressiveness

Answers – Practice Test #4

1. D
2. C
3. A
4. A
5. B
6. C
7. C
8. B
9. B
10. D
11. narcissism
12. bistrategic
13. larger
14. indirect
15. thanatos

CHAPTER 11

GROUPS AND INDIVIDUALS:
THE CONSEQUENCES OF BELONGING

Before You Read...Chapter Summary

What is a group? Why do we tend to want to be a part of a group – or not? What are the "key" components that are common among groups? What are the benefits/costs of being a member of a group? Chapter Eleven addresses all of these topics and more. In the first section, we are first introduced to the term "group," which is defined as people who are perceived to be connected together in a coherent unit. According to this definition, a family is a group, 10 students taking a geometry course constitute a group, members of a church are a group, and the list goes on and on. What, then, do these entities have in common that make each a group? Your textbook delineates four key components that are common to all groups – status, roles, norms, and cohesiveness. If the four components are satisfied, what does a group provide that tends to entice people to join? Within this chapter, you will find information on both the potential costs and benefits of being a member of a group. Unfortunately, within some groups, it is the costs that sometimes outweigh the benefits and, from this, problems can arise.

Within the next section, the topic of the effect of the presence of others, including others who are members of our own group, on behavior is discussed. You will read of an out of the ordinary study investigating the effect others can have on, of all things, cockroaches! You will also become familiar with the constructs of social facilitation and social loafing in this section. With all groups, no matter whether they are large or small, there is bound to be some type of conflict somewhere along the line.

Your textbook, in the next section, takes a look at the conflict that can arise and various ways of diffusing a situation involving conflict. Sometimes this conflict can be the result of a construct known as perceived fairness within the group. The topic of perceived fairness (or unfairness, as the case may be) is also discussed. Finally, this chapter deals with the decision making process within groups. Within this section, you will become privy to the constructs of groupthink and brainstorming.

Before You Read... Learning Objectives

After reading this chapter, you should be able to:
- Define the word "group" and elaborate upon the two different types of groups.
- Discuss the presumed evolutionary motivation behind the group.
- Provide a definition for *entitativity*.
- Name and discuss the key components of groups.
- Provide discussion on the topic of the costs and benefits of joining a group.
- Elaborate upon the idea of the "splintering" of a group.
- Define social facilitation and discuss some of the research findings on this topic.
- Discuss the effect that an audience can have on the performer through the distraction conflict theory.
- Provide information regarding the construct of social loafing.
- Discuss ways of reducing social loafing.
- Define and elaborate upon the idea of individuation.
- Explain the idea of cooperation within a group.
- Discuss conflict within a group, including the social factors that play a powerful role in the initiation of conflict.
- Discuss some useful techniques for resolving conflict.
- Elaborate upon the basic rules for judging if one is being treated fairly in a group setting.
- Explain some of the common reactions to unfairness.
- Define *group polarization*.
- Describe *.groupthink*.
- Discuss the outcome that can be produced when members of a group fail to share information with each other.
- Discuss *brainstorming*.

As You Read...Term Identification

Important Terms to Know
Below are a list of some of the key terms and concepts from this chapter. Make flashcards in order to enhance your recall ability of these terms. Refer to the definitions that are either in boldface or in the margins of this chapter for help. You may also want to include additional terms from this chapter as you deem necessary.

obligatorily interdependent, (p. 378)	ideology (p. 392)	bargaining/negotiation, (p. 404)
group, (p. 380)	schism, (p. 392)	decision making, (p. 408)
common bond group, (p. 380)	social facilitation, (p. 394)	group polarization, (p. 408)
common identity group, (p. 380)	distraction-conflict theory, (p. 395)	groupthink, (p. 409)
entitativity, (p. 380)	additive tasks, (p. 396)	brainstorming, (p. 410)
status, (p. 383)	social loafing, (p. 397)	superordinate goals, (p. 405)
role, (p. 384)	deindividuation, (p. 399)	perceived fairness / justice, (p. 405)
norms, (p. 387)	cooperation, (p. 401)	distributive justice, (p. 406)
cohesiveness, (p. 388)	conflict, (p. 401)	procedural justice, (p. 406)
politicized collective identity (p. 390)	social dilemmas, (p. 401)	transactional justice, (p. 406)

As You Read...Practice Activities

GROUPS: WHEN WE JOIN...AND WHEN WE LEAVE

We Are All Part of One...
(Introduction, page 380)

1.   Oliver is a member of a research team at the university he attends. In addition, he is an active member of a local church, plays the trombone in the city orchestra, and comes from a huge Italian family. In other words, Oliver is a member of quite a few "groups."

What is a group?

_____

_____

_____

Your textbook discusses two different types of groups – the "common-bond" group" and the "common-identity" group. How do these two types of groups differ?

_____

_____

_____

_____

Entitativity...
(Introduction, page 380)

2.   Groups can differ in terms of their entitativity. What, exactly, is entitativity?

_____

_____

_____

What are some of the characteristics of groups that are high in entitativity?

_____

_____

_____

YouTube and Social Psychology...
(What Psychology Tells Us About. page 382-383)

3.   We are a society that highly relies on the internet for many things. Just one of them is entertainment. So goes the website, YouTube. Your author provides a wonderful explanation of the website as well as the purpose that it fulfills.

   This entire section seeks to answer the question, "Is YouTube Just a Website, or is it a Real Group? What answer does this section provide? Provide details in your answer.

   _____

   _____

   _____

Status...
(Status: Hierarchies in Groups, page 383-384)

4.   There are three components that are common to all groups. They include status, roles, norms, and cohesiveness.

   Define the term *status*.

   _____

   _____

   What are some of the factors that can play a role in the acquisition of status within a group?

   _____

   _____

   _____

   _____

   _____

   _____

Roles...
(Roles: Differentiation of Functions within Groups, pages 384-386)

5.   Mark is the president of his fraternity. He is expected to be present at every meeting and to act as the "leader" of the group. Art is the vice-president and is expected to step in whenever the president is unable to perform his duties. Peter is the treasurer and maintains control of the financial aspects of the group. Zack is the secretary. He is required to take the minutes at every

Roles…Continued

meeting and to keep up wit
and telephone numbers.

In other words, each officer h

_____

_____

Viewing the family as your grou

_____

_____

_____

Norms…
(Norms: The Rules of the Game, page 387)

6.   What is a _norm_?

_____

_____

_____

How do norms differ between individualistic and collectivistic cultures?

_____

_____

_____

_____

Cohesiveness…
(Cohesiveness: The Force that Binds, page 388)

7.   Define _cohesiveness_.

_____

_____

Cohesiveness…"Continued

What is meant by the sentence,

What Is
(The

...sive groups have a sense of solidarity"?

_____

_____

_____

_____

In It For Me?
(Benefits of Joining: What Groups Do For Us, pages 388-390)

8.   This section includes a discussion of some of the benefits of joining a group. What are these benefits? Name and discuss each.

A. _____

_____

_____

B. _____

_____

_____

C. _____

_____

_____

Nothing is Free...Where There are Benefits, There Have to Be Costs...
(The Costs of Getting Accepted into a Group, page 390)

9.   Sometimes there are some rather severe costs paid for acceptance into a group. Fraternities are infamous for their "hazing" behavior. In fact, there have actually been college students who have suffered the ultimate consequence, death, as a direct result of a hazing ritual.

The question exists, "What impact does initiation through "extreme" means have on one's commitment to a group?"

Nothing is Free…Where There are Benefits, There Have to Be Costs…Continued

Provide an answer to this question. Make sure to include a reference to the research of Aronson and Mills (1959) and the theory of cognitive dissonance in your answer.

_____

_____

_____

_____

_____

_____

_____

_____

It is Often Difficult to Get Into a Group; Why, Then, Do People Leave a Group?
(The Costs of Membership: Why Groups Sometimes Splinter, page 391)

10.   Once someone has worked really hard to get into a group, they may find that they are not happy within the group and have the desire to leave. Within this section the potential costs of membership are discussed. One the costs of membership is that membership within a group may impinge on one's individual freedom.

Explain how being a member of group can impinge on its members' individual freedom. In addition, explain what the consequences might be if one does not behave as is expected as a group member.

_____

_____

_____

_____

_____

The Anglican Church of England and Ideological Splintering…
(The Costs of Membership: Why Groups Sometimes Splinter, page 391-393)

11.   A major change occurred in the Church of England in 1994: women were allowed into the priesthood. Prior to that time, it was unheard of for a woman to become a priest. This did represent forward movement for women, but it was not entirely positively received. There were

The Anglican Church of England and Ideological Splintering...Continued

some followers of the Church, both male priests as well as parishioners. who vehemently opposed this decision. The result was a schism of the Church with literally hundreds of the faithful leaving the Church in a symbolic move against the decision. Much to the disappointment of those who head the Anglican Church of England, this schism produced an indelible effect and the Church itself, as well as its members, will never be the same.

In 2005, Sani investigated the phenomenon of ideological splintering that took place among members of the Anglican Church of England.

Discuss this research by filling in the following chart.

Participants: _____

_____

_____

Method of Data Collection: _____

_____

_____

_____

Data Collected (Information Sought): _____

_____

_____

_____

_____

_____

_____

The Anglican Church of England and Ideological Splintering...Continued

What were the results of this study?

_____

_____

_____

EFFECTS OF THE PRESENCE OF OTHERS: FROM TASK PERFORMANCE TO BEHAVIOR IN CROWDS

Yes, Even Bugs are Used in Psychological Research...Even The Simple Cockroach...
(Does the Presence of Others Have an Effect on Performance? Ask a Cockroach! page 396-397)

12.   In what probably seems like eons ago to some, Zajonc, Heingartner and Herman (1969) sought to investigate the impact the presence of others had on behavior. Their "participants" proved quite willing to give the study their all. One could tell simply by the wide smiles upon their faces. At least, if cockroaches COULD smile, they certainly would have been smiling. Who wouldn't smile at opportunity to participate in a social psychology research study??!!?

Putting the humor aside, this study led to evidence in support of a study conducted back in 1898 by Triplett. Incidentally, this study, as your book notes, was the first published experiment in social psychology and provided a portal through which thousands have followed.

Discuss the classic cockroach study (Zajonc, Heingartner & Herman (1969). In addition, elaborate on the work of Triplett (1898).

_____

_____

_____

_____

_____

_____

_____

_____

_____

Just Ask Someone with Stage-Fright...Does Performing Before an Audience Affect Performance?
(Does Having an Audience Distract Us? page 394-395)

13.　　Martin is an actor. He has performed before audiences for the past 15 years, but he still experiences a tendency to be distracted by his audience. Is this due to the potential for increased arousal caused by the presence of the audience, as was thought by Zajonc et al. (1898) or is it due to cognitive "overload" (Baron, 1986)?

　　　　Discuss the research findings of Huguet, Galvaing, Monteil, and Dumas (1999) and Hetherington, Anderson, Norton, and Newson (2006).

　　　　_____

　　　　_____

　　　　_____

　　　　Which line of thought do these researchers tend to follow?

　　　　_____

　　　　_____

　　　　_____

SOCIAL LOAFING: LETTING OTHERS DO THE WORK

I Am Just Going to Sit Back and Let You Handle This One...Social Loafing
(Introduction, page 397-399)

14.　　Define *social loafing*.

　　　　_____

　　　　_____

　　　　Now, match the researchers to their research.

　　　　_____　Weldon and Mustari (1988)

　　　　_____　Price, Harrison and Gavin (2006)

　　　　_____　Englehart (2006)

　　　　_____　Latane, Williams and Harkin (1979)

I Am Just Going to Sit Back and Let You Handle This One…Social Loafing…Continued

A.   Results demonstrated support for the idea that social loafing can occur not only when the performance task is cognitive it can also occur when the task is physical.

B.   Results showed that as the size of the group increased, the individual has the tendency to put less effort into task performance.

C.   Results showed that having knowledge and skill related to the task at hand can decrease social loafing.

D.   Results indicated that social loafing in class participation is more likely in a class that is large. This is due to the idea that in a larger class, students are provided with greater anonymity than in a smaller class.

Diminishing the Effects of Others…
(Reducing Social Loafing: Some Useful Techniques, page 399)

15.   Your textbook provides discussion of five techniques been used to demonstrate a reduction in the phenomenon of social loafing. Name each of these methods.

1. _____

2. _____

3. _____

4. _____

5. _____

Going With the Grain…
(Effects of Being in a Crowd, pages 399-400)

16.   Discuss the idea of deindividuation by, first, providing a definition of this construct, and, then, discuss the research findings, pro and con, on deindividuation.

_____

_____

_____

_____

_____

_____

COORDINATION IN GROUPS: COOPERATION OR CONFLICT?

When Both Sides Benefit...
(Cooperation: Working With Others to Achieve Shared Goals, page 401)

17.   What are two reasons that group members may not choose to cooperate with others?

A. _____

_____

B. _____

_____

When Do Individuals Make the Decision to Cooperate and When Is the Decision Made Not to Cooperate? Why? Social Psychologists Have Asked the Same Questions...
(Social Dilemmas: Where Cooperation Could Occur, But Often Doesn't, page 401)

18.   What is a social dilemma, as defined by Komorita and Parks (1994)?

_____

_____

_____

How does the prisoner's dilemma (Insko et al., 2001) fit into this definition?

_____

_____

_____

_____

_____

Does Punishment Work Toward Subsequent Cooperative Behavior?
(Social Dilemmas: Where Cooperation Could Occur, But Often Doesn't, pages 401-402)

19.   Uli is a member of the Theta Psi Alpha sorority. Two weeks ago, the sorority sisters participated in a walk to raise money for AIDS research. Uli is under the impression (though it is inaccurate) that anyone who has AIDS is a homosexual, and she is of the firm belief that homosexuality is, in her own words, "immoral." In light of her beliefs, Uli did not participate in the walk. Now she is being snubbed by her sorority sisters and, in the very least, not happy with this outcome. Will the ostracism Uli is facing have any effect on her desire to cooperate with the group in the future?

Does Punishment Work Toward Subsequent Cooperative Behavior?...Continued

This was the principle question behind the research of Mulder, van Dijk, De Cremer, and Wilke (2006). What answer did this research investigation support?

_____

_____

_____

When People Get Become Members of Groups, Things are Not Always Rose-Colored...
(Conflict: Its Nature, Causes and Effects, pages 402-403)

20.   What is conflict? Give an example of a conflict you have experienced due to your membership in a group.

_____

_____

_____

_____

_____

Do Social Factors Play a Role in Conflict – Well, Yeah...
(Conflict: Its Nature, Causes and Effects, page 402-403)

21.   If you have any recollection of the course you are taking at present, you probably remember the role that social factors have played in concepts discussed throughout the textbook. Conflict is no different.

Your textbook discusses four social factors that play a role in the development of conflict. Name and elaborate upon each of these factors.

A. _____

_____

_____

B. _____

_____

_____

Do Social Factors Play a Role in Conflict – Well, Yeah...Continued

C. _____

_____

_____

D. _____

_____

_____

Now That We Have Conflict...How Will We Resolve It...Some Suggestions...
(Resolving Conflicts: Some Useful Techniques, pages 403-405)

22.   Within the human psyche is the desire to move toward that which is perceived as good and away that which is perceived as bad. So it is with conflict...No one *likes* to be in a state of conflict and will often seek to, if at all possible, resolve the conflict as quickly as they can.

Your textbook provides two techniques that are noted to be the most common ways for seeking a resolution to conflict. Elaborate upon these.

1. _____

_____

_____

_____

_____

2. _____

_____

_____

_____

_____

PERCEIVED FAIRNESS IN GROUPS: ITS NATURE AND EFFECTS

"Though force can protect in emergency, only justice, fairness, consideration and cooperation can finally lead men to the dawn of eternal peace." - Dwight D. Eisenhower
(Basic Rules for Judging Fairness: Distributive, Procedural and Transactional Justice, pages 406-407)

23.   Have you ever been a member of a team? Perhaps, you were a member of a debate team or a member of an athletic team. Let's say you are presently a member of an award winning athletic football team – *The Social Psychology Soldiers*. As a member of this team you are expected, as you know, to fulfill various roles and to adhere to the norms of the game.

One evening after a game, you are just tuning down from the game when your coach (before all of the other players) singles you out. You have the sinking feeling that this is not going to be good and it appears that your feeling is on-the-button accurate. The coach begins by reading from the rule book. The section chosen is in reference to zigging when you are supposed to zag, You knew you had made a mistake immediately after the play was made and you had suspected some form of castigation from the coach. But nothing could have prepared you for the degree of the penalty. You are told that you will have to sit out the next four games and, unfortunately, this will include the "big" game against your team's arch rival – *The Quantum Physics Velocity*. You are outraged, but are able, for the time being, to keep your anger under wraps. After you dress and leave the locker room, though, you "let loose." "How could the coach be so **&^%#@ unfair??!!??"

According to your textbook, you probably perceived the punishment as being unfair by applying three basic rules. What are the three basic rules?

1. _____

_____

2. _____

_____

3. _____

_____

How Would YOU React?
(Reactions to Perceived Unfairness: Tactics for Dealing with Injustice, page 407)

24.   Your textbook discusses several common reactions to unfairness – whether it be from a team coach or in the workplace. Elaborate upon these customary reactions.

_____

_____

How Would YOU React?...Continued

_____

_____

_____

_____

_____

_____

Knowing yourself better than anyone else, if you were actually in the predicament described in activity 23, which reaction would you be more likely to display? Why?

_____

_____

_____

DECISION-MAKING BY GROUPS: HOW IT OCCURS AND THE PITFALLS IT FACES

Moving Toward an End – Group Polarization...
(The Decision Quality of Groups: Less or More Extreme? pages 408-409)

25.   When a group initially becomes a "group", there are always conflicting opinions on various issues and the key to a "good" group is a general consensus. Luckily, through interaction among members and maybe some acquiescence on the part of some members, a decision can be made.

A great deal of research in social psychology has focused on the quality of the decisions made by groups. One construct that has arisen through these investigations is that of *group polarization*. Discuss this construct. Make sure you include the *risky shift* in your discussion.

_____

_____

_____

_____

_____

Two Factors in Route Toward Polarization...
(The Decision Quality of Groups: Less or More Extreme? pages 408-409)

26.   There are two factors involved in answer to the question, "Why do groups show the tendency to move toward increasingly radical views?" What are they?

_____

_____

_____

_____

_____

DANGER...GROUP POLARIZATION AHEAD...
(Groupthink: When Cohesiveness is Dangerous, pages 409-410)

27.   What is *groupthink*?

_____

_____

_____

According to Haslam et al. (2006), how can groupthink be dangerous?

_____

_____

_____

_____

According to Tetlock et al. (1992) and Kameda and Sugimori (1993), why does groupthink occur?

_____

_____

_____

_____

_____

Bias Seen in Decision-Making in Groups...
(Groupthink: When Cohesiveness is Dangerous, page 409-410)

28.   Hornsey and Imani (2004) found evidence of an in-group / out-group bias in decision-making in groups. Discuss their research and the resulting support for this bias.

_____

_____

_____

_____

_____

_____

_____

_____

_____

_____

Bias Seen in Decision-Making in Groups –Part Deux
(Brainstorming: Idea Generation in Groups, pages 410-411)

29.   Gigone and Hastie (1997) and Stasser (1992) found evidence of another bias. Discuss this bias.

_____

_____

_____

_____

Groupthink in Action...
(Does Brainstorming in a Group Result in More and Higher Quality Inventive Ideas? pages 412-413)

30.   Read this passage and then provide an answer to the question posed above. Be sure to include some of the research evidence.

_____

_____

_____

Groupthink in Action...Continued

_____

_____

_____

_____

_____

After You Read... MyPsychLab Connection

(1)   Peer relationships are very important in the development process of an individual. Among the roles that these relationships play, they are an avenue through which people learn sex role and relational skills. How are peer groups formed and how does the peer group tend to change as one ages and matures? For answers to these two questions, and more, *WATCH: Peer Groups in Adolescence.*

(2)   *WATCH: Students Teaching Students.* There is strong research support for the idea that if you teach something to someone you tend to remember approximately 95% of what you have taught. This short video shows this process in action and is well worth a look!

(3)   Students tend to learn much more effectively when they are involved in their learning. This process of involvement in learning is known as cooperative learning. *WATCH: Cooperative Learning* for a view of the processes involved.

After You Read... Practice Test #1

_____1.   The idea that interdependence among group members is necessary for the survival of the species would be an idea espoused by
    A.   Dr. McMartin, a clinical psychologist.
    B.   Dr. McMillon, a school psychologist.
    C.   Dr. McMurphy, an evolutionary psychologist.
    D.   Dr. McDonald, an environmental psychologist.

_____2.   Argyle (2001) found that one of the best predictors of happiness and well-being is
    A.   our financial status.
    B.   the degree of connectedness that we feel toward others.
    C.   the number of groups to which we belong.
    D.   the type of groups to which we belong.

_____3.   Common-bond groups tend to involve
    A.   a large number of members.
    B.   those who have much in common.
    C.   face-to-face interaction.
    D.   a link to the group as a whole.

_____4.   The extent to which the individual members of a group are perceived as a whole is the definition for
    A.   identity bond.
    B.   Gestalt group formation.
    C.   entitativity.
    D.   categorical linkage.

_____5.   Groups high in the construct defined in question 4 tend to
    A.   communicate often, but only through face-to-face contact.
    B.   rarely communicate - but when they do, it is through face-to-face contact.
    C.   share a common goal.
    D.   tend to be dissimilar to each other in various ways.

_____6.   Sarah is the president of her drama club. Joe is the historian. According to the common hierarchy of officers in clubs, Sarah has higher _____ than does Joe.
    A.   role expectations
    B.   status
    C.   motivation
    D.   Both B and C are correct.

_____7.   Hornsey, Jetten, McAuliffe, and Hoff (2006) found that
           A.   individuals who were low in identification with a particular group were not
                  effected by evaluations of a student whose personal goals were different from
                  theirs.
           B.   individuals who were high in identification with a particular group were highly
                  effected by evaluations of a student whose personal goals were different from
                  theirs.
           C.   individuals who were high in identification with a particular group were not
                  effected by evaluations of a student whose personal goals were different from
                  theirs.
           D.   individuals who were low in identification with a particular group were highly
                  effected by evaluations of a student whose personal goals were different from
                  theirs.

_____8.   Groups that are cohesive
           A.   see themselves as homogenous.
           B.   see themselves as heterogenous.
           C.   are oriented toward achieving individual goals.
           D.   Both B and C are correct.

_____9.   Which of the following is NOT a benefit of joining a group?
           A.   Gaining "social" clout.
           B.   Help in reaching our goals.
           C.   Gaining self-knowledge.
           D.   All of the above are benefits of joining a group.

_____10.   The costs of joining a group may include
           A.   denial of membership back into other groups that we have left.
           B.   restriction of personal freedom.
           C.   heavy demands on our time, energy and resources.
           D.   All of the above are correct.

11.   The idea that increased cognitive load can adversely affect one's performance is known as the

       _____.

12.   _____ can be defined as reductions in motivation

       and effort that tend to occur when individuals work as a group.

13.   When two opposing groups see that they have goals that, between the two groups, actually

       overlap, conflict can be reduced and is often replaced by _____ cooperation.

14.   _____ corresponds to the fairness of the system through which

       rewards are distributed.

15.   The saying, "Safety comes in numbers," could adequately be used to explain the construct of

       _____.

After You Read... Practice Test #2

_____1.   Tetlock et al, (1992) and Kameda and Sugimori (1993) found that there are two factors that are crucial in the occurrence of groupthink. They are
   A.   high levels of cohesiveness and definite role expectations.
   B.   low levels of cohesiveness and definite role expectations.
   C.   high levels of cohesiveness and norms that suggest the group is morally superior to other groups.
   D.   high levels of cohesiveness and norms that suggest the group is capable of making mistakes.

_____2.   The tendency to move toward extremes in decisions is known as
   A.   social comparison.
   B.   end polarization.
   C.   group polarization.
   D.   risky shift.

_____3.   When people meet as a group to generate new ideas, they are engaging in
   A.   groupthink.
   B.   polarization.
   C.   group generative action.
   D.   social comparison.

_____4.   Groups that demonstrate _____ entitativity tend to be stereotyped more often than groups with _____ entitativity.
   A.   low; high.
   B.   high; low.
   C.   no; some degree of.
   D.   There is no research evidence that shows a difference between two levels of entitativity.

_____5.   All of the following are ways in which people acquire high status, except
   A.   individuality.
   B.   height.
   C.   prototypicality.
   D.   seniority.

_____6.   In individualistic cultures, the norm is to value
   A.   our group as a whole.
   B.   the individual within the group.
   C.   being different from others.
   D.   Both B and C are correct.

_____7.   The mere presence of others, according to Triplett (1898)
   A.   made bicycle racers race faster when racing in a group.
   B.   seemed to increase racing times.
   C.   served as a motivational factor for racers.
   D.   Both A and C are correct.

_____8.   In the research study conducted by Latane, Williams and Harkins (1979), the independent variable was
   A.   the amount of noise each participant listened to.
   B.   the size of the group.
   C.   the age of the participants.
   D.   the time of day the data was recorded.

_____9.   The best way to reduce social loafing is to
   A.   make the output of each participant readily identifiable.
   B.   reduce the size of the group.
   C.   allow each person the group to assess his or her role in within the group.
   D.   None of the above is correct.

_____10.   The main reason for lack of cooperation in a group is
   A.   that the opinions of each group member do not match.
   B.   that the goals of are not shared.
   C.   lack of motivation.
   D.   the desire for individuality.

11.   One of the most common strategies for resolving conflict is _____.

12.   In the principle of distributive justice, we tend to apply the _____ rule of distribution of the rewards according to the contributions of each member so that each member gets his or her share depending of what he or she has put in.

13.   _____ refers to the idea that we rely on others for knowledge and information sharing.

14.   Collectivistic cultures value the _____ more than the individual person.

15.   One problem with group membership is that it tends to restrict one's _____ freedom.

After You Read... Practice Test #3

_____1. Cost is to benefit as
  A. restriction of personal freedom is to self knowledge.
  B. self knowledge is to restriction of personal freedom.
  C. monetary is to emotional.
  D. monetary is to self knowledge.

_____2. Zajonc (1965) found that the mere presence of others
  A. increases psychological arousal.
  B. increases physiological arousal.
  C. decreases psychological arousal.
  D. decreases physiological arousal.

_____3. Social loafing involves decreases in
  A. motivation.
  B. effort.
  C. sensation.
  D. Both A and B are correct.

_____4. Deindividuation is defined as a psychological state characterized by
  A. reduced self awareness.
  B. increased arousal.
  C. a sense of independence.
  D. a feeling of non-dependence.

_____5. Faulty attribution is to faulty communication as
  A. annoyance is to error.
  B. false is to true.
  C. causes are to effects.
  D. error is to annoyance.

_____6. Deciding on one out of several possible courses of action is the definition of
  A. decision making.
  B. decision shift.
  C. decision polarization.
  D. decision tasking.

_____7. Mrs. McAllister teachers sixth grade at Owens Elementary School. She is going to have her students do a group project. She, though, having majored in social psychology in college, knows the idea behind social loafing and wants her students to do well on the project without conflict. To minimize this effect, Mrs. McAllister
  A. grades the students not only on the group contributions, but also on individual contributions.
  B. makes the groups very small in size with no more than 4 people per group.
  C. allows the children to assign themselves to groups rather than her assigning them to groups herself.
  D. None of the above is correct.

_____8.   One's position or rank within their group is their
      A.   rank order.
      B.   rank position.
      C.   status quo.
      D.   status.

_____9.   The role individuals play in one group
      A.   does not pre-determine them to play the same role in another group.
      B.   destines them to play that role in another group.
      C.   erases them from the competition to play a particular role in another group.
      D.   None of the above is correct.

_____10.   When we are aroused, we tend to perform better on
      A.   complex tasks.
      B.   easy tasks.
      C.   familiar tasks.
      D.   Both B and C are correct.

11.   When an actor has to divide his or her attention between the audience and the task, there is an increase in _____.

12.   _____ within a group can increase task motivation and make groups more satisfying.

13.   When a part of a risk-prone group, an individual may exhibit the tendency to move towards more _____ than if the individual were to make a decision on his or her own.

14.   When group members share information that is inaccurate, it tends to _____ their decision making accuracy.

15.   A _____ is defined as an assembly of people who are bonded together in a coherent unit.

After You Read... Practice Test #4

_____1. According to Englehart (2006), social loafing is most likely to occur in which situation?
A. Three men are getting together to play poker.
B. Five girls are going out in their neighborhood as a group to sell Girl Scout cookies.
C. One firefighter has volunteered to clean the firehouse.
D. Two members of a local church congregation are preparing sandwiches for the homeless.

_____2. The tendency of group members to seek a consensus among all group members is known as
A. groupthink.
B. group polarization.
C. social acceptance.
D. group polarization.

_____3. Which of the following is the strongest example of deindividuation?
A. Rob dons a mask and robs a convenience store.
B. Mary makes a goal in a soccer game.
C. George is a member of a group and chooses to leave the group because he does not completely agree with their principles.
D. None of the above would be an example of deindividuation.

_____4. Helping that is mutual and through which both parties benefit is called
A. consensus.
B. social acceptance.
C. cooperation.
D. social facilitation.

_____5. When individuals lose their individuality through membership in a group, they are experiencing
A. social diversion.
B. individuality shift.
C. deindividuation.
D. polarization towards an extreme.

_____6. Renee is a flamenco dancer. She has learned, through the experience of performing before an audience every Friday evening, that she actually gets what she calls a "rush" from the audience. This is positive example of what?
A. Social facilitation.
B. Cooperation.
C. Group polarization.
D. Both A and C are correct.

_____7.   David's band is trying to make a decision about attending a battle of the bands competition. David tends to be very shy and likes to play before small audiences. He realizes that the audience will be HUGE in this case. The other band members, though, are excited about the competition and really want to participate. David decides that the other members will provide a sort of "buffer" from his shyness and decides to play. This is an example of
   A.   social polarization.
   B.   social comparison.
   C.   social facilitation.
   D.   social reliance.

_____8.   The Mighty Elbows, a group of "professional" arm wrestlers, are going to work with a local charity to build a home for the homeless. There are 15 people in the group and Quincy, a social psychology major at the local university, realizes that the possibility of the existence of social loafing is very real. This is particularly true because Mark tends to be a little "lazy." In an effort to reduce the chance of social loafing, Quincy
   A.   provides snacks and drinks for the day.
   B.   makes sure Mark gets a good night's rest and is aware that this is a group project.
   C.   invites another group to participate with them.
   D.   makes sure that every member of the "elbows" has an assigned task and knows how important it is that he completes that task.

_____9.   Hermione is a cheerleader. Her best friend, LaTosha, is a member of the band. LaTosha is normally a very quiet, almost shy person; but, when she is with the band, she becomes another person. The other day Hermione looked up into the stands and saw LaTosha actually leading a cheer among the band members. This is apparently an action resulting from
   A.   social polarization.
   B.   deindividuation.
   C.   social comparison.
   D.   social loafing.

_____10.   Roles can be
   A.   attained.
   B.   assigned.
   C.   ascribed.
   D.   All of the above are correct.

11.   There are two normally opposing groups that are working together to raise money for cancer research. The fact that both groups are working towards a common goal make this goal a

_____ goal.

12.   In the process of groupthink, _____ norms suggest that the

group is perfect, has made a decision, and that decision is the only valid response to the situation.

13.   In the Stanford Prison Experiment, results showed that the _____

began to act within their assigned roles.

14. Cohesive groups have a sense of _____ in that they tend to see themselves as homogenous and orientated towards achieving a common goal.

15. Hetherington, Anderson, Norton, and Newson (2005) found that when one eats with others and watches TV during this time, his or her eating tends to _____.

When you have finished... Crossword Puzzle

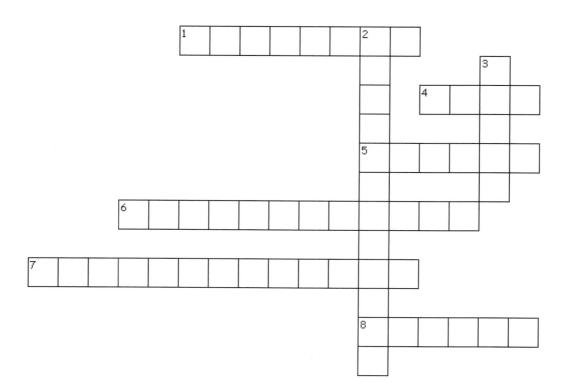

Across

1.   Emphasizes the existence of incompatible interests and a recognition of this fact by all of the parties involved
4.   Implicit rule of how we ought to behave
5.   Position or rank within a group
6.   The extent to which people are perceived as a coherent whole
7.   Reduction in motivation and effort that occurs when individuals work as a group
8.   Splintering of a group into distinct factions

Down

2.   Forces that cause members to remain as part of a group
3.   People who perceive themselves to be bonded together in a coherent unit to some degree

Created by Puzzlemaker at DiscoverySchool.com

When you have finished… You be the Researcher

Your task is to design a study investigating the relationship between the number of people in a group and the construct of social facilitation. Remember, social facilitation can result in either improved performance or a reduction in the quality of a performance.

You are to determine your hypothesis, who your participants are, the method(s) of data collection you will use, and the hypothetical results. You will then draw conclusions from your results.

You will report your study and its' findings in APA format using the research of Zajonc, Heingartner and Herman (1969) as one of the sources for your introduction. The other **three** sources will come from your library research on the topic.

Remember the "participants" used in the research of Zajonc, Heingartner and Herman (1969). Who or "what" will your participants be???!!?? Research does NOT have to be boring…

Answers - As You Read...Practice Activities

1. A group is a collection of people who perceive themselves as being bonded to one another in a coherent unit to some degree.

    A common bond group is one in which individuals within the group are tied to each other in some way. There is much face to face contact within a common bond group.

    A common identity group is one in which group members are connected through the category as a whole. That is, they are more connected to the group than to each other.

2. Entitativity is defined as the extent to which the group is perceived as a coherent whole.

    Groups that are high in entitativity tend to have four characteristics:

    1. The members often interact with each other.

    2. The group is important to its members.

    3. Members share a common goal.

    4. Members are similar to each other.

3. Similarly to "real" groups, members of YouTube can either be high or low identifying members. Viewers tend to be loyal to those bloggers within the YouTube community. There also tends to be a polarization to the point of view of others within the YouTube population. Therefore, one could, certainly, determine that YouTube is a real group.

4. Status refers to one's position or rank within a particular group.

    Some factors that play a role in the acquisition of status within a group include:

    1. Physical attributes, including height.

    2. An individual's behavior. Is the individual a prototypical member of the group?

5. A role different tasks that are assigned to certain individuals within a group.

6. A norm is an implicit rule that tells us how to behave in certain situations. Norms are part of all societies.

    The norm is individualistic cultures is to be different than others and to stand out from the group. The norm in c collectivistic cultures is to be a part of the group and harmony among group members.

7. Cohesiveness can be defined as all of the forces that cause members to remain as part of the group.

    Cohesive groups see themselves as one entity, are supportive of each other, have high confidence levels, and perform much better than non-cohesive groups.

8. The benefits of joining a group include:

    1. Groups help us gain self-knowledge.

    2. Groups help us reach our goals.

    3. Groups help us accomplish goals that we, alone, could not accomplish.

9. The impact of an initiation through extreme means tends to increase our

commitment to the group. Aronson and Mills (1959) provided support for this tendency in their study. This is consistent with the theory of cognitive dissonance in which individuals begin to feel discomfort when their attitudes and behaviors are opposed.

10. Groups tend to intrude on one's individual freedom by making the group's norms superior to one's individual norms. If one does not behave as is expected for a group member, they are subjected to sanctions by the group. These sanctions may include being kicked out of the group.

11. Participants: One thousand priests and deacons in the Church of England.

   Method of data collection: Personal interview

   Data collected: Priests and deacons were asked their views about the new policy of allowing women to become priests within the Church. They were also asked to give their opinion of the extent to which this change had affected the Church. In addition, an assessment was made to determine how much each identified with the Church, the degree to which they felt personally distressed by the ordination of women, and whether or not they believed that their views would be heard.

   Results: Priests and deacons who left the Church did so because they felt that the ordination of women had changed the fundamental doctrines of the Church. They also felt very strongly that their opinions did not count. Their group identity was, simply put, threatened by this change which led to the schism of the Church of England.

12. In 1969, Zajonc, Heingartner and Herman arranged the cockroaches in a maze and had them run the maze. They also had a cockroach audience that observed the participants as they ran the maze. The participants knew that they were being observed by the audience. Findings showed that cockroaches that were being watched tended to run the maze faster than those who were not being observed.

   Triplett (1898) found this same phenomenon when he noted that cyclists tended to ride faster when they were being observed than when not being observed. He also found that adolescents who were winding fishing line tended to wind faster when they were being observed.

13. Huguet, Galvaing, Monteil, and Dumas (1999) found that the presence of others generates increased arousal due to the cognitive demands of paying attention both to the audience and to the task of performing. Hetherington, Anderson, Norton, and Newson (2006) found that those who ate a meal with others while watching TV tended to eat faster than those not involved in watching TV or eating with others.

   The line of thought followed is that increased cognitive demands increase timing of task performance.

14. Social loafing refers to the idea that the presence of others can result in a decrease in motivation and effort to perform the task. This increases with the number of others present.

   Matching: A, C, D, B

15. 1. Make sure each participant is responsible for the completion of a particular task.

    2. Increasing the group members' commitment to a successful completion of the task.

    3. Increase the value or importance of the task.

4. Viewing the idea that each member's contribution is not redundant to the contributions of others.

16. Deindividuation refers to the idea that being anonymous makes individuals less responsible for their behavior.

Discuss the research of Zimbardo (1970), Postmes and Spears (1998), Stott, Adlang, Livingstone, and Schreiber (2007), as well as Johnson and Downing (1979).

17. 1. The goals are not shared by the individual.

2. Cooperation may not allow the individual to portray the "good" image he or she is hoping to depict.

18. A social dilemma is defined as a situation in which every individual can increase his or her gains by behaving in a selfish manner, but if the majority of individuals behave in the same way, the outcomes experienced by all are reduced.

In the prisoners' dilemma, two suspects are caught by police and either one or both can choose to cooperate or compete. If both of the suspects cooperate, they will both gain. If both compete, each will lose. If one competes and one cooperates, the one who cooperates will gain, while the other one loses.

19. Since Uli has been ostracized in the past, this will tend to lower her desire to cooperate in the future.

20. Conflict involves that existence of incompatible interests and the acknowledgment of this fact by all parties involved.

Give an example of a conflict you have experienced due to membership in a group. This group may be your family, if you choose.

21. 1. Faulty attributions = errors that we make concerning what has led to another's behavior.

2. Faulty communications = individuals may communicate with others in a way that irritates the other party.

3. Conflict may come from poor initial performance by the group. Group members may blame each other for this assessment.

22. 1. Bargaining = Synonymous with negotiation. Opposing sides exchange offers, counteroffers, and concessions, either directly or through representatives. If successful, an amicable solution is reached. If not, deadlock may result which will tend to intensify the conflict.

2. Superordinate goals = These are goals that both sides try to obtain and that tend to tie the interests of both groups together.

23. 1. Distributive justice = involves the results we and others achieve. The equity rule states that rewards should be divided according to the group members according to their contributions. Therefore, if one puts in more than another individual, he or she should obtain a larger reward.

2. Procedural justice = involves the fairness of the procedure that determine the distribution of rewards.

3. Transactional justice = involves the way in which the information about the outcomes and procedures are given to us.

24. Common reactions to unfairness include:

    A. Regarding distributive justice, people focus on changing (in this case, reducing) their degree of their contributions or insist upon larger rewards.

    B. Regarding procedural justice or transactional justice, people tend to often turn towards covert techniques to even the score.

25. Group polarization refers to the idea that groups tend to adopt more extreme position than members are likely to adopt alone. This change towards the more extreme positions is known as the risky shift.

26. 1. Social comparison.

    2. During group discussions, most disagreements tend to favor the group's initial preference.

27. Groupthink occurs when cohesiveness reaches very high levels. Groupthink is a powerful inclination to for decision making groups to lock into a certain decision and to assume that this decision cannot be wrong.

    According to Haslam et al. (2006), groupthink can be dangerous when the decisions that members lock onto are very poor decisions.

    According to Tetlock et al. (1992) and Kameda and Sugimori (1993), groupthink occurs because of a high level of cohesiveness and due to emergent groups norms. Emergent group norms are norms that suggest that the group is not capable of making a wrong decision, is morally superior to others, and that the decision is made.

28. Hornsey and Imani (2004) asked their participants, Australian college students to read comments that were either positive or negative. The comments were attributed either to an Australian, an individual from another country who had never lived in Australia, or to a person from another country who had, at one time, lived in Australia. Students then evaluated the extent to which the individual's comments were constructive.

    When the comments were positive, it made no difference. When the comments were negative, the comments and the person making them were viewed as more negative when this person was an out-group member.

29. Gigone and Hastie (1997) and Stasser (1992) found that bias can occur when decisions are made reflecting shared information. Unfortunately, this is a problem when the information shared does not point to the best decision.

30. The answer is "not necessarily." You are to provide research evidence to support this claim.

Answers – Cross Word Puzzle

Across

1. conflict
4. norm
5. status
6. entitativity
7. socialloafing
8. schism

Down

2. cohesiveness
3. group

Answers – Practice Test #1

1. C
2. B
3. C
4. C
5. C
6. B
7. A
8. A
9. D
10. D
11. distraction-conflict theory
12. social loafing
13. overt
14. procedural justice
15. group polarization

Answers – Practice Test #2

1. C
2. C
3. A
4. A
5. D
6. D
7. D
8. B
9. A
10. B
11. bargaining
12. equity
13. obligatory interdependence
14. group
15. personal

Answers – Practice Test #3

1. A
2. B
3. D
4. A
5. D
6. A
7. A
8. D
9. A
10. D
11. cognitive load
12. cohesiveness
13. risk
14. decrease
15. group

Answers – Practice Test #4

1. B
2. B
3. A
4. C
5. C
6. A
7. C
8. D
9. A
10. D
11. superordinate
12. emergent group
13. guards and prisoners
14. solidarity
15. increase

CHAPTER 12

SOCIAL PSYCHOLOGY:
APPLYING ITS PRINCIPLES TO LAW, HEALTH, AND BUSINESS

Before You Read...Chapter Summary

Chapter Twelve begins with a discussion of the differences in the crime rate between the 1970/1980 time period and the early 1990's. The change, which was definitely for the better, is ultimately credited to William Bratton who was named chief of police in 1994 and Rudy Giuliani, mayor of New York. Your author includes this discussion is to bring a point to the surface – that we really do see psychology all around us. In this case, Chief Bratton used many of the principles you have already learned in your textbook. In this chapter, you will increase your knowledge base of social psychology. Section one addresses how social influences play a role in the events that take place prior to a case going to court. For example, this section provides a lengthy discussion of the ways in which social influence can be used in the initial police interrogation as well as in the lineup procedure. Section one also speaks to the effects that the media can have on our perception of defendants. Have you every wondered about the accuracy of eye witness testimony? You will find an answer to your questions in this chapter when a discussion of the accuracy of eye witness testimony is presented. It appears to be a long-standing opinion of some that the constructs of prejudice and stereotyping are alive and well and living in our justice system. You will learn about the physical characteristics of both the defendants and the jurors that can influence the court proceedings.

Section two of this chapter concentrates on the connection between social psychology and health. Here, you will learn about the role that attitudes can play in one's personal health. You will also learn about obesity and its threat to health. Finally, in this section, you will find an extensive discussion concerning the effects of high level stress on human beings. In addition, to discussing the effects of stress, you will also learn of several ways that can be employed to alleviate stress.

The final section of this chapter, explores the connection between social psychology and work. Within this section, you will read of some of the causes of job satisfaction. In addition, you will learn of the idea of prosocial behavior in the workplace as well as some of the basic forms in which this prosocial behavior is displayed. Finally, you will find a discussion of leadership behavior in the workplace.

Before You Read... Learning Objectives

After reading this chapter, you should be able to:

- Discuss the role social influence plays in police interrogation, lineups, and media coverage of legal cases prior to their going to trial.
- Understand the two approaches used in police interrogations.
- Discuss the role of *social influence* plays in the use of deadly force by the police.
- Give support to the idea that *eyewitness test*imony is inaccurate.
- Expand on the roles of emotion, time, memory distortion and initial construction of such memories play in the inaccuracy of eyewitness testimony.
- Delineate ways in which eyewitness testimony can increase in accuracy.
- Explain how prejudice and stereotyping can influence the legal system.
- Answer the question – "Can the effects of prejudice on legal proceedings be reduced?.
- Discuss the connection between *social psychology* and *health*.
- Understand the role of attitudes in personal health.
- Discuss obesity as a major threat to one's health.
- Provide a discussion of the causes, effects and control of stress.
- Discuss some of the major causes of stress and what effect stress can have on personal health.
- Explain the role stress can play on health.
- Answer the question – how are work related attitudes related to job satisfaction?
- Name some of the causes of job satisfaction.
- Discuss the phenomenon of prosocial behavior at work.
- Name and explain some of the basic forms of prosocial behavior at work.
- Understand how helping at work can both benefit the organization and the individual.
- Discuss the role of leadership in group settings.
- Explain why some people make good leaders and other do not.
- Name and discuss the basic dimensions of leadership behavior.
- Explain the role of the follower.
- Discuss the difference between transactional and transformational leaders.
- Describe how one can make a good impression in a job interview.

As You Read...Term Identification

Important Terms to Know
Below are a list of some of the key terms and concepts from this chapter. Make flashcards in order to enhance your recall ability of these terms. Refer to the definitions that are either in boldface or in the margins of this chapter for help. You may also want to include additional terms from this chapter as you deem necessary.

inquisitorial approach, (p. 420)	obese, (p. 435)	sportsmanship, (p. 447)
adversarial approach, (p. 420)	stress, (p. 436)	courtesy, (p. 447)
lineup, (p. 423)		social dilemma, (p. 447)
misuse of deadly force, (p. 424)	hassles, (p. 438)	distributive justice, (p. 448)
eyewitness testimony, (p. 425)	immune system, (p. 439)	procedural justice, (p. 448)
memory construction, (p. 427)	social support, (p. 440)	leadership, (p. 449)
memory, (p. 427)	industrial organizational psychologists, (p. 442)	
fuzzy-trace theory, (p. 428)	job satisfaction, (p. 443)	great person theory of leadership, (p. 449)
cognitive interviews, (p. 428)	positive affectivity–negative affectivity, (p. 445)	initiating structure, (p. 451)
defendant, (p. 429)	organizational citizenship behavior, (p. 447)	consideration, (p. 451)
double blind procedure, (p. 429)	altruism, (p. 447)	transactional leaders, (p. 453)
health psychology, (p. 432)	conscientiousness, (p. 447)	
self efficacy, (p. 434)	civic virtue, (p. 447)	

As You Read...Practice Activities

SOCIAL PSYCHOLOGY AND THE LEGAL SYSTEM

Connecting What You Already Know with Our Legal System...
(Social Psychology and the Legal System, pages 420-425)

1.   What types of social influence are seen within the legal system?

    _____

    _____

    _____

    _____

Eni Meni Mini Mo – To Which Approach Do We Go?
(Police Interrogations: Using Social Influence to Get at the Truth, pages 420-422)

2.   Mario is a police detective and is often in charge of interrogating suspects. There are two ways in which Mario can go about performing this duty. Name and discuss each approach.

    1. _____

    _____

    2. _____

    _____

Coercive - Coercion...
(Police Interrogations: Using Social Influence to Get at the Truth, page 420-422)

3.   Tim's family is very concerned. Tim was arrested for beating up a fellow student while the two were at a frat party. Tim, though, swears left and right that he is not guilty. The night that he was arrested, he was under the influence of alcohol and admitted that he had committed the crime when, in actuality, he had not. In other words, Tim was "coerced" into making a confession.

    Under what conditions do individuals tend to admit to crimes that they did not commit?

    _____

    _____

Coercion Reduction 101...
(Police Interrogations: Using Social Influence to Get at the Truth, page 420-422)

4.   Your textbook delineates on potential avenue through which can be avoided. Discuss this
        possibility.

        _____

        _____

        _____

The Pertinence of Location...
(Police Interrogations: Using Social Influence to Get at the Truth, page 420-422)

5.   Location is an important factor in many decisions. For example, let's say you are buying a house.
        You have three young children, two of which will be attending elementary school next year and
        you want to live in a neighborhood that is zoned to a particular school. Therefore, you will most
        likely pay particular attention to houses that are for sale in one of the neighborhoods zoned to the
        desired school.

        Likewise, location is important to the interrogation process. Discuss the importance of the
        location in which police interrogations take place.

        _____

        _____

        _____

Other Tactics of Interrogation...
*(Additional Tactics of Interrogation: How Social Influence is Actually Used in Such Procedures,
page 422)*

6.   Name the additional tactics as discussed in your textbook.

        _____

        _____

        _____

        Now, discuss the research of Kassin and Kiechel (1996) regarding the tactics discussed above.

        _____

        _____

        _____

Other Tactics of Interrogation...Continued

_____

_____

Dos Typos...
Lineups: How Subtle Social Pressure Sometimes Leads to Tragic Errors, page 423)

7.   What is a *lineup*?

_____

_____

What is the difference between a *sequential* and a *simultaneous lineup*?

_____

_____

_____

_____

Everyone Line Up...
(Lineups: How Subtle Social Pressure Sometimes Leads to Tragic Errors, page 423)

8.   What impact do the instructions given to witnesses have on the lineup procedure?

_____

_____

The Media – A Positive or a Negative Thing??
(Effect of Media Coverage on Perceptions of Defendants, pages 423-424)

9.   Sally has been selected to participate as a juror in a trial involving a gentleman who is accused of murdering his wife's mother. The first day the jury is given instructions not to watch the TV news or listen to news-talk radio for the duration of the trial. Why was this instruction given? In other words, what effect do the media have on our perception of the person on trial?

_____

_____

_____

A Heated Debate: Should the Police be able to Use Deadly Force if They Deem it Necessary?
(Social Influence and Judgments Concerning the Use of Deadly Force by Police, pages 424-425)

10.   This has been a long-standing debate. Should the police be allowed to use deadly force if they feel it is necessary? To add something extra to the pot, should the police be allowed to use deadly force if they feel it is necessary even if that might mean shooting someone who may not be armed? You most likely have your own ideas concerning this issue.

Discuss the research conducted by Perkins and Bourgeois (2006) investigating the issue of the use of deadly force.

_____

_____

_____

_____

_____

_____

No Wonder Eyewitness Testimony is Often NOT Allowed in Court...
(Social Cognition and the Legal System: Why Eyewitness Testimony is Often Inaccurate, pages 425-426)

11.   What is meant by *eyewitness testimony*?

_____

_____

According to Wells (1993), Loftus (2003) and Zaragoza et al. (2001), how reliable is eyewitness testimony?

_____

_____

_____

_____

Eyewitness Testimony is Highly Unreliable – But, Why?
(The Role of Emotion: Affect and Cognition Revisited, page 426)

12.   Alexandra was a witness to a fatal car accident last year. Immediately following the accident, Alexandra was questioned by police and gave her interpretation of what had happened in the accident. She was then asked to view a lineup. Alexandra was very quick to point out a

Eyewitness Testimony is Highly Unreliable – But, Why?...Continued

gentleman with long hair, a beard, a height of 6'4" and a weight of around 215 lbs. Since that time Alexandra has read information regarding eyewitness testimony and is concerned that she may have pointed out the wrong gentleman. In other words, she is concerned that she may have made an error. Unfortunately, this is more the rule than the exception.

Why do errors in eyewitness testimony occur so often?

_____

_____

_____

Another Obstacle To Be Overcome…
(Time and Intervening Information, page 426)

13.   Time is another obstacle to the accuracy of eyewitness testimony. Explain how time can be an obstacle.

_____

_____

_____

Possibly A "Fuzzy Plant"- or Is it a "Planty Fuzz?"
(Memory Distortions and Constructions, pages 427-428)

14.   What is *memory construction*?

_____

_____

_____

From where do we get these false memories? Name and discuss the two ways discussed within your textbook.

1. _____

_____

2. _____

_____

Can We Improve the Accuracy of Eyewitness Testimony? If So, How…
(Increasing Eyewitness Accuracy, pages 428-429)

15.   Danny is taking a criminal justice class this semester. In this class, they are currently discussing the accuracy of eyewitness testimony. Thus far, the class has discussed how inaccurate eyewitness testimony is; but, has not gone into how the accuracy in eyewitness testimony can be improved.

You are a friend of Danny's and have just studied eyewitness testimony in your social psychology class. Danny asks you for your opinion on how the accuracy can be improved. Knowing what you know, you provide Danny with two suggestions. What are they?

1. _____

_____

2. _____

_____

3. _____

_____

Seeing a Lineup Through the Eyes of a Social Psychologist…
(Increasing Eyewitness Accuracy, page 428-429)

16.   In what ways is a police lineup analogous to a social psychology experiment? You may use the following schematic to provide an answer to this question.

Primary Experimenter: _____

Participants: _____

_____

Stimulus: _____

Response Data: _____

_____

Research Design: _____

_____

Seeing a Lineup Through the Eyes of a Social Psychologist...Continued

Hypothesis: _____

_____

Probability:

_____

_____

Using "Fillers" as a Method of Improving Accuracy...
(Increasing Eyewitness Accuracy, page 428-429)

17.   Your textbook identifies additional ways in which eyewitness accuracy can be improved. One of these is the use of "fillers" in the lineup. What are the others?

_____

_____

_____

_____

_____

An Early Classic – Musterberg (1907)
(Early Evidence that Even "Expert" Eyewitnesses Are Inaccurate: Munsterberg's Ingenious Research, pages 426-427)

18.   Are eyewitnesses to crimes really accurate? Are there limits to their memory and their emotions that lead eyewitnesses to serious error?

These two questions catapulted Munsterberg into the classics in social psychology hall of fame. How did Munsterberg address these two questions and what were his findings?

_____

_____

_____

_____

_____

Characteristics of the Defendant and How They Affect Jury Decisions...
(The Influence of Prejudice and Stereotypes on the Legal System, pages 429-431)

19.   Rose has been accused of stealing approximately $1,500 worth of clothing from a local department store. Today her case is coming before the court. Rose is physically attractive, white, and of a high socioeconomic status.
        According to research findings, what is the jury likely to decide?

_____

_____

Defendant Characteristics and How They Affect Jury Decisions – Continued...
(The Influence of Prejudice and Stereotypes on the Legal System, page 429-431)

20.   Match the researcher(s) with their findings:

_____ Downs and Lyons (1991)

_____ Cruse and Leigh (1987)

_____ Mazzella and Feingold (1994)

_____ Harris and Weiss (1995)

_____ Schutte and Hosch (1997)

       A.   Women were more likely than men to vote for conviction.
       B.   Attractive defendants tend to receive a lighter sentence and gain more sympathy from jurors than do unattractive defendants.
       C.   In a rape trial, men are more likely than women to conclude that the sexual interaction was consensual.
       D.   If someone is physically attractive, female and of high socioeconomic status they are more likely to be acquitted than are people who do not fit into this categorization.
       E.   In cases involving assault, women are more likely to found guilty than are male defendants because assault is considered to be an unacceptable behavior for women.

And, According to The Model of Information Processing...
(The Influence of Prejudice and Stereotypes on the Legal System, page 429-431)

21.   The way jurors process information has also been shown to have an effect on decision making. What is this influence?

_____

_____

_____

Subtle and Nonconscious Prejudice and Jury Deliberations...
(Can The Effects of Prejudice on Legal Proceedings Be Reduced? Pages 430-431)

22.   In 2006, Botwell et al., investigated how jury deliberations may possibly serve to reduce the impact of subtle and nonconsious prejudice. Describe this research using the following outline.

Participants: _____

_____

Procedure: _____

_____

_____

_____

Independent variable(s): _____

_____

_____

Dependent variable: _____

_____

Results: _____

_____

_____

A Link – Social Psychology and Health...
(Social Psychology and Health, pages 432-433)

23.   Dr. Stanley Martinez is a social psychologist who is interested in the link between psychological constructs and health. In particular, he is interested in the connection between workplace stress and one's long-term health. There is a very high probability that Dr. Martinez is, more appropriately, a health psychologist.

What is *health psychology*?

_____

_____

Longitudinal Research: Research Conducted Over a LONG Period of Time…
(Social Psychology and Health, page 432-433)

24.   Wiley and Camacho, 1980, conducted a longitudinal study over a ten year period investigating beneficial health practices. These included sleep habits (7 – 8 hours per night), eating breakfast daily, refraining from smoking, drinking alcohol in moderation or not drinking alcohol at all, maintaining a normal weight, and exercising regularly. What did Wiley and Camacho find?

_____

_____

_____

Attitudes Also Play a Role…
(The Role of Attitudes in Personal Health: Promoting a Healthy Lifestyle, pages 433-435)

25.   Levy et al., conducted a study in 2002 in which they measured participants' self-perceptions of aging. In other words, they investigated their participants' beliefs about what was going to happen to them as they grew older. Discuss this study.

_____

_____

_____

_____

_____

_____

The Fat and Thin of It…
(Obesity: A Social Psychological Perspective on a Major Threat to Health, pages 435-436)

26,   There are three types of factors that contribute to weight gain around the world. Name and discuss each.

1._____

_____

2._____

_____

_____

The Fat and Thin of It...Continued

3._____

_____

Thin Appears to Be the Norm...
(Anti-Fat Attitudes, page 436)

27.   Hebl and Mannix (2003) investigated the growing prejudice towards people who are very obese.
       Discuss this study and its findings.

_____

_____

_____

_____

Now, discuss the study of Crandall et al. (2001) investigating prejudice towards those who are
obese.

_____

_____

_____

_____

STRESS...
(Stress: Its Causes, Effects, and Control, pages 436-441)

28.   George has just found out that his job is being eliminated from the company due to downsizing.
       Yesterday, he discovered that his blood pressure was, as he terms it, "ski high" and last week he
       was told that his son needed braces ASAP due to a misalignment of his teeth. In other words,
       George is experiencing a high degree of something we call STRESS!!

What is stress?

_____

_____

Sources of Stress...

(Major Sources of Stress and Their Effects on Personal Health, pages 437-439)

29.   David's grandfather died. Marcia's grandchild is recovering from surgery. Alice's husband has just found out that he has cancer. Tammie recently discovered that she was pregnant. Mark's job is requiring much more of his time recently. Rick is having major financial problems and may lose his house. Evan's son wrecked his car last weekend and the car had to be totaled. Talk about STRESS!!!

Though stress is defined in one way throughout all of the situations above, the effects that stress has on the individual experiencing the stress varies from person to person. Holmes and Rahe (1967) investigated the effect of stress on the individual. Discuss their study. Be sure to include a discussion of the results.

_____

_____

_____

_____

Stress...Acute or Chronic??

(Major Sources of Stress and Their Effects on Personal Health, page 437-439)

30.   Describe the work of Cohen et al. (1998). Make sure that you provide a definition for acute stress and chronic stress in your answer.

_____

_____

_____

_____

At Times, Life Can be Such a Hassle...

(Major Sources of Stress and Their Effects on Personal Health, page 437-439)

31.   How many times have you said to yourself or to someone else that you life is full of "hassles?" What did you mean by this? That is, what is a hassle? Name four of the hassles in your present life.

_____

_____

_____

_____

Okay, Now for the Particulars...How Does Stress Influence our Health?
(How Does Stress Affect Health? Pages 439-440)

32.   What is the mechanism by which stress affects our health?

_____

_____

_____

_____

What is the impact of stress upon the immune system? Within your answer include the effect of stress on lymphocytes and cortisol. You should also explain what lymphocytes and cortisol are.

_____

_____

_____

_____

Direct versus Indirect...
(How Does Stress Affect Health? Page 439-440)

33.   In question 32, the *direct* effects of stress were addressed. What are some of the *indirect* effects of stress?

_____

_____

_____

_____

Sometimes the Acknowledgment of the Presence of the Stress is Half the Battle...
(Coping with Stress, pages 440-441)

34.   There are many ways in which individuals try to cope with the stress within their lives. One way that individuals attempt to cope with stress is through seeking social support.

What is social support?

_____

_____

Sometimes the Acknowledgment of the Presence of the Stress is Half the Battle…Continued

Using your thinking skills, how do you think that social support would act as a "buffer" against stress?

_____

_____

_____

_____

_____

An Added Value of Pets…
(Coping with Stress, pages 440-441)

35.   There is one "common sense" source of social support. It is man's best friend – the dog – as well as other kinds of pets. How can a pet provide social support? What kind of social support can a pet provide?

_____

_____

_____

_____

What is the connection between pets and blood pressure?

_____

_____

Did You Know That Married Men Live Longer Lives Than Unmarried Men??!!?
(Coping with Stress, page 440-441)

36.   What is the connection between stress and marital status?

_____

_____

SOCIAL PSYCHOLOGY AND THE WORLD OF WORK

The Workplace as a "Social" Setting...
(Introduction, page 442)

37.   Allister P. Mortimore, PhD, is a psychologist who studies behavior and cognition in the workplace. Therefore, Dr. Mortimore is what type of psychologist?

_____

Two Attitudes Common to the Workplace...
(Work-Related Attitudes: The Nature and Effects of Job Satisfaction, pages 442-446)

38.   We spend a lot of time working and, therefore, in the workplace. According to your textbook, we tend to harbor some very strong attitudes towards our workplace as well as our job, itself. Within this section, these two types of attitudes are named. What are the terms that belong with these two types of attitudes?

Attitudes concerning our job, itself = _____.

Attitudes concerning the company (workplace) = _____

_____.

Of Course, I am Satisfied with My Job...Now, Tell Me Why...
(Job Satisfaction: Its Causes, pages 443-446)

39.   Research into why individuals are satisfied with their jobs has pointed toward two groups of factors. Name these two groups.

1. _____

2. _____

Now, discuss the first group by providing some of the research findings delineated within your textbook.

_____

_____

_____

_____

_____

_____

Of Course, I am Satisfied with My Job...Now, Tell Me Why...Continued

Finally, discuss the second group by providing some of the research findings delineated within your textbook.

_____

_____

_____

_____

_____

_____

_____

_____

Twins and Job Satisfaction...
(Job Satisfaction: Its Causes, pages 443-446)

40. Sarah and Tarah are twins. If there were to have participated in the 1989 study conducted by Arvey et al., what would this say about their levels of job satisfaction? That is, what, exactly, were the results of this study?

_____

_____

_____

_____

_____

What percentage of the variation in job satisfaction tends to be due to genetic factors?

_____

Does Happiness Tend to Increase One's Production?
(Are Happy Workers Productive Workers? The Attitude-Behavior Link Revisited, pages 445-446)

41. Your task, here, is to answer the question posed above using research evidence.

_____

_____

Does Happiness Tend to Increase One's Production?...Continued

_____

_____

_____

_____

_____

_____

_____

_____

A Look Back – Prosocial Behavior…
(Organizational Citizenship Behavior: Prosocial Behavior at Work & The Nature of Prosocial Behavior at Work: Some Basic Forms, pages 446-449)

42.　　After Chapter Nine, it is without a doubt that the definition of prosocial behavior is etched forever in your mind. That being said, provide a definition of prosocial behavior.

_____

_____

　　Now, apply the definition of prosocial behavior to the concept of organizational citizenship behavior or OCB.

_____

_____

_____

_____

Matching…How Much Fun Can You Have in One Day?!?
(The Nature of Prosocial Behavior at Work: Some Basic Forms, page 447)

43.　　Individual employees help others at work in a wide variety of ways. Research has, though, placed these acts into five basic categories.

Matching…How Much Fun Can You Have in One Day?!?…Continued

In this activity, match the category with its description.

_____   Conscientiousness

_____   Altruism

_____   Sportsmanship

_____   Civic Virtue ,

_____   Courtesy

A.   When one makes efforts to avert any interpersonal issues with others.
B.   Participating in and displaying concern for the organization itself.
C.   Helping other individuals perform their jobs.
D.   Displaying a willingness to tolerate poor work conditions without complaining.
E.   Going above and beyond.

If You are In a Social Quandary – You are In a Social Dilemma:
(Helping Others at Work as a Social Dilemma, pages 447-448)

44.   A social dilemma can be defined as a situation in which one's short-term personal interests are at odds with long-term collective interests. Apply the idea of the social dilemma to the concept of the social fence.

_____

_____

_____

Non-compliance in the Workplace? Certainly not…
(Helping Others at Work as a Social Dilemma, page 447-448)

45.   What is "non-compliance behavior?"

_____

_____

_____

Non-compliance in the Workplace? Certainly not...Continued

Apply the concept of non-compliance behavior to the idea of the social delayed trap.

_____

_____

_____

Influential Factors...
(Helping at Work: Other Factors that Influence its Occurrence, page 448)

46.   There are several factors that influence whether or not an individual will help another person at work. Complete the following word search puzzle to find some of these factors.

```
J L R N B T R I L I V D G Q A
P F A B G N S W C K E K X E O
L N T N E M T I M M O C J A B
D M T Z O K L L M C C N N N F
H B I P J I E U R R U N W F R
Z S T E V I T U B I R T S I D
B J U S P R O C E D U R A L R
E R D G I L G H A X X F T J Y
F Q E C I T S U J R U S U T F
L U S A Q P S O D O E P I W N
H W V O D L U D C I C T A W H
G W U M Y T F B D I N Y N O W
D W M O D Z H Z T E A S W I M
Z X W X L S F X D X H L V L E
X A V J Q A M I X Y T M I P G
```

Words To Find

ATTITUDES
COMMITMENT
FAIR
INTERACTIONAL
PROCEDURAL

BREADTH
DISTRIBUTIVE
IDENTITY
JUSTICE
SOCIAL

You Rub My Back and I Will Rub Yours...
(The Effects of Helping at Work: Beneficial for Both Organizations and Individuals, pages 448-449)

47. John was hospitalized last year when he broke his leg after falling from a ladder. In John's absence, Ron made sure that Ron's work was kept up to date. In addition, Ron made sure that John came back to a clear desk so that he would not have to play "kept-up" if he was still experiencing some set backs as a result of his injury.

 A week ago, Ron experienced some chest pain while out to dinner and was rushed to the hospital. It was found that Ron had had a major heart attack and he is now in the cardiac care unit in the hospital. He is expected to have open heart surgery in the next few days when his weakened condition has improved somewhat.

 Because of Ron's state and feeling obligated to give back to Ron what he (Ron) had given to him when he was hospitalized, John is planning to keep Ron's workload up to date. John intends to do this as a favor for Ron, so that he (Ron), too, will not have to worry about being behind when he returns to work.

 This scenario is illustrative of what principle?

 _____

 What is the pattern that has been found within research regarding this principle?

 _____

 _____

 _____

Leader = The Person in Charge...
Leadership: Influence in Group Settings, pages 449-454)

48. What is primarily involved in leadership and being a leader?

 _____

 _____

 _____

Dr. Martin Luther King, Jr. – A Great Person....
(Why do Some Persons but Not Others Become Leaders? Pages 449-450

49. Dr. Martin Luther King, Jr., President Ronald Reagan, Margaret Thatcher, Pope John Paul, as well as many others well-fit the definition of what it means to be a "great" person.

Dr. Martin Luther King, Jr. – A Great Person….Continued

What is this definition?

_____

_____

_____

Name two other individuals YOU would consider to be "great" persons.

1._____

2. _____

What are some "leadership characteristics?"

_____

_____

_____

Adolf Hitler – A Cruel, but Charismatic, Leader…
(Why do Some Persons but Not Others Become Leaders? Pages 449-450)

50.   Adolf Hitler is, perhaps, known as one of the most charismatic leaders in the history of the world. In fact, he was so charismatic that he managed to persuade and encourage those under him to kill an estimated 15 million persons, including Jews, homosexuals, gypsies, the infirmed, and the disabled.

When a leader is charismatic, what are two of the characteristics that he or she embodies?

1. _____

2. _____

Ryan and Haslam…
(Why do Some Persons but Not Others Become Leaders? Pages 449-450)

51.   The research findings of Ryan and Haslam (2007) suggests that women are more likely to be chosen to be in a position of leadership when what?

_____

_____

Ryan and Haslam...Continued

Why does this appear to be true?

_____

_____

_____

Dos Dimensions...
What do Leaders do? Basic Dimensions of Leader Behavior, pages 450-452)

52.   Discuss the two dimensions mentioned in your textbook that relate to an individual's overall
        approach to leadership.

        1. _____

        _____

        _____

        2. _____

        _____

        _____

Influence is a Two-Way Street...
(Leaders and Followers: Two Sides of the Same Coin, page 452)

53.   What is the interplay between leaders and followers?

        _____

        _____

        _____

Another Visit to the Charismatic Leader...
(Transactional and Transformational Leaders: Different Approaches, Different Effects, pages 450-453)

54.   What is a transformational leader?

        _____

        _____

Another Visit to the Charismatic Leader…Continued

What is the definition of charismatic? How is this term related to the transformational leader?

_____

_____

_____

_____

Transactional as Opposed to Transformational…
(Transactional and Transformational Leaders: Different Approaches, Different Effects, page 450-453)

55.   What is a transactional leader?

_____

_____

_____

_____

The First Impression…
(How to Make a Good First Impression in Job Interviews, pages 454-455)

56.   Discuss research findings on impression management.

_____

_____

_____

_____

_____

After You Read... MyPsychLab Connection

(1)   Have you ever thought about how the actual wording of a sentence or question can influence our response? If I were to tell you that a car "contacted" another car – how fast would you estimate that the car was traveling? On the other hand, if I were to ask you how fast a car was traveling when it "crashed" into another car – how fast would you estimate that the car was traveling? *WATCH: Eyewitness Testimony* for a description of a study conducted by Elizabeth Loftus regarding this phenomenon.

(2)   How do men tend to handle stress? The answer may be in ways in which you might not think. *WATCH: Men and Stress* to find out.

(3)   How do women tend to handle stress? The answer is quite different to the ways in which men handle it. You might just be surprised! *WATCH: Women and Stress* to find out.

After You Read... Practice Test #1

_____1.	Attorney use several social psychological constructs in their work. These include which of the following?

    A.	Aggression. C.	Persuasion.

    B.	Prosocial behavior. D.	Tolerance.

_____2.	Social influence plays an important role in ALL of the following EXCEPT

    A.	police interrogations. C.	arrests.

    B.	lineups. D.	media coverage of court cases.

_____3.	Inquisitional is to adversarial approach as

    A.	proving guilt is to seeking the truth.

    B.	forcefulness is to leniency.

    C.	seeking the truth is to proving guilty.

    D.	leniency is to forcefulness.

_____4.	Lassiter et al. (2002) conducted a study investigating the use of videotaping during police interrogations. This study

    A.	tested the hypothesis that jurors tend to have a preconceived idea about videotaped interrogations and are very unlikely to be seen as true

    B.	tested they hypothesis that jurors have the tendency to see any viewed confession as true and voluntary because the defendant is the center of attention.

    C.	there was one condition in which the camera focused primarily on the suspect.

    D.	there were two conditions – in one the camera focused primarily on the s suspect; while, in condition II, the camera was focused mainly on the interrogator.

_____5.	Gudjonsson and Clark (1986) found that both authority and location of the interrogation are important. The two serve to

    A.	reinforce the person's beliefs that the one asking the questions is an expert who possesses detailed knowledge of the case.

    B.	reinforce the person's beliefs that the one asking the questions is a lawyer.

    C.	reinforce the person's beliefs that the one asking the questions is only interested in getting a guilty confession from the individual being interrogated.

    D.	reinforce the person's beliefs that the one asking the questions is only there is coerce the individual being interrogated.

_____6.	Kassin and Kiechel (1996) found that police sometimes use false polygraph results, false fingerprint data, inaccurate eyewitness reports, and false information about the confession of a fellow suspect in order to

    A.	put the suspect at ease.

    B.	encourage the suspect to lie and give a confession to something that he did not do.

    C.	make sure the suspect knows how much power the person interrogating him or her has.

    D.	persuade the suspect to confess.

_____7.   Sequential is to simultaneous as
    A.   one at a time is to all at once.
    B.   all at once is to one at a time.
    C.   happening over a week's period is to happening in one day.
    D.   two at a time is to all at once.

_____8.   When one speaks of "the media", he or she is speaking of ALL of the following
    EXCEPT
    A.   a class lecture.
    B.   a magazine.
    C.   CNN.
    D.   *The New York Times*

_____9.   Evidence given by individuals who have observed a crime defines
    A.   interrogation.
    B.   arrest.
    C.   lineup.
    D.   eyewitness testimony.

_____10.   According to the fuzzy trace theory
    A.   we tend to make decisions based on previous experience.
    B.   we tend to make decisions based on our level of motivation.
    C.   we tend to make decisions based on characteristics of our personality.
    D.   we tend to make decisions based on the gist of our memories.

11.   When an eyewitness is asked to report everything that he or she can remember. He or she is

    being asked to do a(n) _____.

12.   A procedure in which a witness is first shown a lineup of innocent non-suspects only is called

    a(n) _____.

13.   In a(n) _____ procedure, neither the researcher nor the

    participants know which experimental group the participants are in.

14.   Munsterberg's 1907 study was conducted in an unusual setting. The study was conducted during

    a meeting of the proceeding of the _____.

15.   A(n) _____ is best defined as the person on trial.

After You Read... Practice Test #2

_____1.   All of the following characteristics have been shown to influence jury decisions, except
A.   race.
B.   gender.
C.   ethnic background.
D.   marital status.

_____2.   Findings among African Americans living in the United States have shown that
A.   African Americans are less likely than whites to be convicted of murder.
B.   African Americans, if convicted, are more likely to receive the death penalty.
C.   Whites are proportionally over-represented on death row.
D.   Both A and B are correct.

_____3.   Amber is a tall, slim woman with blonde hair and a smile that lights up a room. In other words, Amber is quite physically attractive. Today, she is on trial for theft. According to the prosecutor, Amber was caught stealing clothing from a local clothing retailer. Research findings have consistently shown that
A.   it is more difficult for attractive individuals to get adequate representation in court.
B.   an attractive individual has more of a chance of receiving a light sentence than someone who is not physically attractive.
C.   an attractive individual will tend to receive less sympathy from women than from men.
D.   All of the above are correct.

_____4.   Van is a male and Sarah is a female. Both are on trial for murder. According to research findings, Sarah, as well as other females, are
A.   more likely to be treated with leniency.
B.   more likely to be found guilty of crimes involving weapons than are males.
C.   more likely to receive a fair jury decision.
D.   more likely to be convicted of a crime than are males.

_____5.   Regarding the way in which jurors process information
A.   about 30% have already made up their minds by the time the opening statements are made.
B.   as the trial progresses, 75% – 85% begin to favor one side over the other.
C.   confirmation biases may arise.
D.   All of the above are correct.

_____6.   False memories are
A.   memories for events that have actually happened; the person remembering the events, though, is not sure if the memories are accurate.
B.   memories for events that never took place.
C.   memories for negative information.
D.   memories for the gist of the information stored in the individual's memory.

_____7.   The belief held by an individual, that he or she is capable of accomplishing what they set out to accomplish is known as
    A.   self-confidence.
    B.   self-efficacy.
    C.   self-reliance.
    D.   self-esteem.

_____8.   Social factors have been shown to contribute to the epidemic of obesity in the United States. These factors include all of the following except
    A.   people are not walking as much as they used to, possibly due to fear of crime.
    B.   the abundance of high calorie meals and snacks.
    C.   the fast food industry.
    D.   the lack of finances – enough money to buy healthy foods.

_____9.   Major is to minor as
    A.   life event is to hassle.
    B.   hassle is to life event.
    C.   death of a spouse is to having to wash clothes.
    D.   Both A and C are correct.

_____10.   Acute is to chronic as
    A.   brief is to Long-term.
    B.   long-term is to brief.
    C.   the common cold is to cancer.
    D.   Both A and C are correct.

11.   _____ is defined as a response to events that have the tendency to disrupt, or threaten to disrupt, our physical and/or psychological functioning.

12.   Pam recently lost her father to cancer. Unfortunately, her father was the last relative that she had who was living. Fortunately, though, Pam has a large group of friends and co-workers with whom she is very close. Pam will be able to draw the much needed emotional encouragement she needs right now from this vast group of individuals. This group of individuals is Pam's

_____.

13.   Attitudes toward one's job is to attitudes toward the company for which one works as

_____ is to _____.

14.   Helping others to perform their jobs is the definition of _____.

15.   In a type of social dilemma known as a(n) _____ there is a trade off between short-term individual coasts and the long-term collective benefits.

After You Read... Practice Test #3

_____1.   The mechanism through which our body recognizes and destroys potentially harmful substances and intruders such as bacteria, viruses, and cancerous cells are our
   A.   lymphatic system.
   B.   hormonal system.
   C.   immune system.
   D.   glandular system.

_____2.   According to your textbook, pets, including dogs and cats,
   A.   can lower one's blood pressure.
   B.   provide nonjudgmental social support.
   C.   reduce stress in their owners.
   D.   All of the above are true.

_____3.   Psychologists who specialize in studying all forms of behavior and cognition in work settings are called
   A.   industrial-organizational psychologists.
   B.   employment psychologists.
   C.   organizational psychologists.
   D.   company employment psychologists.

_____4.   Research investigating job satisfaction has found
   A.   job satisfaction is highly related to one's pay.
   B.   those who have been at a particular job for an extended period tend to like their jobs the least.
   C.   type A personalities are more satisfied with their jobs than type B personalities.
   D.   those with a lower status at work are more satisfied with their jobs than those who are of a higher status.

_____5.   Civic virtue is to sportsmanship as
   A.   helping others perform their jobs is to showing a willingness to tolerate unfavorable conditions without complaining.
   B.   showing a willingness to tolerate unfavorable conditions without complaining is to going above and beyond the requirements at work.
   C.   participating in and showing concern for the life of the organization is to showing a willingness to tolerate unfavorable conditions without complaining.
   D.   making efforts to prevent interpersonal problems with others is to participating in and showing concern for the life of the organization.

_____6.   Do people get the rewards that reflect the size of their contributions to the organization is the definition for
   A.   interactional justice.
   B.   procedural justice.
   C.   distributive justice.
   D.   fair justice.

_____7.   All of the following except _____,are common characteristics
that seem to be consistent among leaders:
A.   their cognitive abilities
B.   aspects of their personality
C.   their motives and skills
D.   All of the above are correct.

_____8.   According to your textbook, a leader who has charisma, has tremendous ambition, and is
outstanding at communicating with others. Examples of charismatic leaders, include all
of the following except
A.   Adolf Hitler.
B.   John F. Kennedy.
C.   Winston Churchill.
D.   All of the above can be thought of as charismatic leaders.

_____9.   Are some people more suited for leadership than others? In other words, do some people
possess leadership attributes and others not possess them? How do situational factors
mix with leader attributes? Ryan and Haslam (2007) sought to answer this question.
What did they find?
A. Organizations facing very different conditions are more likely to choose women to be
their leaders than companies that face more ordinary conditions.
B. Organizations facing very difference conditions are more likely to choose men to be
their leaders than companies that face more ordinary conditions.
C. Different groups require different types of leaders.
D. Basically, all leaders are the same.

_____10.   Leaders who are high in task-orientation, have the primary concern of
A.   maintaining harmony in the office setting.
B.   establishing good working relationships with other employees.
C.   getting the job done.
D.   Both A and C are correct.

11.   Leaders who are low in the dimension of _____ tend to really not

care how they get along with their subordinates.

12.   _____ is a type of managerial style in which the manager has a

tendency to constantly look over the shoulders of his or her subordinates and tells subordinates

how to do all tasks.

13.   When a manager is highly admired and trusted by his or her subordinates , this manager is said to

be high in the characteristic of _____.

14.   When a manager acts as a mentor to his or her subordinates and is very interested in the

subordinates' needs for achievement, he or she is said to be high in the characteristic of

_____.

15.   _____ refers to an employee's attitude toward

his or her job.

After You Read... Practice Test #4

_____1.   Kassin and Kiechel (1996) found that
A.   police officers need to rely on force in order to get a confession.
B.   police officers should be supportive of the suspect(s) – a technique based on ingratiation.
C.   police officers do not have to use force to get a confession.
D.   Both B and C are correct.

_____2.   A _____ lineup is a lineup in which the suspects are presented one at a time.
A.   simultaneous
B.   singular
C.   sequential
D.   progressive

_____3.   When a person is given biased instructions for the lineup procedure, he or she
A.   is more likely to point out the correct suspect
B.   is more likely to feel pressure to choose one of the suspects
C.   is less likely to feel pressure to choose one of the suspects
D.   biased instructions make no difference

_____4.   The greater the publicity of a crime
A.   the lesser the tendency of jurors to convict whoever is accused of committing the crime
B.   the greater the tendency of jurors to acquit whoever is accused of committing the crime
C.   the greater the tendency of jurors to convict whoever is accused of committing the crime
D.   publicity makes no difference in conviction or acquittal

_____5.   Testimony that is given by persons who have witnessed a crime is termed
A.   natural testimony
B.   false testimony
C.   eyewitness testimony
D.   exact testimony

_____6.   The tendency of witnesses to attribute their memories for information regarding a crime to the wrong source is
A.   suggestibility
B.   source Monitoring
C.   sequential tendency
D.   None of the above is correct.

_____7.   Sometimes we may produce memories for events that never took place or for experiences that we have never had. The process through which these memories are formed is called
A.   memory consolidation
B.   memory production
C.   memory construction
D.   memory development

_____8.   According to Wells and Luus (1990), a police lineup is analogous to a social psychology experiment. In this analogy, the suspect is compared to the
A.   participant
B.   experimenter
C.   primary stimulus
D.   hypothesis

_____9.   In this type of lineup, the witness is first shown a lineup of only innocent persons.
A.   Double-blind lineup.
B.   Blind lineup.
C.   Blank lineup.
D.   Filler lineup.

_____10.   If justice were blind, as is portrayed by pictures and statues of justice as being blindfolded, juries would be unaffected by such characteristics as all of the following except
A.   race.
B.   gender.
C.   ethnicity.
D.   the evidence.

11.   _____ are the people who are on trial.

12.   When one adds together all of the small stresses in one's life to all the hassles in one's life the result is one's total _____.

13.   According to Holmes and Rahe (1967), The greater the number of stress points one accumulates, _____.

14.   The stress response tends to reduce circulating levels of _____ and tends to increase levels of the hormone _____.

15.   Brown et al. (2003) found that individuals who _____ high levels of social support were significantly less likely to die over a five year period.

When you have finished... Crossword Puzzle

Across

1.   Influencing someone by leading questions and similar techniques

5.   Response to events that disrupt, or threaten to disrupt out physical and psychological functioning

6.   Memories for events that did not happen

7.   Person who is on trial

Down

2.   Testimony given by individuals who have witnessed a crime

3.   Interview in which eyewitnesses are asked to report everything that they can remember

4.   Procedure in which neither the researcher nor the participants know what is true or correct

Created by Puzzlemaker at DiscoverySchool.com

When you have finished... You be the Researcher

You are given an assignment to design two hypothetical research studies. One will be correlational and one will be experimental. Your study is to investigate the link between one's self-esteem and job satisfaction.

You are to design a **correlational study** to explore the relationship between the two variables by answering the questions below:

1. What is your hypothesis (es)?

2. How will you measure the two variables?

3. What will your sample look like? How will they be chosen? Number of participants desired?

4. Let's say you have already conducted the experiment and obtained a correlation of .81. What does say about the relationship between self-esteem and job satisfaction?

Now, you are to design **an experiment** using the same variables:

1. What is your hypothesis (es)?

2. How will you measure the two variables?

3. What is your independent variable? How many levels do you have?

4. What is your dependent variable?

5. What does your sample look like? Is the sample random? How was this sample chosen?

6. How will you analyze the data? With statistics? Which type? Why?

7. What will we learn from this study that we could not learn from the study above?

Answers - As You Read…Practice Activities

1. Social influence is seen within our legal system in the roles of the attorneys, police and who are participants in the legal system. For example, the police attempt to influence any individual who is being questions to tell them the truth. Attorneys attempt to persuade jurors to a decision of guilty or innocent.

2. (1) Inquisitional Approach = a search for the truth.

   (2) Adversarial Approach = an approach in which the goal is to prove guilt

3. Individuals tend to admit to crimes they did not commit when they are in highly stressful and emotion charged setting which tends to make an individual highly agitated and very confused.

4. The avenue suggested is the requirement that all police interrogations be videotaped. The videotaping will, supposedly, serve to prevent police from using strong arm tactics and will also allow jurors to see the actual interrogation. By the jurors seeing the videotaped interrogation, they will, for themselves, be able to determine if the confession was coerced or not.

5. Police investigators often will conduct formal interrogations in "intimidating" locations such as police stations/headquarters as opposed to a less intimidating setting than the suspect's house.

6. Additional tactics of interrogation include the use of subtle approaches. This may include blaming the victim which is, in actuality, an approach using ingratiation. This technique is one that,

if used, can eliminate any questions concerning coercion of a confession.

Other techniques include presenting the suspect with false polygraph reports, fake fingerprint data, inaccurate eyewitness identification, and false information about a confession of a fellow suspect. All of these techniques are used to persuade the person being questioned to confess.

Kassin and Kiechel (1996) used college students as their participants. The participants were led to believe that they were participating in an experiment on reaction time. Every participant interacted with a female assistance who read of list of letters. The participants were to respond to the list by typing the letter on a keyboard. All participants were given the warning not to press the ALT key because pressing this key would cause the program to crash and all data would be lost. The pace of the study was either fast (high vulnerability) or slow (low vulnerability). After the experiment had begun, all computers ceased proper function and the apparently upset experimenter came into the room. The experimenter accused the participant to pressing the ALT key. There was also an accomplice who either stated that he or she had seen the participant hit the ALT key or stated that he or she had not seen the participant hit the ALT key.

Sixty-nine percent of the participants signed a false confession. Twenty-eight percent internalized their guilt by later telling another student, privately, that he or she had really pressed the ALT key.

7. A lineup is a procedure in which witnesses to a crime are shown several people, one or more of whom may be suspects in the case, and are asked to identify any of the person(s) that they

recognize as being involved in the crime.

A sequential lineup is a lineup in which suspects are presented one at a time and witnesses indicate whether or not they recognize any of the persons in the lineup.

A simultaneous lineup is a lineup in which all suspects are shown at one time and witnesses are asked to indicate whether they can identify the person who committed the crime.

8. There are two types of instructions that are commonly given. (1) Neutral instructions = asked to simply identify the person who committed the crime. There is no indication as to whether or not the criminal is present in the lineup. (2) Biased instructions = suggest that the criminal is present and the task is to pick this person from the others.

9. Media coverage does not, typically, emphasize evidence that may point towards a person's innocence. Because of this, there is a strong tendency to form a negative impression of the suspect. This is due to the primacy effect which refers to the tendency for information we first receive to strongly influence our decisions. In addition, people tend to believe what they hear from the media. Both of these issues can cause one to belief that the suspect is guilty even prior to the trial.

10. Perkins and Bourgeois (2006) asked participants in their study to read descriptions of the fatal shooting of a suspect. The descriptions were varied in respect to the number of (police officers present (2 or 6) and the number of shots fired (4, 8, 16, or 32). The participants then rated the extent to which the police actions were a misuse of deadly force. Ratings were gained through a Likert scale ranging from no misuse of deadly force to absolute misuse of deadly force.

The hypothesis was that the greater number of police present and the more shots fired, the more use of force would be seen as inappropriate. Data collected supported one part of the hypothesis. It was found that the greater number of police present, the more justified deadly force was perceived to be. The greater number of shots fired, the more the use of deadly force was seen as inappropriate. The explanation for these findings is that when there are more police present and all of them decide to fire at the suspect, the suspect must have really done something suspicious or dangerous.

11. Eyewitness testimony is defined as evidence given by persons who have witnessed a crime.

Wells (1993) found that witnesses often falsely identify innocent persons as criminals.

Loftus (2003) found that witnesses often make mistakes about important details involve in the crime.

Zaragoza et al. (2001) found that we sometimes have the tendency to remember events that actually did not take place.

12. Errors occur so often in eyewitness testimony because intense emotions tend to exert effects on information processing. Anytime one has seen a crime committed, it constitutes an intensely emotional charge situation and this is not conducive to an accurate assessment.

13. If there is a time interval between one's viewing the event and testifying about what was seen, the witness is almost certainly exposed to misleading post-even information. This comes from

police questioning, news stories, and statements made by others. This information may become incorporated into the witness's memory and has the propensity to influence what is remembered. Basically, what is happening is that the new information is interfering with the old information.

14.   Memory construction is the development of memories for events that never took place.

The two ways in which false memories are constructed include planting of the false memories and the fuzzy trace theory. Planting of false memories is often done unintentionally and occurs through exposure to the words and actions of others.

Fuzzy trace theory postulates that we make decisions and judgments while focusing on the general idea or gist of the information stored in memory. Therefore, we tend to remember information consistent with the gist of the information rather than from the real memories.

15.   (1)   Conduct improved interviews with witnesses. One way this might be done is by conducting a cognitive interview in which the eyewitness is asked to report anything and everything he or she can remember about the event. This provides the eyewitness with retrieval cues, which can improve memory.

(2)   Eyewitnesses can also be asked to describe events from different perspective and in different order.

(3)   Also, efforts can be made to improve police lineups.

16.   Primary Experimenter: the officer conducting the lineup

Participants: the eyewitnesses

Stimulus: the suspect

Response Data: eyewitness positive identification

Research Design: the arrangement of the lineup

Hypothesis: the suspect is guilty

Probability: data are stated in terms of probability because neither the lineup nor experiments can provide absolute certainty

17.   The second method mentioned in your textbook is the presentation of pictures of the crime scene and the victim to the witness before identification is made. In addition, there is the avoidance of biased instructions. Also, use of a double blind procedure which is a procedure in which neither the witness nor the person presenting the lineup knows who is the true suspect.

18.   While a meeting of a scientific association was being conducted, the proceedings were interrupted by a series of events. One of the events involved a clown in a colorful costume bursting into the room while being followed by a black gentleman carrying a gun. The clown and the gentleman began arguing. One of the individuals fell down and the other jumped on him. Moments later a shot range out. Both men, then, ran out of the room.

The president of the association was in on what was happening. All of the other attendees had no idea what had

happened or why it had happened. The people within the room were then asked to write down what they could remember about what had happened. It was stated that they should write this down in an effort to help policemen investigate the event.
Results showed that the attendees were highly inaccurate in their descriptions of the event. Only one of the participants provided a completely accurate description. The conclusion of the experimenter was that eyewitness testimony is highly inaccurate and participants can, at best, be correct about half of the time.

19. Because of her physical attractiveness, her high socioeconomic status, and her gender, Rose has a greater probability of being acquitted than she does found guilty.

20. 2, 5, 4, 3, 1

21. About 1/3 of jurors have already made up their minds prior to the trial. As the trial progresses, between 75 and 85% begin to favor one side. This bias tends to affect how any subsequent information or evidence is processed. Confirmation bias may go into play with jurors remembering only the information that is consistent with their initial opinion of the defendant.

22. Participants: Students and prospective jurors.

Procedure: Participants read about a sexual harassment suit in which a supervisor demanded sexual favors from a subordinate.

Independent variable (s): The race of the supervisor and the subordinate (African American or White) and gender (male or female).

Dependent variable (s): Rating of responsibility of the person making the

complaint and how much monetary compensation the victim should receive from the company.

Results: Racial and gender prejudice exerted significant effects. The person making the complaint was held more responsible for what happened to him or her when the supervisor was Black than when the person was White. Less compensation was awarded when the supervisor was Black. When the supervisor was Black, the subordinate was supposed to have known better than to go the person's hotel room for a drink.

A mock trial was held in which the jurors met and then were to recommend compensation for the victim, effects of race and gender then, for the most part, disappeared. What had happened was that the impact of the variables prior to deliberation were eliminated by the deliberations

The findings suggested that the process of the jury deliberations can, at times, help counter the impact of various characteristics of the defendants and probably the jurors also.

23. Health psychology is defined as a branch of psychology that investigates the connection between psychological variables and health. This suggests that health and illness are determined by an interaction of genetic, psychological, and social factors.

24. The findings showed that there are numerous links between health related behaviors and personal well being. The most noteworthy finding was that those who reported demonstrating all or most of the health promoting behaviors were less likely to die during the ten year study period than were those who practiced few or none of the health promoting behaviors.

25.   Levy et al. studied their participants over a 22 year period. First, the researchers measured their participants' self perception of aging. Then, the participants were divided into those who had a predominantly positive perception of their aging and those who had a predominantly negative perception of their aging. The two groups were followed for 22 years. Findings indicated that those who had the positive beliefs were more likely to continue living throughout the duration of the study. More precisely, the positive group tended to live an average of 7.5 years longer than those with the negative attitudes.

26.   (1)   Genetic factors = due to situations faced by our ancestors in which periods of famine were alternated with periods of plenty, eating an abundance made us more likely to survive during famines and to have children which served to maintain the species. Because of this, today we display the tendency to gain weight when we overeat.

(2)   Environmental factors = the size of our portions has increased greatly over the past few years. We have adapted to this change in size, some of us by increasing the amount of what we eat.

(3)   Social factors = People do not exercise as much as they used to. Also, we tend to have more enticing media campaigns for high calorie foods and snacks. In addition, the family sit-down dinner is disappearing. We are a fast paced society and families are eating at different times and often this is away from home. Social norms are also influential. We believe from the ads that we see that it is good to be thin. The abundance of these ads tends to give us the message that if we are overweight we are not alone.

27.   In Hebl and Mannix's study, participants role played the part of an employer choosing among several job applicants. The information they received about each applicant included a photograph of the applicant sitting next to a women who was either of normal weight or overweight. Applicants were rated lower when they were seated next to an overweight person than one of normal weight.

Crandall et al. found that findings such as those obtained by Hebl and Mannix are primarily due to the fact that there is the widespread belief that people who are overweight are responsible for their being overweight.

28.   Stress is defined as an individual's response to events that interrupt, or threaten to interrupt, one's physical or psychological functioning.

29.   In 1967, Holmes and Rahe asked a group of participants to assign points (from 1 to 100) to life events according to how much "readjustment" each would require. The researchers then connected the total points accumulated from this study with any changes the participants had to their personal health during a single year. Holmes and Rahe found that the greater the number of "stress points", the greater the likelihood of their becoming seriously ill.

30.   Cohen et al. (1998) asked their participants to describe stressful events they had experienced during the past year. Participants were also asked to specify the onset and offset of each event. The researchers then gave the participants nose drops, which contained a low dose of a virus that has been shown to cause the common cold. Results showed that those participants who reported chronic stress (stress lasting a month or more) were more likely to develop a cold than the participants who reported acute stress

(stress that is brief in duration). Also, the longer the duration of the stress, the greater the risk of developing a cold.

31. A hassle is a stress that is an annoyance. Hassles are very low in their intensity; but, are very high in their frequency.

32. Stress drains our reserve. This, in turn, induces negative feelings (including depression) and keeps us physiologically off balance. In other words, stress tends to upset our internal chemistry.

Stress can negatively influence our immune system which is defined as the mechanism through which out bodies recognize and destroy potentially harmful substances – bacteria, viruses, and cancerous cells. Long-term exposure to stress affects the level of lymphocytes in our bloodstream. Lymphocytes are white blood cells that serve to fight infection and disease. Stress can reduce the number of lymphocytes in our bloodstream. Long-term stress can also increase levels of cortisol in our bodies. Cortisol is a substance that suppresses aspects of our immune system. So, therefore, if we have increased levels of Cortisol, our immune system becomes compromised.

33. Indirect effects include our health-related behaviors (do we visit a physician when we need to?) as well as our fitness-related behaviors (do we eat a balanced diet?).

34. Social support is defined as a support system developed by drawing on the emotional and other resources provided by others.

The definition really provides an answer to the second question. Social support gives us someone to fall back on when we need some support or just an ear to listen.

35. Pets can provide nonjudgmental social support. This is due to the fact that they tend to love their owners no matter what. Even animals whose "people" treat them abusively will still display love for their owners.

Pets have been shown to actually reduce blood pressure in humans.

36. People who are married are buffered from stress. It has been found that individuals, who are divorced or separated, when compared to those who are married, often show reduced functioning in their immune systems.

37. Industrial-Organizational Psychologist.

38. Attitudes concerning our job, itself = job satisfaction.

Attitudes concerning the company (workplace) = organizational commitment.

39. NOTE: You may or may not have listed the groups in the order that is displayed here. If you did not, simply switch answers between group one and group two.

The two groups of factors are organizational factors and personal factors.

Organizational factors that have been shown to affect job satisfaction include the following:

People tend to report higher satisfaction when…
A. they feel that the reward system in their workplace is far.
B. they like and respect their bosses and feel that he or she has their best interests at heart.
C. they can participate in some of the decisions that will or do affect them.

D.   the work they perform is interesting as opposed to boring and repetitive.

E.   they are neither overloaded not overloaded with work.

F.   they are comfortable in the physical work environment.
A factor that does not appear to exert a significant effect on job satisfaction:

A.   Pay = it has been discovered that job satisfaction is not as highly connected with pay as we would think. What appears to be more important than the actual pay is a feeling that the pay is fair. That is, the pay is well in line with what the employee thinks he or she should be making.

Personal factors that have been shown to affect job satisfaction include the following:

A.   Seniority = the longer one has been working in a given job, the higher their status and the greater their satisfaction with the job.

B.   Status = the more the job is matched with the individual's personal interests, the greater the satisfaction.

C.   Personality traits can affect job satisfaction. Individuals who are type A personalities tend to have greater satisfaction with their jobs than those who are type B.

40.   Arvy et al. (1989) investigated job satisfaction in 34 pairs of identical twins who had been raised apart since a very early age. Results revealed that the level of job satisfaction reported by the pairs showed a strong correlation. Also, the correlations were higher than the correlations that are found within non-related persons.

As much as 30% of the variation in job satisfaction appears to be from genetic factors.

41.   This is from the section *Making Sense of Common Sense*. Within your answer you can provide evidence from the researchers and their results as discussed within this section.

42.   Organizational citizenship behavior (OCB) is a type of prosocial behavior that occurs within the workplace that may or may not be rewarded by the organization.

43.   E, C, D, B, A

44.   A social fence is a type of social dilemma. A social fence is when individuals help others within the workplace and the actions involved in the helping are not usually part of the person's job. It is strictly voluntary.

45.   Non-compliance behaviors are due to decisions not to help other individuals or to do something that is contrary to the group or organization's values. Basically, non-compliance behavior leads to neglecting one's job or showing substandard performance while on the job.

In the social delayed trap, there is a short-term benefit, but a long-term collective cost.

46.　**(Over,Down,Direction)**

ATTITUDES(3,2,S)　　　　　　BREADTH(1,7,SE)
COMMITMENT(12,3,W)　　　　DISTRIBUTIVE(15,6,W)
FAIR(12,8,NE)　　　　　　　　IDENTITY(8,15,NE)
INTERACTIONAL(14,13,NW)　　JUSTICE(9,9,W)
PROCEDURAL (5,7,E)　　　　　SOCIAL (7,9,SE)

```
+ L + + + + + + + + + + + +
+ + A + + + + + + + + + + +
+ + T N E M T I M M O C + + +
+ + T + O + + + + + + + + +
+ + I + + I + + + + + + + R
+ + T E V I T U B I R T S I D
B + U + P R O C E D U R A L +
+ R D + + + + A + + F + + Y
+ + E C I T S U J R + + + T +
+ + S A + + + O + + E + I + +
+ + + + D + + + C + + T + + +
+ + + + + T + + + I N + N + +
+ + + + + + H + + E A + + I +
+ + + + + + + D + + L + + +
+ + + + + + + I + + + + + +
```

47. The scenario is indicative of the principle of reciprocity.

   The pattern that has been identified is that the more OCB's that one performs, the more likely they are to be helped in return.

48. The main principle of leadership and being a leader is having influence. Influence is defined as changing the behavior and thoughts of other members of the group so that they work together to attain the group's common goals.

49. A "great" person is one who possesses certain traits that set them apart from most other human beings. These traits are possessed by all such leaders, regardless of when and where they lived. Some leader characteristics include the leader's cognitive abilities, aspects of his or her personality, the leader's motives, values, social skills, expertise, and problem solving skills. These characteristics interact with situational factors so that some of the characteristics are helpful only under some circumstances and not in others.

50. If a leader is charismatic, he or she has tremendous ambition and exceptional communication skills.

51. The organization is facing very difficult conditions.

   The reason this appears to be true is that women are assumed to possess traits that will help them deal better in a crisis than would a man.

52. The first is initiating structure or task orientation. Leaders who are high in initiating structure are very concern with getting the job done. Leaders who are low in initiating structure tend to engage in such actions, but to a lesser degree.

   The second is consideration or person-orientation. Leaders who are high in consideration tend to focus on establishing good relationships with their subordinates and on being liked by them. Those who are low in consideration do not particularly care how well they get along with their subordinates. Neither one of the styles is superior to the other. Both have good and bad qualities. High consideration can improve group morale, but efficiency can suffer. High initiating structure, efficiency may be high, but subordinates tend to feel that the leader does not really care about them. This causes their commitment to the organization to suffer.

53. Both leaders and followers exert influence. On a more basic level, there can be no "leaders" without "followers."

54. A transformational leader is a leader that exerts powerful effects over millions of people and, by doing so, changes society.

   Charismatic is defined as someone who exerts profound power over their followers. This power is so profound that it is almost magical.

55. A transactional leader is a leader that we meet in our everyday lives. Like the transformational leader, they exert their power over followers, but it is done in a different way. They work within the system offering praise and rewards for good performance. They clarify goals and provide recognition for those who achieve them. They are highly effective in an ordinary work setting.

56. Flattery
   Be prepared
   Look your best
   Emphasize your strengths
   Agree with the interviewer as much as possible
   Be realistic

Answers – Practice Test #1

1. C
2. C
3. C
4. B
5. A
6. D
7. A
8. A
9. D
10. D
11. cognitive interview
12. blank lineup control
13. double blind
14. scientific association
15. defendant

Answers – Practice Test #2

1. D
2. B
3. B
4. A
5. D
6. B
7. B
8. D
9. D
10. D
11. stress
12. social support
13. job satisfaction; organizational commitment
14. altruism
15. social fence

Answers – Practice Test #3

1. C
2. D
3. A
4. D
5. C
6. C

7. D
8. D
9. A
10. C
11. consideration.
12. micromanagement.
13. idealized influence.
14. individualized consideration.
15. job satisfaction.

Answers – Practice Test #4

1. C
2. C
3. B
4. C
5. C
6. B
7. C
9. C
10. D
11. defendants.
12. stress quotient.
13. the greater the likelihood of one becoming ill
14. lymphocytes; cortisol.
15. provide

Answers – Cross Word Puzzle

Across

1. suggestibility
5. stress
6. false
7. defendant

Down

2. eyewitness
3. cognitive
4. doubleblind

NOTES

NOTES

NOTES

NOTES

NOTES

NOTES

NOTES

NOTES

NOTES

NOTES

NOTES

NOTES

NOTES

NOTES

NOTES

NOTES